Cell

1993

Random Packings and Packed Towers

Design and Applications

Random Packings and Packed Towers

Design and Applications

Ralph F. Strigle, Jr.

 Chemical Process Products

 Gulf Publishing Company
Book Division
Houston, London, Paris, Tokyo

Random Packings and Packed Towers
Design and Applications

100 246 1261

Library of Congress Cataloging-in-Publication Data

Strigle, Ralph F.
   Random packings and packed towers.
   Includes bibliographies and index.
   1. Packed towers. I. Title.
TP159.P3S77   1987   660.2'842   87-8670
ISBN 0-87201-669-2

First Printing, June 1987
Second Printing, June 1988

iv

CONTENTS

Gas Dehydration, Sulfuric Acid Manufacture, Absorption with
Chemical Reaction, Amine Systems, Hot Carbonate Systems,
Example Problem, Notation, References.

Reflux Ratio, Demethanizers, Depropanizers, Chemical
Separations, Example Problem, Notation, References.

FOREWORD

Packed columns have been used for contacting gases and liquids in the chemical industry since the beginning of this century. The first packing, the Raschig ring, was invented in 1915, and many of the packed column design procedures used today were the subject of some of the earliest theoretical work in chemical engineering during the 1920s and 1930s.

The development of a proven technology for commercial-scale packed columns has taken much longer, since by definition it must be based on the experience of many successful applications. Although large-diameter (greater than 3 m) packed columns have been accepted for more than 20 years for gas absorption (for example, in sulfuric acid production or carbon dioxide removal), only in the last five years have they been accepted for distillation.

Thus it has taken 70 years or more for the packed column to come of age. With this maturity gained, it is timely to publish descriptions and design guides for the practical use of packed columns in many different industries.

Very little research is now done at universities on packed columns, although the theoretical interpretations are inadequate for many of the proven applications. For example, the apparently elementary problem of predicting from first principles the pressure drop and maximum capacity for countercurrent flow of a gas and/or liquid in packed beds requires further study. In the field of gas absorption with chemical reaction, there is still a great gulf between the extensive academic work (which explains the process in terms of the effect of the chemical reaction on the liquid-film resistance) and the practical design procedures in general use (which describe it in terms of an empirical gas-film mass transfer coefficient and a gas partial-pressure driving force).

This state of the art is not surprising. Packed columns are used in applications as different as vacuum distillation, high-pressure gas absorption with reactive salt solutions, and/or gas/liquid heat exchange, all in large-diameter towers. Thus, the only source of reliable data is the full-scale plant. It is unreasonable to expect that design procedures may be derived from laboratory work on small packings in small-diameter columns working at near atmospheric pressure and temperature.

Nevertheless, the conditions encountered in one vacuum distillation are usually similar to those in another vacuum distillation, and one heat transfer pumparound bed is similar to another. Thus, by classifying the fields of application, practical experience may be recorded and accumulated over years, and in response to the pressures of competitive tendering, the best route to an optimum design is eventually established. It is in this way that simple but proven design procedures have been developed even for those situations where the most fundamental relationships are too complex for convenience, or indeed remain unknown.

Norton Chemical Process Products is well known in the industry for publishing technical performance data from the laboratory tests it performs on its products. Now, in this book, it has released design procedures developed from extensive experience in supplying packings and internals in every type of packing application. It is perhaps worth noting that Norton Chemical Process Products was formed from two long established companies, United States Stoneware Company in the United States and Hydronyl Limited in the United Kingdom. Thus, this experience of more than 60 years embraces the first use of packings in most if not all applications since the invention of the Raschig ring.

In many of these developments, the author, Ralph Strigle, has played a leading role, evaluating and guesstimating for the initial application of a new packed tower technology, and then developing design procedures as plant data became available and the business matured. More than 20 years ago he worked on the then-new use of ceramic Intalox® saddles in large-diameter sulfuric acid plant absorbers, and on the first use of metal packings in oil refinery heat transfer pumparound beds. More recently he has been very much involved in the new large-diameter distillation column breakthrough, and in particular, in high-pressure packed demethanizers.

This book then is the condensation of the experience of the author's working lifetime. It describes in simple terms many of the methods which are used to design packed columns for a wide range of practical applications. It is meant for the engineer who intends to design or evaluate a packed tower to solve a practical problem. For the discerning academic, it provides examples of experience that are worth exploring in theoretical terms, and it may stimulate new interest in a currently neglected field.

K. E. Porter
Professor of Chemical Engineering
Aston University

PREFACE

More than a third of a century has elapsed since *Tower Packings and Packed Tower Design* was prepared by Max Leva. During this period, the chemical industry has grown to maturity. The traditional heavy chemicals business has peaked in size and profitability in most industrialized countries. Since World War II, the organic chemical industry has become a petrochemical industry, with hydrocarbons serving as the primary feedstocks. Ethylene and methanol have replaced sulfuric acid and ammonia as the major chemical building blocks.

No longer is this industry able to show an annual double-digit growth rate. Profitability in this mature business climate depends on advanced technology. As a result, design techniques suitable for an environment in the 1950s will not produce viable designs for operations conducted in the 1980 and '90s. This book records some design procedures based on practical experiences that have been demonstrated to produce satisfactory column designs. The theoretical bases for these design procedures in most cases were developed many years ago. These theories are available in most academic texts used in chemical engineering courses on mass transfer. However, in many practical situations the direct application of these theoretical concepts is complicated by the lack of physical and chemical constants, or because the data in the academic texts are based on small-size columns in operation near atmospheric pressures. In practice, some large-diameter packed columns must operate at high pressures, or with systems that foam and are dirty.

The theoretical methods have been supplemented by empirical design procedures based on extensive commercial experience. Sometimes this experience has been acquired by simple revamps of previously operating columns. In other cases, extensive and costly modifications were required to accomplish the desired column operation.

Most engineers find themselves faced with the design of a mass transfer device only a few times a year. In such circumstances, the designer welcomes a single source of design information. This book is an attempt to describe the mechanism of operation of tower packings and modern design methods. The procedures presented have been used successfully to design more than 1,200 columns within the last 6 years. These towers have diameters as large as 46 ft and develop as many as 128 theoretical stages of separation.

The applications of packed columns are many and varied. The use of packed columns for mass transfer has increased as a percent of the total of all devices utilized. Several new types of tower packing shapes have been developed and have achieved significant degree of acceptance. Additional research in the field of mass transfer has produced superior design methods. Norton Chemical Process Products has continued the development in this field pioneered by its predecessor, United States Stoneware Company.

The major areas of application of packed columns are reviewed in this book so the reader might appreciate the advantages of packed columns as compared with other, perhaps more traditional, devices. In addition, new applications such as high-vacuum distillation and high-pressure fractionations have been carried out advantageously in packed columns. Each chapter has an example to familiarize the reader with the mechanics of the design calculations.

No attempt is made to discuss economics in this volume. Capital equipment prices and installation costs vary significantly with material of construction and plant location. Further, each organization has different methods for determining total costs and varying criteria for return on investment. Suffice to say that costs of various devices should be compared on an installed basis, not just by equipment prices.

Ralph F. Strigle

1

HYDRAULICS OF OPERATION

This chapter describes the various hydraulic phenomena that occur in a bed of random dumped tower packing shapes. First, those factors that influence only gas-phase flow are considered. Then, the more complex hydraulics that result when liquid is introduced onto the packed bed are examined. Finally, a method for predicting pressure drop in two-phase flow through the packed bed is developed.

A packed bed provides a mechanism for mass or heat transfer through which the gas and liquid phases usually flow countercurrently in the column. The presence of tower packing elements provides a resistance to the flow of these fluids that is greater than it would be in an empty column shell. Resistance to the liquid flowing downward is not normally of great importance because the liquid flows under the influence of gravity.

The gas that flows upward, however, must overcome the resistance offered by the tower packing elements. If only the gas phase is flowing through the packed bed, the bed might be treated as an extension of the theory of gas flow through beds of granular solids. For small particles and low gas flow rates, the Reynolds number (Re) is low and the gas phase is in laminar flow. Under these conditions, the form drag loss accounts for almost all of the pressure drop as the kinetic energy loss is low. This drag coefficient is inversely proportional to the Reynolds number.

Kozeny modeled a packed bed as a series of parallel, small diameter tubes of equal length and diameter [1]. Carmen applied the work of Kozeny to experimentally determine pressure drops for the flow through packed beds [2]. This work produced the Carmen-Kozeny equation for gas-phase pressure drop:

$$\Delta P = \psi \, \frac{Vu'}{\epsilon^3} \left[\frac{1 - \epsilon}{D_p} \right]^2 \tag{1-1}$$

1

However, in most applications, the gas phase is in turbulent flow. Equation 1-1 does not apply where kinetic energy losses are high, as is the case for large values of the Reynolds number. Burke and Plummer used a model similar to that of Kozeny and derived an equation to express the pressure drop for packed beds with the gas phase in turbulent flow [3].

$$\Delta P = \psi \, \frac{V^2 \rho_G}{D_p} \left[\frac{1 - \epsilon}{\epsilon^3} \right] \tag{1-2}$$

In this equation the pressure drop per unit of bed depth is a function of the second power of the gas flow rate as long as there is only single-phase flow. Pressure drop also is influenced by the void fraction of the packed bed. A smaller void fraction in a packed bed obviously results in a higher local gas velocity at a constant superficial gas mass flow rate. Packing size also influences pressure drop. Ergun combined the equation for form drag loss with the equation for kinetic energy loss to produce an equation for the pressure drop through a packed bed [4].

$$\Delta P = \psi_1 \, \frac{V u'}{\epsilon^3} \left[\frac{1 - \epsilon}{D_p} \right]^2 + \psi_2 \, \frac{V^2 \rho_G}{D_p} \left[\frac{1 - \epsilon}{\epsilon^3} \right] \tag{1-3}$$

This equation has been applied with some success to packed beds where the pressure drop is small compared to the column operating pressure.

INFLUENCE OF PACKING SHAPE

Flow channels do not have a fixed shape or diameter in a packed bed. The hydraulic radius (flow channel area divided by wetted perimeter) varies significantly with the channel shape. Further, these flow channels are not straight nor are they of uniform length. Because the pressure drop per foot of bed depth is constant, the actual gas velocity varies with the hydraulic radius as well as the effective length of the flow channel. Even with single-phase flow through a packed bed, the effect of packing shape is not well defined. The development of packing shapes remains an empirical art in which the pressure drop produced in the actual packed bed must be experimentally determined.

Over the years, many shapes have been proposed for tower packing elements but only a few are used widely. Various packing shapes are shown in Figures 1-1 through 1-11. Probably the oldest random dumped tower packing shape in substantial commercial use is the Raschig ring.

(text continued on page 8)

Figure 1-1. Raschig ring (ceramic).

Figure 1-2. Raschig ring (metal).

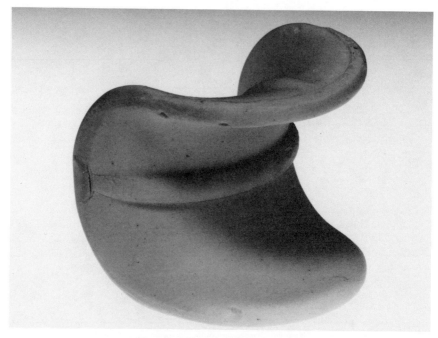

Figure 1-3. Berl saddle (ceramic).

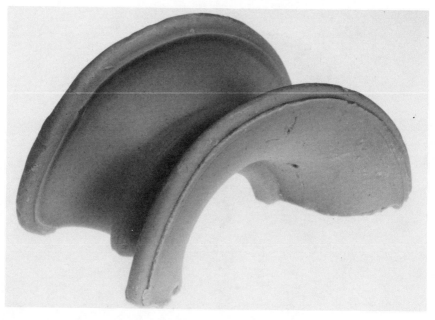

Figure 1-4. Intalox® saddle (ceramic).

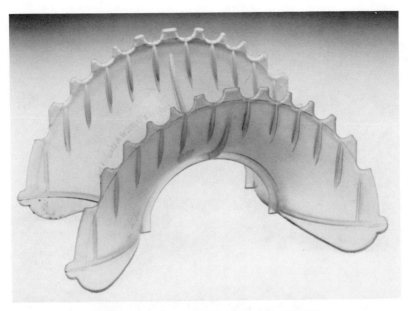

Figure 1-5. Super Intalox® saddle (plastic).

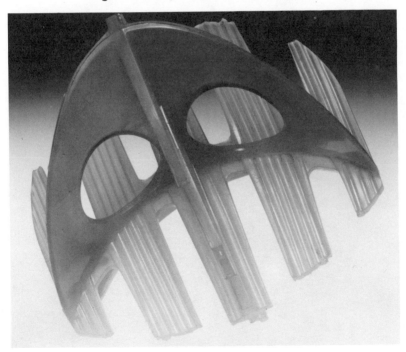

Figure 1-6. Maspac® packing (plastic)

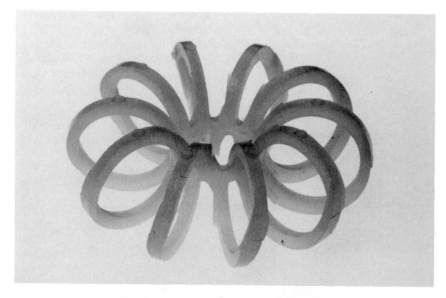

Figure 1-7. Tellerette® packing (plastic).

Figure 1-8. Pall ring (plastic).

Figure 1-9. Pall ring (metal).

Figure 1-10. Hy-Pak® packing (metal).

Figure 1-11. IMTP® packing (metal).

(text continued from page 2)
This packing is a simple cylinder with a length equal to its outside diameter. It is manufactured from ceramics, metals, plastics, and carbon. Two modifications of this shape are the Lessing ring and the cross-partition ring. Both of these shapes use internal partitions. These packings have been installed in both a dumped and a stacked manner. A further modification of the basic cylindrical shape involves installation of a helix inside the cylinder. The interior of this ring may contain a single, a double, or a triple helix. This spiral ring packing normally is made from ceramic and only should be installed by stacking.

The first of the modern dumped packings was the Berl saddle, developed in the late 1930s. This shape has a significantly increased surface area per unit of packed volume compared to the Raschig ring. Another improved shape was the Intalox® (trademark Norton Chemical Process Products) saddle developed in the early 1950s. This design has two different radii of curvature that provide a greater degree of randomness in the packed bed.

Two unique packing shapes are Maspac® (trademark Clarkson Controls and Equipment Co.) packing developed by Dow Chemical Company, and the Tellerette® (trademark The Ceilcote Co.) packing developed by Dr. A. J. Teller. These packings are manufactured only in plastics.

In the early 1950s a significant improvement was made in the Raschig ring shape by B.A.S.F. Aktiengesellschaft. Their development, called the Pall ring, consists of a cylinder of equal length and diameter with ten fingers punched from the cylinder wall which extend into the packing element interior. Although the Pall ring has the same geometric surface area as the Raschig ring, the interior surfaces of the Pall ring are much more accessible to gas and liquid flows due to the openings through the wall. Pall ring modifications, such as Hy-Pak® (trademark Norton Chemical Process Products) packing, subsequently have been developed to further increase the interfacial area the packing element makes available for gas and liquid contact.

A further modification on the Pall ring was developed by Mass Transfer Limited. Their Cascade® (trademark Mass Transfer Ltd.) Mini-Ring also is a cylinder with fingers punched from the wall projecting into the interior of the ring; however, the height of the cylinder is only one-third the outside diameter. This shape is said to orient itself preferentially when dumped into a packed bed.

A newer packing element combines advantages of the shape of the Intalox® saddle with that of a modern ring packing. This Intalox® Metal Tower Packing, or IMTP® (trademark Norton Chemical Process Products) packing, was developed by Norton Company in the late 1970s and is manufactured from metals only.

Packing element shape greatly influences resistance to flow (aerodynamic drag factor). However, the resistance to flow, even single-phase flow, produced by a packed bed cannot be predicted from first principles. Ceramic Intalox® saddles and ceramic Raschig rings have similar void fractions, but greatly different pressure drops (shape factors) as shown in Table 1-1. With more recently developed packings, a similar situation exists between Intalox® Metal Tower Packing and metal Pall rings as shown in Table 1-2. The shapes of IMTP® and ceramic Intalox® saddle packings produce less pressure drop than metal Pall ring and ceramic Raschig ring packings, respectively, for the same gas mass flow.

In single-phase gas flow (where there is no liquid wetting the packing surface), the dry line relates the pressure drop to the gas rate:

$$\Delta P = \psi \frac{G^{*2}}{\rho_G} \text{ or } \Delta P = \psi V^2 \rho_G \qquad (1\text{-}4)$$

The constant relating pressure drop to $V^2 \rho_G$ in Equation 1-4 for the dry line is actually the summation of the effects of packing shape factor, bed void fraction, and hydraulic radius of the packing as indicated in Equa-

Table 1 – 1
Characteristics of Ceramic Packings

Packing	Void Fraction	Bulk Weight lb/ft³	Single Phase Pressure Drop (in. H₂O/ft)	
			G† = 900	G† = 1600
1 in. Intalox® Saddles	0.721	43.9	0.30	0.96
1½ in. Intalox® Saddles	0.734	41.8	0.16	0.52
2 in. Intalox® Saddles	0.748	39.6	0.12	0.39
1 in. Raschig Rings	0.707	46.1	0.44	1.38
1½ in. Raschig Rings	0.720	44.0	0.27	0.87
2 in. Raschig Rings	0.737	41.4	0.22	0.73

† G is gas mass velocity in lb/ft² · h

Table 1 – 2
Characteristics of Metal Packings

Packing	Void Fraction	Bulk Weight lb/ft³	Single Phase Pressure Drop (in. H₂O/ft)	
			G† = 1500	G† = 2700
#25 IMTP® Packing	0.962	18.8	0.38	1.24
#40 IMTP® Packing	0.971	14.5	0.24	0.79
#50 IMTP® Packing	0.977	11.3	0.15	0.50
1 in. Pall Rings	0.942	29.0	0.46	1.49
1½ in. Pall Rings	0.956	22.0	0.32	1.03
2 in. Pall Rings	0.965	17.5	0.22	0.72

† G is gas mass velocity in lb/ft² · h

tion 1-2. This constant can be determined from dry line pressure drop measurements for any particular type and size of packing as long as the gas-phase flow is turbulent.

IRRIGATED PACKED BEDS

For packed beds used in gas and liquid contacting, the liquid can flow in the opposite direction to the gas (countercurrent operation), or it can flow in the same direction as the gas (concurrent operation). The theory of pressure drop in irrigated packed beds is not as well developed as that for single-phase flow.

With countercurrent liquid and gas flow, as soon as a flowing liquid phase is introduced onto the packed bed, the pressure drop will be greater than that developed only with gas flow. Data collected over many years, representing 4,500 pressure-drop measurements, have been correlated for each packing in a plot of log ΔP vs. log G, as illustrated by Figure 1-12. The region of low gas flow rate gives an indication of how the liquid flow rate parameters on such a pressure-drop plot parallel the dry line up to high liquid rates. This is true because the liquid holdup is a low value that primarily is a function of liquid rate at low gas rates. The highest gas rate at which pressure drop can be expressed by Equation 1-4, with ψ modified to account for the effect of liquid rate, sometimes has been called the lower loading point.

At low liquid rates, the log ΔP vs. log G plot gives liquid rate parameters that appear to start parallel to the dry line but gradually increase in slope as the gas flow rate increases. The rate of slope change of each of these curves is constant up to rather high gas flow rates. Of course, the rate of slope change of the dry line is zero. The rate of slope change of the other liquid rate parameters increases with increasing liquid flow

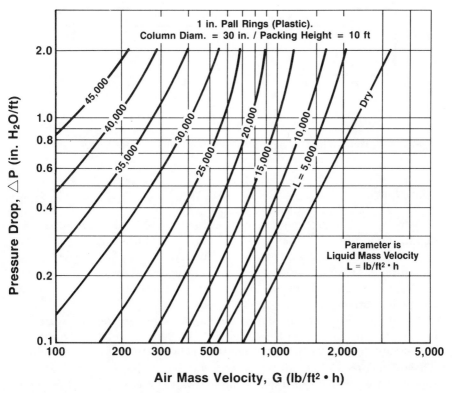

Figure 1-12. Pressure drop vs. gas rate (1-in. Pall Rings (Plastic)).

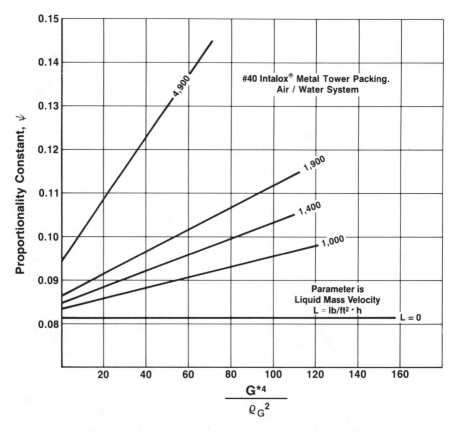

Figure 1-13. Rate of pressure drop change (#40 Intalox® Metal Tower Packing).

rates. Thus, a plot of ψ in Equation 1-4 vs. G^{*4}/ρ_G^2 gives a straight line for any fixed liquid rate as shown in Figure 1-13.

As the pressure drop goes below a value of 0.10 in. H_2O/ft of packed depth, the modified Equation 1-4 predicts a pressure drop that is lower than the experimentally determined value. At a very low pressure drop, measurement tolerances, as well as static head due to the gas phase, may be significant. In addition, at low gas rates the gas phase may not be in completely turbulent flow.

As the gas flow rate increases, the vapor begins to interact with the liquid affecting the liquid flow regime. At higher gas rates, the rate of change of pressure drop increases more rapidly than a constant value. This is because liquid holdup increases with increasing gas rate. This gas rate has been called the upper loading point. Operation at higher gas rates is considered to be in the loading region of the packing [5].

Above this gas rate the column will reach a maximum capacity that will be determined either by massive liquid entrainment in the gas phase or by excessive liquid holdup in the packed bed. Conventional flooding as a maximum capacity limit is produced by liquid holdup of sufficient magnitude to invert phases within the interstices of the packed bed. In distillation, maximum operational capacity is determined by the amount of liquid entrainment required to reduce separation efficiency (see Chapter 6).

HIGH LIQUID RATE PERFORMANCE

The plot of log ΔP vs. log G also shows another hydraulic phenomenon that occurs at high liquid rates, as illustrated in Figures 1-12 and 1-14. The slopes of these liquid rate parameters at low gas rates are less than 2 at liquid rates above 40 gpm/ft^2 for 1-in. size packings or 55 gpm/ft^2 for 1½-in. size packings. Extrapolation of these curves leads to the

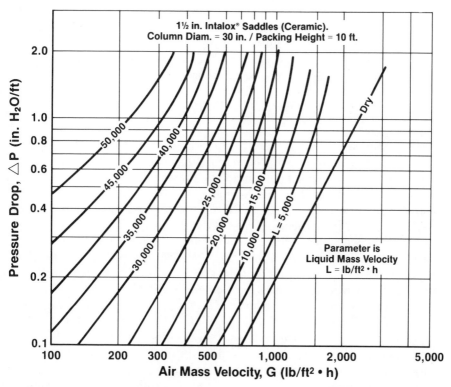

Figure 1-14. Pressure drop vs. gas rate (1½-in. Intalox® Saddles (Ceramic)).

conclusion that there still will be a pressure drop as the gas flow rate approaches zero. At a high liquid flow rate, depending on the size of the packing, the packed bed voids largely tend to be filled with liquid, and some of the gas phase actually is aspirated down the column in the liquid phase. A sufficient liquid retention time in the base of the column will permit these aspirated gas bubbles to rise to the surface of the liquid pool and escape back into the gas phase. The packed bed, therefore, produces a pressure drop that is an indication of the internal gas flow passing upward through the bed. This internal gas flow is the sum of the externally introduced gas flow rate plus the recirculated gas released from the liquid at the bottom of the column.

Ordinarily, packed columns are not designed at liquid rates above those just enumerated because pressure drop cannot be predicted by the usual correlations. The prudent designer will use a large enough packing to avoid this area of operation. For example, 2-in. packings do not exhibit this phenomenon below a liquid rate of 70 gpm/ft^2 and 3½-in. packings have been operated at liquid rates as high as 125 gpm/ft^2.

The preceding flow rates apply for mobile liquids. High liquid viscosity tends to diminish the acceptable liquid flow rate. Smaller sizes of packings are more restricted than larger sizes by increasing liquid viscosity. The foregoing maximum design liquid rates are based on a liquid viscosity no higher than 1.0 cps for 1-in. size packings, 1.8 cps for 1½-in. size packings, and 3.2 cps for 2-in. size packings.

LIQUID HOLDUP IN PACKED BEDS

There are two different types of liquid holdup in a packed bed: static and operating. Static holdup represents that volume of liquid per volume of packing which remains in the bed after the gas and liquid flows stop and the bed has drained. Normally, this static holdup is not large and thus not of great significance. The static holdup is dependent on the packing surface area, the roughness of the packing surface, and the contact angle between the packing surface and the liquid. In addition, capillary forces will hold liquid at junctions between individual packing elements. Well designed tower packings normally do not trap stagnant pools of liquid within the packing element itself.

Operating holdup is that volume of liquid per volume of packing that drains out of the bed after the gas and liquid flows to the column stop. Operating holdup primarily is a function of liquid flow rate [6]. The gas rate has only a small effect on liquid holdup below the loading region. Liquid surface tension has practically no effect on operating holdup for high surface tension liquids such as water. For ordinary organic liquids

(σ about 27 dyne/cm) at low liquid rates, the operating holdup will be about 12% lower than for water. Holdup will be reduced up to 20%, for low surface tension systems (σ about 13 dyne/cm) at low liquid rates. At liquid rates above 7 gpm/ft^2 this effect of surface tension on liquid holdup diminishes. These measurements were determined at atmospheric pressure and should not be extrapolated to high-pressure distillations.

Liquid holdup increases with increasing liquid viscosity. Usual liquid holdup graphs show an air/water system and thus apply to a liquid viscosity of about 1.0 cps. If the liquid viscosity is increased to 2.0 cps the liquid holdup will increase by 10%. At 16 cps liquid viscosity, the holdup will be about 50% greater. If liquid viscosity is reduced to 0.45 cps, the holdup will be about 10% lower. At a liquid viscosity of only 0.15 cps, the holdup will be reduced by 20%.

Viscous liquids tend to bridge the small void openings in beds of smaller size packings resulting in a rapid loss of gas handling capacity as liquid rates are increased. It is recommended that only 1½-in. and larger size packings be used for handling liquids of 50 cps or higher viscosity.

The pressure drop through a packed bed represents not only the frictional loss and kinetic energy loss through the packing, but also the force exerted by the operating liquid holdup. Thus, at the same pressure drop, the packed bed has less volumetric liquid holdup in high liquid-density systems. Conversely, with low density liquids, the volumetric liquid holdup can be significantly greater than for water at the same pressure drop.

At atmospheric pressure and in vacuum services, the static head produced by the gas is small and can be neglected. However, in high pressure fractionators requiring large numbers of theoretical stages, the static head of vapor can be appreciable from condenser to reboiler. This correction should be added to the calculated pressure drop in the determination of bottom column pressure and reboiler temperature.

PRESSURE-DROP CALCULATION

Calculating pressure drop is of considerable importance in atmospheric absorbers, heat transfer services, and vacuum distillations. Although pressure-drop plots are available for most commercial types and sizes of random dumped tower packings, these data usually have been collected on an air/water system. While the air flow rate can be corrected for changes in gas density, no adequate method exists for handling the effect of liquid properties.

It is highly desirable for the designer to have a generalized correlation to predict pressure drop in a packed bed. Development of a single correlation to represent all the different applications of packings (absorption, distillation, etc.), as well as widely differing pressures of operation, is an ambitious undertaking. Reliable design of a packed column requires an understanding of the reasons some systems are less well predicted by a generalized pressure-drop correlation than other systems.

Over the years, the Sherwood, et al., universal flooding correlation, proposed for random dumped tower packings operated in countercurrent flow, has been modified to provide a generalized pressure-drop correlation [7]. Leva first modified this correlation to include parameters of constant pressure drop [8]. The abscissa of this correlation is known as the *flow parameter:*

$$X = \frac{L}{G} \left[\frac{\rho_G}{\rho_L} \right]^{0.5} \tag{1-5}$$

This flow parameter is the square root of the ratio of liquid kinetic energy to gas kinetic energy. The ordinate of this correlation includes the gas flow rate, the gas and liquid densities, the a_p/ϵ^3 ratio (which is characteristic of the particular tower packing shape and size), and a liquid viscosity term. Lobo, et al., proposed the use of a packing factor to characterize a particular packing shape and size [9]. They determined that the a_p/ϵ^3 ratio did not adequately predict packing hydraulic performance. Eckert further modified this correlation and calculated the packing factors from experimentally determined pressure drops [10].

An extensive study was performed at Norton Company's Chamberlain Laboratories to determine the optimum location of these pressure-drop parameters. The data bank of 4,500 pressure-drop measurements was subjected to a statistical analysis. Pressure drops ranged from 0.05 in. H_2O/ft to 2.0 in. H_2O/ft and flow parameter values from 0.005 to 8. It was found that more than one-half (55%) of the packing types and sizes would produce a constant packing factor at all pressure drops. Packings smaller than 1-in. size often showed a small increase in the packing factor as the pressure drop was reduced. A few high-voidage, large-size packings showed a small decrease in the packing factor as the pressure drop was reduced. The locations of the pressure-drop parameters on the correlation, shown in Figure 1-15, were essentially the same whether a variable packing factor (to allow for these small deviations) or a constant packing factor, was employed.

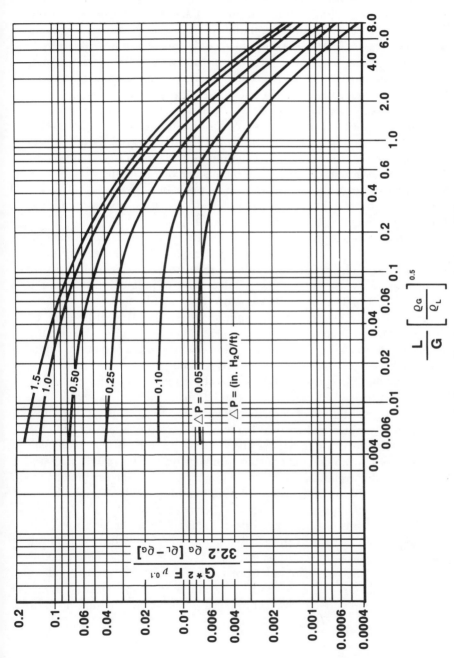

Figure 1-15. Generalized pressure-drop correlation.

The resultant correlation predicts pressure drop within $\pm 17\%$ of measured values throughout its entire range. In the most widely used range of abscissa values (from 0.01 to 1.0) and for pressure drops from 0.25 to 1.0 in. H_2O/ft, the correlation predicts the pressure drop to an accuracy of $\pm 11\%$. In its present form, this correlation probably represents the maximum accuracy possible, considering the many shapes and sizes of packings available. If greater accuracy is necessary, a separate correlation is required for each packing type and size.

For abscissa values less than 0.02, which indicates the operation is under vacuum, special pressure-drop equations can be developed from the packing dry line. In such operations, the liquid rate usually is low and thus the liquid holdup is small. When holdup is only a few volume percent, the void fraction reduction of the packed bed is slight. Actual measurements indicate the pressure drop in operation can be significantly lower than that predicted from Figure 1-15 using an abscissa value of 0.02. (See Chapter 7 for further discussion.)

Abscissa values greater than 1.0 are produced either by operations involving very high liquid-to-gas mass flow ratios or by high gas-to-liquid density ratios. The stripping of light hydrocarbons under high pressure is an example of the latter case. (Calculation of pressure drop in high pressure fractionators is discussed more fully in Chapter 8.)

As previously stated, at high liquid rates, pressure drop may be greater than that predicted from the generalized correlation, especially when smaller packing sizes are used. For operations carried out at liquid rates greater than those recommended for the packing size used, pressure drop should be calculated from a chart for the particular packing rather than from the generalized correlation.

The classical method of depicting the generalized pressure-drop correlation (as illustrated in Figure 1-15) uses a logarithmic scale for both the abscissa and the ordinate. Using this graph requires a difficult interpolation between parameters of constant pressure drop. Figure 1-16 presents a rearranged correlation that utilizes a linear scale for the ordinate. Further, to facilitate use of the correlation in distillation calculations, the ordinate has been expressed in terms of the capacity factor (C_s). Also, the gravitational constant (32.2) has been included in the ordinate value.

The packing factors given in Table 1-3 are for use with these generalized pressure-drop correlations (Figures 1-15 and 1-16). These packing factors have been determined from experimental pressure-drop data; therefore, they are empirical rather than theoretical in nature. The use of pressure drop to determine column size is discussed in detail in Chapter 3.

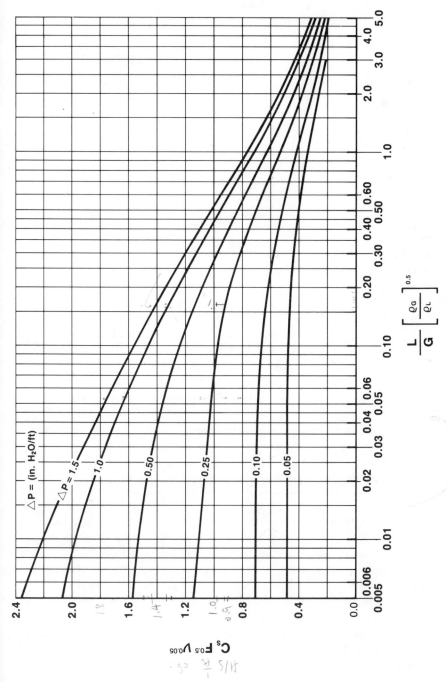

Figure 1-16. Alternate generalized pressure-drop correlation.

Table 1 – 3
Packing Factors (F) — Random Dumped Packings

	Nominal Packing Size (in.)							
	½	⅝	¾	1	1¼	1½	2	3 or 3½
IMTP® Packing (Metal)		51		41		24	18	12
Hy-Pak® Packing (Metal)				45		29	26	16
Super Intalox® Saddles (Ceramic)				60		30		
Super Intalox® Saddles (Plastic)				40			28	18
Pall Rings (Plastic)		95		55		40	26	17
Pall Rings (Metal)		81		56		40	27	18
Intalox® Saddles (Ceramic)	200		145	92		52	40	22
Raschig Rings (Ceramic)	580	380	255	179	125	93	65	37
Raschig Rings (1/32 in. Metal)	300	170	155	115				
Raschig Rings (1/16 in. Metal)	410	300	220	144	110	83	57	32
Berl Saddles (Ceramic)	240		170	110		65	45	

EFFECTS OF SURFACE TENSION AND FOAMING

There is no general agreement on the effect of liquid surface tension on the capacity of a packed bed. Eckert's series of tests using aqueous methanol solutions showed that reducing surface tension had no effect on the capacity of a packed bed, as long as that was the only different factor [10]. Further experiments with surfactants incorporated in aqueous systems showed a marked increase in pressure drop. However, when antifoams were added to the liquid, the pressure drop was lowered almost back to the level produced by a methanol solution with the same surface tension. Eckert deduced that foaming had caused the increase in pressure drop and that surface tension of a nonfoaming liquid had no effect on capacity. Later tests conducted by an independent research organization confirmed this conclusion.

Subsequent experience indicates that these experiments produced accurate conclusions with respect to absorption operations, since the tests were performed in this manner. In distillation operations, however, low surface tension liquids most commonly are encountered in the fractionation of light hydrocarbons under high pressure. The effects of surface tension in such applications are discussed in Chapter 8.

The presence of foam in a packed bed causes a marked increase in pressure drop [11]. The foam represents a very low-density liquid phase that can significantly reduce the void fraction within the packed bed. It has been suggested that a packed bed could be utilized to measure the foaming tendency of a system. This could be accomplished by running various gas flow rates through a packed bed countercurrent to a nonfoaming, pure, inert liquid and measuring the resulting pressure drops. The liquid under test could then be introduced into the column and pressure drops measured again at the same gas flow rates. Any pressure drop increase would give a measure of the degree of liquid foaming. Further, such a test would indicate whether foaming would be induced by gas flow rates above a certain critical value.

In many systems, there appears to be an operating froth present on the liquid's surface, especially when mass transfer occurs between the gas and liquid phases. A knowledgable designer will take into account the percentage increase in pressure drop this froth produces above that for a nonfoaming system.

In some systems, foam is induced because of the work done by the gas phase on the liquid phase. In such systems the pressure drop will increase at a faster rate with an increasing gas flow rate than it will with a nonfoaming system. The experienced designer operates the packed bed in these systems at a lower-than-normal gas flow rate, thus avoiding excessively high pressure drops.

A few systems produce stable foams in which the rate of foam generation equals or exceeds the rate of foam collapse at desired operating flows. Under these conditions, use of suitable antifoams is necessary for satisfactory packed bed operation. It may not be necessary to eliminate the foam completely, but merely to reduce it to a level that can be tolerated by the packed bed. Stable foams usually result from surface active agents and are controlled by the addition of antifoams. However, excessive quantities of antifoams themselves may produce a foaming system.

Pure liquids, or totally miscible solutions, normally are nonfoaming. Some low surface tension, halogenated organic liquids tend to foam slightly. Hydrocarbons with a molecular weight of 100 or more, organic liquids with a viscosity of 0.5 cps or greater, and partially immiscible liquids may foam moderately.

Heavy foaming can be expected in systems involving heavy oils, amines, or insoluble fine solids. Corrosion products or chemical breakdown end products often collect on the liquid surface and cause foaming. Filtration or adsorption operations commonly are employed to remove such contaminants from the system.

CONCURRENT FLOW OPERATION

Packed columns that operate with concurrent gas and liquid flows are not widely used. Countercurrent operation provides the greatest efficiency because mass transfer driving forces are at a maximum. However, in those operations where only a single mass transfer stage is required, concurrent operation may offer advantages.

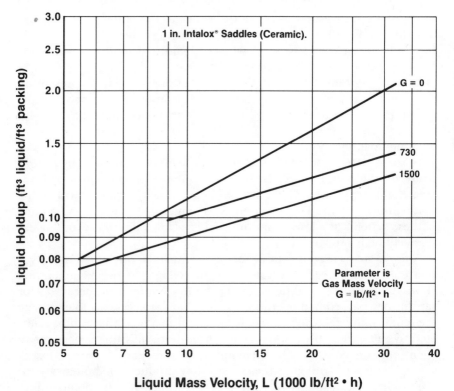

Figure 1-17. Concurrent flow liquid holdup (1-in. Intalox® Saddles (Ceramic)). (From Dodds [12]. Reproduced by permission of the American Institute of Chemical Engineers.)

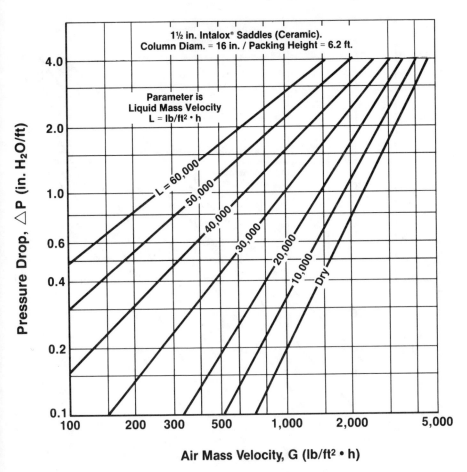

Figure 1-18. Pressure drop vs. gas rate—concurrent flow (1½-in. Intalox® Saddles (Ceramic)).

A packed bed in concurrent flow has no conventional flooding limitation because liquid holdup tends to decrease with an increasing gas rate as shown in Figure 1-17 [12]. The curve at zero gas flow shows the usual effect of liquid flow rate on operating holdup. As gas flows downward through the bed, it accelerates the liquid velocity, thus reducing the volumetric holdup.

When liquid is added to a packed bed in concurrent flow, the pressure drop increases, as shown in Figures 1-18 and 1-19, which apply to 1½-in. ceramic Intalox® saddle and 2-in. plastic Pall ring packings, respectively. The parameters of constant pressure drop in Figure 1-18 are not curved as is the case for Figure 1-14, where the same packing was oper-

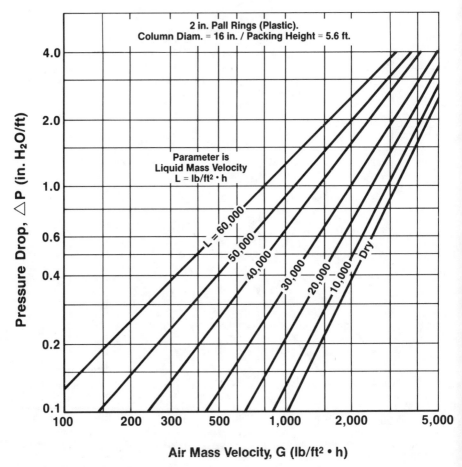

Figure 1-19. Pressure drop vs. gas rate—concurrent flow (2-in. Pall Rings (Plastic)).

ated in countercurrent flow. The dry line indicates that pressure drop is a function of the second power of the gas flow rate. At a liquid rate of 40 gpm/ft^2, the pressure drop in Figures 1-18 and 1-19 increases as the gas rate to the 1.7 power. As the liquid rate increases to 80 gpm/ft^2, the pressure drop increases as the gas rate to only the 1.1 power. At a very high liquid rate of 120 gpm/ft^2, the pressure drop increases as the gas rate to the 0.9 power, less than directly.

The pressure drop represents a loss of energy by the gas phase. As liquid flow is increased, more energy is required to accelerate the liquid velocity. This absorption of energy by the liquid phase represents an increasing percentage of the pressure drop as the liquid flow becomes greater.

As can be seen from Figures 1-18 and 1-19, the pressure drop in concurrent flow can be 1.0 or 2.0 or even 4.0 in. H_2O/ft of packed depth. Because of the higher allowable pressure drop, the capacity of a given diameter column is much greater in concurrent than in countercurrent flow operation. Gas and liquid contact intensity is greatly increased at higher flow rates; thus mass transfer rates can be elevated in concurrent flow.

In those systems where there is practically no vapor pressure of solute above the liquid phase, concurrent flow operation should be considered. Such applications include:

1. Absorption of low concentrations of ammonia by dilute acids.
2. Removal of traces of H_2S or CO_2 by absorption into caustic soda solutions.
3. Drying of chlorine gas with recirculated concentrated sulfuric acid.

This highly turbulent contact produced in concurrent flow is especially useful in removing fine solids from a gas stream. Removal efficiency improves as power input increases. This application is discussed more completely in Chapter 2.

EXAMPLE PROBLEM

An existing CO_2 absorber is 84 in. ID and operates at a pressure of 400 psia. The inlet gas analysis is as follows:

Component	Mol %
CH_4	2.7
CO_2	7.3
C_2H_6	75.0
C_3H_8	15.0

The inlet gas is bone dry and at a temperature of 85°F. The feed liquid is a 30 wt% aqueous diethanolamine solution containing 0.10 mol CO_2/mol DEA. The exit gas is to contain 0.5 mol % CO_2 and will be at 110°F, which is the same temperature as the inlet liquid.

What is the maximum capacity of this absorber if the effluent liquid contains 0.45 mol CO_2/mol DEA? The tower will be packed with #2 Hy-Pak® packing and, because of the foaming tendency of this system, the pressure drop is not to exceed 0.25 in. H_2O/ft at the point of maximum loading.

The inlet gas has a molecular weight of 32.8 and a density of 2.78 lb/ft^3 at operating conditions. The absorbant liquid has a density of 62.8 lb/ft^3 and a viscosity of 2.5 cps. The 30 wt% DEA solution contains 2.853 lb-mol of DEA per 1,000 lb of liquid feed. Absorbing 0.35 mol CO_2/mol DEA indicates that 0.999 lb-mol of CO_2 will be absorbed in each 1,000 lb of DEA solution feed. The inlet gas stream contains 7.875 lb-mol of CO_2 per 100 lb-mol of inert gas. The specifications require only 0.503 lb-mol of CO_2 be present per 100 lb-mol of dry inert exit gas. Therefore, 7.372 lb-mol of CO_2 must be absorbed for each 100 lb-mol of inert gas feed to the column.

By material balance on the CO_2 absorbed, the inlet inert gas flow is 13.55 lb-mol per 1,000 lbs of liquid feed. The total inlet gas flow is 14.61 lb-mol (or 479.2 lb of gas) per 1,000 lb of liquid feed. The effluent liquid stream contains 43.9 lb of absorbed CO_2 per 1,000 lb of liquid feed. The dry exit gas is humidified to an equilibrium water content above the feed DEA solution. Thus, the exit gas stream contains 0.30 mol % water vapor. The liquid effluent flow will be 1,043.2 lb for each 1,000 lb of liquid feed.

With this information the flow parameter at the bottom of the column, which is the point of maximum loading for an absorber, can be calculated:

$$X = \frac{1,043.2}{479.2} \left[\frac{2.78}{62.8}\right]^{0.5} = 0.458$$

From Figure 1-16, at this abscissa value and a pressure drop of 0.25 in. H_2O/ft, the ordinate value is 0.72. Therefore, because the #2 Hy-Pak® packing has a packing factor of 26 from Table 1-3,

$$0.72 = C_s(26)^{0.5}(2.5)^{0.05}$$

or

$$C_s = 0.135 \text{ fps}$$

Thus, the allowable gas mass velocity at this pressure drop is 6,278 lb/ft^2·h at the bottom of the bed. The maximum inlet gas rate for this 84-in. ID column is 241,600 lb/h at a pressure drop of 0.25 in. H_2O/ft of packed depth. The inlet flow of 30 wt% DEA solution is 504,200 lb/h. This is an irrigation rate of 26.0 gpm/ft^2, which is suitable for this size packing as previously discussed.

Although the maximum loading normally occurs at the absorber bottom, the top conditions should be checked. The exit gas flow is 219,800 lb/h with a density of 2.59 lb/ft³. The flow parameter at the top of the bed has a value of 0.466. The C_s at the top of the column is 0.127 fps, which gives an ordinate value of 0.678 on Figure 1-16. The pressure drop at the top of the packed bed is 0.22 in. H_2O/ft, which is lower than at the bottom of the bed as expected.

NOTATION

a_p	Surface area of packing (ft²/ft³)
C_s	Capacity factor (fps)
D_p	Packing diameter (ft)
F	Packing factor
G	Gas mass velocity (lb/ft²·h)
G*	Gas mass velocity (lb/ft²·s)
L	Liquid mass velocity (lb/ft²·h)
Re	Reynolds number
V	Superficial gas velocity (fps)
X	Flow parameter
u′	Viscosity (lb/ft·h)
ΔP	Pressure drop (in. H_2O/ft)
ϵ	Void fraction
ν	Kinematic liquid viscosity (cst)
ρ_G	Gas density (lb/ft³)
ρ_L	Liquid density (lb/ft³)
σ	Surface tension (dyne/cm)
ψ	Proportionality constant

REFERENCES

1. Kozeny, G. J. Sitzber, "Akad. Wiss. Wein, Math-naturw," *Kl. Abt.*, IIa, Vol. 136, 1927, p. 271.
2. Carman, P. C., *Journal of Society of Chemical Industry*, Vol. 57, 1938, p. 225 T.
3. Burke, S. P., and Plummer, W. B., *Industrial and Engineering Chemistry*, Vol. 20, 1928, p. 1196.
4. Ergun, S., *Chemical Engineering Progress*, Vol. 48, No. 2, 1952, p. 89.
5. Leva, M., *Tower Packings and Packed Tower Design*, 2nd ed., United States Stoneware, Chap. 2, 1953, p. 35.
6. Shulman, H. L., Ulrich, C. F., and Wells, N., *American Institute of Chemical Engineers' Journal*, Vol. 1, No. 2 , 1955, p. 247.
7. Sherwood, T. K., Shipley, G. H., and Holloway, F. A. L., *Industrial and Engineering Chemistry*, Vol. 30, 1938, p. 765.

8. Leva, M., *Chemical Engineering Progress,* Vol. 50, No. 10, 1954, p. 51.
9. Lobo, W. E., et al., *Transactions of American Institute of Chemical Engineers,* Vol. 41, 1945, p. 693.
10. Eckert, J. S., *Chemical Engineering Progress,* Vol. 57, No. 9, 1961, p. 54.
11. Larkins, R. P., and White, R. R., *American Institute of Chemical Engineers' Journal,* Vol. 7, No. 2, 1961, p. 231.
12. Dodds, W. S., et al., *American Institute of Chemical Engineers' Journal,* Vol. 6, No. 3, 1960, p. 390.

2

AIR POLLUTION CONTROL

Tower packing is used extensively in the scrubbing of corrosive, ob-
noxious, or hazardous gases, vapors, and particulates from an air
stream. Packed fume scrubbers operate on the principle of presenting a
large surface wetted by a liquid (usually water) over which the air flows
turbulently. Scrubbing is accomplished by impingement of particles on
the wetted packing surface and by absorption of soluble gas or vapor
molecules from the air by contact with the wetted surface.

GAS SCRUBBER TYPES

Packed scrubbers generally are arranged in one of four ways based on
the manner in which the liquid is contacted with the gas stream. Concur-
rent-flow scrubbers make up two of these classifications; in both cases
the liquid and gas flow in the same direction.

In a horizontal concurrent scrubber, the gas velocity carries scrubbing
liquid into the packed bed and the device actually operates as a wetted
entrainment separator. Normally, superficial gas velocity is limited to a
maximum of 9.6 fps due to liquid reentrainment at higher velocities.
Packed bed thickness is restricted because the depth of liquid penetration
into the tower packing is limited by the allowable gas velocity.

A vertical concurrent scrubber can operate at very high gas velocities
so that pressure drops from 1 in. H_2O/ft to as high as 3 in. H_2O/ft are
common. There is no flooding limit of the packing because the liquid
holdup in the packed bed decreases as the gas rate increases (see Figure
1-17). Contact time between gas and liquid is a function of bed depth as
well as the gas velocity. Absorption driving forces are reduced because
the exit gas is in contact with the highest concentration of contaminant in
the liquid phase. The exit-gas phase may contain substantial liquid en-

trainment that must be removed before this gas is discharged into the atmosphere.

The third class of scrubber is called cross-flow. This device contacts a horizontally flowing gas stream with a vertically descending liquid flow. Thus, cross-sectional area for gas flow is different from the area for liquid flow. Liquid flow rates as low as 2.6 gpm per 1,000 cfm of gas may be possible with this arrangement rather than a minimum liquid rate of 4.2 gpm per 1,000 cfm when the gas flow area is the same as the liquid flow area.

Mass transfer driving forces are intermediate between vertical concurrent scrubbers and countercurrent scrubbers. If the absorbed solute obeys Henry's law in the liquid phase, the mass transfer driving force will limit solute removal efficiency to about 90% for typical chemical fumes assuming scrubbing water flow is limited. However, if the absorption of solute is followed by a rapid chemical reaction in the liquid phase so that there is no appreciable vapor pressure of solute above the solution, the mass transfer driving force will be the same as for a countercurrent scrubber.

The most widely used type of scrubber operates with gas and liquid in countercurrent flow as the liquid flows vertically downward under the influence of gravity. Maximum gas flow rate is limited by liquid entrainment or by pressure drop. Packed bed depth as well as gas velocity controls contact time between the gas and liquid phases. Mass transfer driving forces are maximized because the exit-gas stream contacts the entering liquid, which contains a minimum or zero solute concentration.

The pressure drop through the tower packing is very important because the cost of power to move the gas stream through the scrubber may be the largest operating cost factor. Most tower packing manufacturers can provide experimental pressure drop data specific to the air/water system. If this information is not available, the pressure drop can be determined from the generalized pressure-drop correlation shown in Figure 1-15 or Figure 1-16.

Countercurrent scrubbers generally have these characteristics:

- Designed to operate at a pressure drop between 0.25 and 0.60 in. H_2O/ft of packed depth.
- Air velocity normally between 5.5 fps and 8.0 fps if modern, high-capacity plastic tower packings are used.
- Inlet concentrations of contaminant in the gas stream normally do not exceed 5,000 ppm by volume.
- Liquid irrigation rates typically are from 2 to 8 gpm/ft^2 of column cross-sectional area.

Plastic packings have been used extensively in scrubbers because of their light weight, low cost, and resistance to mechanical damage. Such packings offer a wide range of resistance to chemical attack by acids, alkalis, and many organic compounds. However, it should be recognized that plastic packings can be deformed by excessive temperatures or by exposure to certain solvents.

PARTICULATE REMOVAL

Removal of a solid or liquid particulate involves a physical capture by wetting after the particle has penetrated the liquid surface. There is no limit to the amount of particulate capture that can be achieved as long as the liquid-film properties remain unchanged during the scrubbing operation.

Wet packed scrubbers are at least 99% efficient for removing particles of 10-micron or larger equivalent particle diameter. Removal efficiencies of 90% to 95% can be expected even on 6-micron particle material. Generally, for a given type of wet scrubber, the greater the power applied to the system the higher the collection efficiency for the particulate material. However, in a countercurrent packed scrubber, the power applied (as reflected by pressure drop) is limited by hydraulic flooding of the packing. Thus, for a three-micron average particle diameter, 75% to 80% removal efficiency can be obtained. With a 1-micron average particle diameter, the power input would limit removal efficiency in a countercurrent scrubber to about 35 wt % of the entering particulate.

To obtain impingement and capture of a particle, the liquid must wet the particulate, and make it a part of the liquid phase as a means of removing it from the gas stream. The inertial effect (which depends on the mass of the particle and its velocity) must be sufficient to allow the particle to follow a different path than that of the gas stream. This causes it to impinge on the surface of the wetted packing elements. The optimum packing, therefore, should present an adequate impingement surface for particle capture while producing a low pressure drop. The tower packing must have surfaces that can be continuously wetted and must resist entrainment of liquid into the gas phase.

The removal efficiency depends on the kinetic energy possessed by the particle, which is:

$$KE = \frac{wV^2}{2g} \tag{2-1}$$

The mass at constant specific gravity is a function of the cube of the equivalent particle diameter. For example, to capture a 3-micron particle with the same efficiency as a 5-micron particle, the gas velocity must be increased by 2.15 times. Because pressure drop is proportional to the square of the gas velocity, the scrubber must operate at 4.62 times the pressure drop for the 3-micron particle to be captured with the same efficiency as 5-micron particle removal.

A concurrently operated vertical scrubber removes the restriction of power input with respect to hydraulic flooding of the packed bed. Therefore, this device can operate at higher gas velocities and greater pressure drops than a countercurrently operated scrubber. With increased power input possible, concurrently operated packed scrubbers are much more effective for the removal of particles from one- to three-micron equivalent diameter than countercurrent units. Table 2-1 shows typical size ranges for common particulate emissions [1]. Tobacco smoke has been included in this list to provide a comparison of size with commonly encountered particulates.

Table 2 – 1
Typical Industrial Particulate Emissions

Particulate	Size Range (Microns)
Ground Limestone	40 to 900
Fly Ash	2 to 700
Cement Dust	3 to 80
Electroplating Mist	5 to 50
Sulfuric Acid Mist	0.5 to 30
Insecticide Dust	0.5 to 9
Alkali Fumes	0.1 to 5
Galvanizing Flux	0.1 to 1
Oil Smoke	0.03 to 0.90
Magnesium Oxide Smoke	0.01 to 0.40
Tobacco Smoke	0.01 to 0.40
Zinc Oxide Fumes	0.01 to 0.40

Source: Eckert [1].

GAS SCRUBBING

Gas or vapor removal is more complex than particulate removal because the constituent removed from the air stream is dissolved in the liquid phase and may change the liquid properties. A solution of any volatile material exhibits a vapor pressure of the solute above the liquid phase. This vapor pressure increases with solute concentration and liquid temperature. Contaminant removal continues only so long as the partial pressure of that constituent in the gas phase exceeds the vapor pressure of that solute above the liquid phase. Contaminant removal rate is a function of this driving force pressure difference as well as the mass transfer coefficient.

Calculating fume scrubber efficiency requires an understanding of mass transfer principles. When a solute is transferred from one phase to another, resistance to mass transfer results in a concentration gradient. If solute is transferred from a vapor phase to a liquid phase, the solute concentration in the vapor phase must be greater than the equilibrium concentration in the liquid phase. It usually is assumed that the interface between the two phases consists of a gas film in contact with a liquid film. Further, at the interface, solute concentration in the gas film is in equilibrium with the solute concentration in the liquid film. A gas stream contaminant must pass from the main body of gas through the gas film, then through the liquid film, and finally dissolve into the main body of liquid. In this approach to absorption, it is assumed that the resistances to mass transfer are represented by the gas and liquid films.

The driving force for mass transfer in the gas phase is a pressure difference. The solute transferred from the main gas phase through the gas film is:

$$N = AZk_Ga(p - p') \tag{2-2}$$

The partial pressure of contaminant in the gas phase is a function of concentration:

$$p = yP \tag{2-3}$$

Thus Equations 2-2 and 2-3 may be combined and rewritten as:

$$N = AZk_GaP(y - y') \tag{2-4}$$

The driving force in the liquid phase is a concentration difference. The solute transferred through the liquid film to the main liquid phase is:

$$N = AZk_La(x' - x) \tag{2-5}$$

Unfortunately it is difficult to determine the solute concentration in the gas film or in the liquid film. However, it can be assumed that over a small solute concentration change, a linear equilibrium relationship exists that relates the concentrations in the gas and liquid phases for at least one theoretical stage. The relationship between the two phases can be expressed in terms of the equilibrium curve slope:

$$m = \frac{y' - y^*}{x' - x} \tag{2-6a}$$

or

$$m = \frac{y - y'}{x^* - x'} \tag{2-6b}$$

Equation 2-4 can be rewritten as:

$$y - y' = \frac{N}{AZk_GaP} \tag{2-7}$$

Equation 2-6 can be substituted into Equation 2-5 to produce:

$$N = \frac{AZ}{m} k_La(y' - y^*) \tag{2-8}$$

so that:

$$y' - y^* = \frac{mN}{AZk_La} \tag{2-9}$$

Adding the driving forces for the two films yields:

$$(y - y') + (y' - y^*) = \frac{N}{AZk_GaP} + \frac{mN}{AZk_La} \tag{2-10}$$

Eliminating the interfacial concentration term produces:

$$y - y^* = \frac{N}{AZ}\left[\frac{1}{k_GaP} + \frac{m}{k_La}\right] \tag{2-11}$$

The solute transferred per unit time depends on the concentration gradient, the interfacial area, and the system's mass transfer resistance. Resistance to mass transfer is postulated to consist of a gas-phase resistance and a liquid-phase resistance in series. These resistances are the reciprocals of the mass transfer rates. Thus the overall resistance to mass transfer expressed in terms of the gas phase is:

$$\frac{1}{K_G a P} = \frac{1}{k_G a P} + \frac{m}{k_L a} \qquad (2\text{-}12)$$

This is the familiar two-film theory of mass transfer with the gas-phase mass transfer coefficient expressed in the usual units of partial-pressure driving force.

The solute transferred in terms of the overall gas-phase mass transfer coefficient is:

$$N = A Z K_G a P(y - y^*) \qquad (2\text{-}13)$$

Likewise the overall resistance to mass transfer expressed in terms of the liquid phase is:

$$\frac{1}{K_L a} = \frac{1}{m k_G a P} + \frac{1}{k_L a} \qquad (2\text{-}14)$$

Similarly, the solute transferred in terms of the overall liquid-phase mass transfer coefficient is:

$$N = A Z K_L a(x^* - x) \qquad (2\text{-}15)$$

REMOVAL EFFICIENCY DETERMINATION

As previously stated, the mass transfer rate is considered to be determined by the gas-film resistance operating in series with the liquid-film resistance. The film that offers the predominant mass transfer resistance is called the controlling film. Contaminants that have a limited solubility in the liquid phase (a high value of m) usually are considered to be a liquid-film-controlled system. Contaminants that are highly soluble in the liquid phase (a low value of m) usually are considered to be a gas-film-controlled system.

A calculation can be made for the solute transferred based on the compositions of the main-body gas phase and the main-body liquid phase. It requires only a knowledge of the equilibrium relationship between y and x. For low concentrations of a non-reacting solute in the liquid phase, the equilibrium partial pressure of solute above the liquid phase is expressed by Henry's Law:

$$p^* = Hx \qquad (2\text{-}16)$$

At low concentrations of solute and ambient temperature operation, the Henry's Law constant (H) can be considered a fixed value. Using the two-film theory would require a knowledge of the value of H to evaluate the driving force magnitude as well as the mass transfer coefficient.

In certain applications where the dissolved solute would exhibit a high vapor pressure above the resultant solution, a reactive chemical is added to the liquid phase. The function of this reactant is to combine rapidly with the absorbed solute so as to eliminate or substantially reduce the vapor pressure of the solute above the liquid phase. In these situations the mass transfer driving force is maximized. Further, the scrubbing solution can be recirculated while still obtaining a high fume removal efficiency. For example, the use of an alkaline scrubbing liquid for removal of chlorine from a gas stream is common practice.

PRACTICAL APPLICATIONS

In fume scrubbing operations, often it is not possible to define the gas flow rate or contaminant concentration with great precision. Obviously, the scrubber design cannot be more exact than the definition of the scrubbing problem. However, there has been much experience in the scrubbing of many common contaminant gases, which permits the use of simplifying assumptions to provide a rapid design procedure. The empirical overall mass transfer coefficients derived from this experience allow for assumptions such as a small partial pressure of solute above the effluent liquid.

If a large excess of scrubbing water is used, solute concentration in the liquid phase (x) approaches zero. If a chemical that reacts with the solute is present in the liquid phase, the value of H may approach zero. In either case, the mass transfer driving force approaches a value of yP. Since total system pressure (P) is constant, a ln mean average driving force can be used:

$$\Delta p_{LM} = P\left[\frac{y_i - y_o}{\ln(y_i/y_o)}\right] \qquad (2\text{-}17)$$

Then Equation 2-13 may be expressed as:

$$N = K_GaAZ\Delta p_{LM} \tag{2-18}$$

When very low concentrations of solute are being removed from the gas phase, the solute transferred from the gas stream is:

$$N = Gm(y_i - y_o) \tag{2-19}$$

Equations 2-17, 2-18, and 2-19 may be combined to give:

$$Gm(y_i - y_o) = K_GaAZP\left[\frac{y_i - y_o}{\ln(y_i/y_o)}\right] \tag{2-20}$$

Equation 2-20 can be simplified to produce:

$$Gm = \frac{K_GaAZP}{\ln(y_i/y_o)} \tag{2-21}$$

and then arranged to:

$$\ln(y_i/y_o) = \frac{K_GaAZP}{Gm} \tag{2-22}$$

A rapid design can be carried out using a graphical procedure. A semi-log plot of solute removal efficiency at constant Gm/A gas rate per unit of column area can be made against the packed depth with K_Ga as the parameter.

The percent removal efficiency of contaminant is:

$$E = 100(1 - y_o/y_i) \tag{2-23}$$

This graphical design procedure will apply to most fume scrubbers that operate at atmospheric pressure.

LIQUID-FILM-CONTROLLED SYSTEMS

For a liquid-film-controlled system, the effect of gas rate on the over-all K_Ga value is small and will not significantly alter graphical calculations. The plots in Figures 2-1, 2-2, and 2-3 permit rapid determination of the packed height required for fume scrubbers in such systems. As can be seen, the packed depth necessary for a given solute removal efficiency becomes greater with increasing gas rate. *(text continued on page 41)*

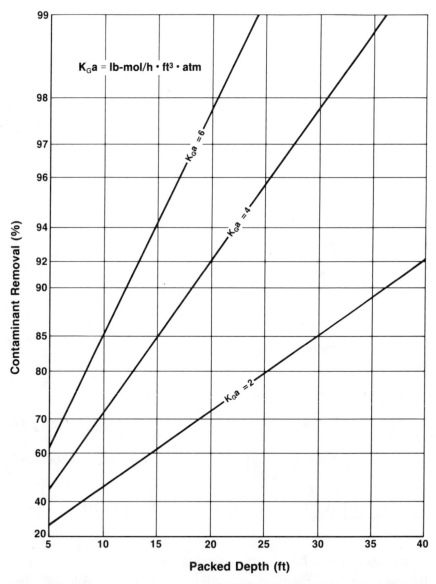

Figure 2-1. Packed depth requirements for liquid-film-controlled systems (3.5 fps gas rate). (From *1983 Equipment* [2]. Reprinted by permission from ASHRAE Handbook.)

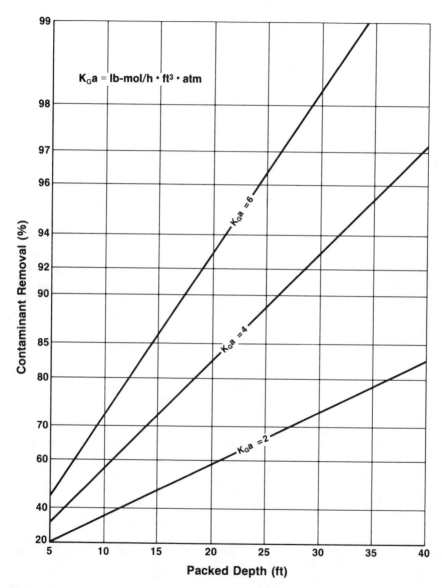

Figure 2-2. Packed depth requirements for liquid-film-controlled systems (5.0 fps gas rate). (From *1983 Equipment* [2]. Reprinted by permission from ASHRAE Handbook.)

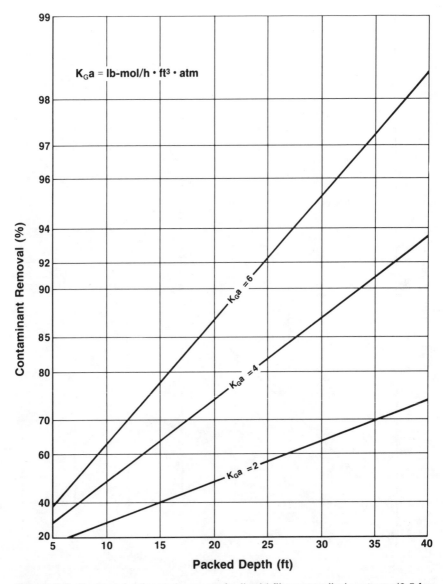

Figure 2-3. Packed depth requirements for liquid-film-controlled systems (6.5 fps gas rate). (From *1983 Equipment* [2]. Reprinted by permission from ASHRAE Handbook.)

Table 2 – 2
K_Ga Values for Liquid-Film Controlled Systems

Gas Contaminant	Scrubbing Liquid	Overall K_Ga Value (lb-mol/h • ft³ • atm)
Carbon Dioxide	4% NaOH	1.5
Hydrogen Sulfide	4% NaOH	4.4
Sulfur Dioxide	Water	2.2
Hydrogen Cyanide	Water	4.4
Formaldehyde	Water	4.4
Chlorine	Water	3.4
Bromine	5% NaOH	3.7
Chlorine Dioxide	Water	4.4

Note: K_Ga Values apply to 2 in. plastic Super Intalox* packing at a gas velocity of 3.5 fps and a liquid rate of 4 gpm/ft².

Source: *1983 Equipment* [2]. Reprinted by permission from ASHRAE Handbook.

(text continued from page 37)

Liquid-film-controlled systems usually provide low K_Ga values that are less than 6 lb-mol/h•ft³•atm. Table 2-2 shows the comparative base K_Ga values for various systems [2]. These base values apply to a gas rate of 3.5 fps superficial velocity, a liquid irrigation rate of 4 gpm/ft², and atmospheric pressure operation. Values shown are for 2-in. plastic Super Intalox® packing.

The packed depth required for other sizes or types of tower packings is a function of the ratio: K_Ga value for 2-in. plastic Super Intalox® packing to K_Ga value for the other packing. Table 2-3 gives relative K_Ga values for tower packings commonly used in fume scrubbers.

Liquid flow rate has a significant effect on the overall K_Ga value. A doubling of the liquid irrigation rate typically will increase the overall K_Ga value by 25%. Table 2-4 gives the correction factor for the K_Ga value that applies to liquid rates other than the base value of 4 gpm/ft². The K_Ga values given in Table 2-2 are typical for liquid temperatures from 60° to 75°F. Higher liquid temperatures normally increase K_Ga values. However, a maximum K_Ga value may be achieved for the particular system. This occurs because at higher temperatures the diffusion rate of the solute dissolved in the liquid phase increases but the solubility of a gaseous solute in the liquid phase usually decreases. Although the K_Ga value theoretically is independent of the driving force (Δp_{LM}), the effect of the solubility (m or H) is shown by Equation 2-12.

Table 2 – 3
Relative K_Ga Values for Tower Packings

Type of Packing	Size (in.)			
	1	1½	2	3 or 3½
Plastic Super Intalox® Saddles	1.49	—	1.00	0.63
Metal Hy-Pak® Packing	1.52	1.28	1.12	0.76
Metal Pall Rings	1.62	1.32	1.13	0.65
Plastic Pall Rings	1.38	1.19	1.05	0.63
Ceramic Intalox® Saddles	1.42	1.19	0.99	0.57
Ceramic Raschig Rings	1.21	1.02	0.84	0.51
Plastic Tellerette® Packing	1.52	—	1.38	—
Plastic Maspac® Packing	—	—	1.00	0.62

Source: *1983 Equipment* [2]. Reprinted by permission from ASHRAE Handbook.

Table 2 – 4
Effect of Liquid Rate on Scrubber Efficiency

Liquid Rate (gpm/ft²)	Relative K_Ga Value
2.0	0.80
3.0	0.91
4.0	1.00
5.0	1.07
6.0	1.14
8.0	1.25
10.0	1.34

GAS-FILM-CONTROLLED SYSTEMS

In a gas-film-controlled system, the effect of liquid rate on the overall K_Ga value is essentially the same as for a liquid-film-controlled system such as that shown in Table 2-4. In addition, in such a system the gas rate has a significant effect on the overall mass transfer coefficient. Similarly, Figures 2-4, 2-5, and 2-6 allow a rapid determination of the packed depth required for fume scrubbers in gas-film-controlled systems. In these plots the overall K_Ga value has been corrected for the effect of the gas flow rate. Because the K_Ga value increases with an increasing gas flow rate, the solute removal efficiency drops only slightly for a fixed packed depth as the gas rate is increased in such a system.

(text continued on page 46)

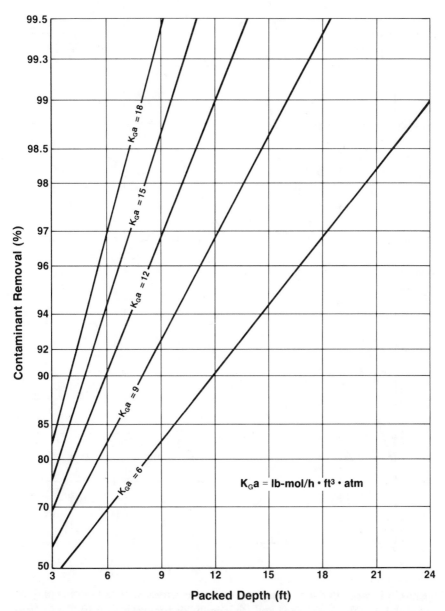

Figure 2-4. Packed depth requirements for gas-film-controlled systems (3.5 fps gas rate). (From *1983 Equipment* [2]. Reprinted by permission from ASHRAE Handbook.)

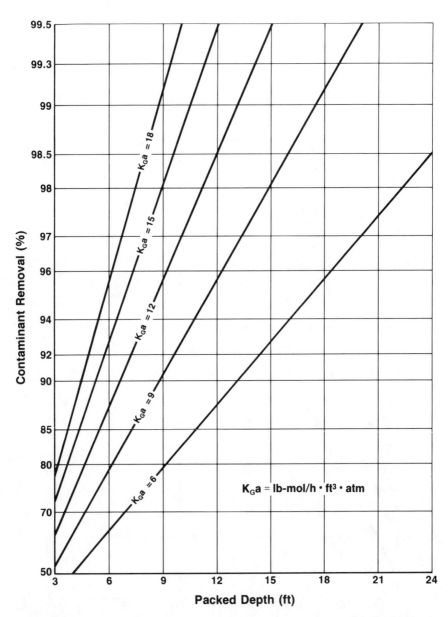

Figure 2-5. Packed depth requirements for gas-film-controlled systems (5.0 fps gas rate). (From *1983 Equipment* [2]. Reprinted by permission from ASHRAE Handbook.)

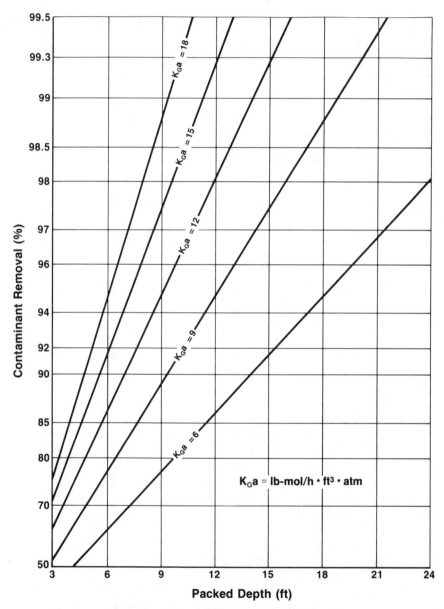

Figure 2-6. Packed depth requirements for gas-film-controlled systems (6.5 fps gas rate). (From *1983 Equipment* [2]. Reprinted by permission from ASHRAE Handbook.)

(text continued from page 42)

Gas-film-controlled systems normally have higher K_Ga values than liquid-film-controlled systems. Table 2-5 shows the base K_Ga values for typical gas-film-controlled systems at 3.5 fps superficial gas velocity and 4 gpm/ft² liquid irrigation rate [2]. These values apply for 2-in. plastic Super Intalox® packing and for liquid temperatures from 60° to 75° F. The packed depth required for other tower packings is a function of the ratio: K_Ga value for 2-in. plastic Super Intalox® packing to K_Ga value for the packing selected as shown in Table 2-3. The packed depth required also is inversely proportional to the relative K_Ga values corrected for liquid rate as given in Table 2-4.

Table 2 – 5
K_Ga Values for Gas-Film Controlled Systems

Gas Contaminant	Scrubbing Liquid	Overall K_Ga Value (lb-mol/h · ft³ · atm)
Hydrogen Chloride	Water	14
Hydrogen Fluoride	Water	6.0
Ammonia	Dilute Acid	13
Chlorine	8% NaOH	10.8
Sulfur Dioxide	11% Na₂CO₃	8.9

Note: K_Ga values apply to 2 in. plastic Super Intalox* packing at a gas velocity of 3.5 fps and a liquid rate of 4 gpm/ft².

Source: *1983 Equipment* [2]. Reprinted by permission from ASHRAE Handbook.

If the scrubbing liquid contains a chemical that reacts with the contaminant absorbed from the gas stream, at least 33% excess of this chemical over the amount theoretically required should be provided when determining the circulating liquid rate. Hydrogen chloride dissolved in water develops a negligible partial pressure of the contaminant when the solution has a concentration less than 8 wt% HCl. However, if ammonia is dissolved in water, there is an appreciable partial pressure of the contaminant above the resulting solution even at 1 wt% NH_3 concentration. To use Figures 2-4, 2-5, and 2-6 in fume scrubber design for this system, the scrubbing liquid must contain enough dilute acid to keep the liquid phase pH below seven.

SCRUBBER SIZE DETERMINATION

To use Figures 2-1 through 2-6, in the design of a countercurrent scrubber, the column diameter first must be selected to fix the superficial gas velocity. Next, a convenient liquid irrigation rate between 2 and 8 gpm/ft² of column cross-sectional area is chosen. Most commercial scrubbers use liquid irrigation rates between 3 and 6 gpm/ft². However, the minimum liquid feed rate for scrubbing with water normally provides a solute concentration not greater than 0.002 mol fraction in the effluent liquid.

It is necessary to know the base K_Ga value for the system to be handled in the scrubber. If experimental data or industrial experience is not available, the base K_Ga value should be selected from Tables 2-2 or 2-5 for the system that most closely resembles that under consideration. The percent removal efficiency is determined from the solute concentration in the inlet-gas stream and the allowable concentration of that solute in the exit-gas stream.

If the base K_Ga value for the system involved is less than 6.0 lb-mol/ h · ft³ · atm, Figures 2-1 through 2-3 usually apply. If the base K_Ga value is greater than 6.0 lb-mol/h · ft³ · atm, Figures 2-4 through 2-6 normally should be used. The base K_Ga value chosen should be adjusted for the effect of liquid rate using the values shown in Table 2-4. The removal efficiency desired is located on the ordinate of Figures 2-1 through 2-6 and the packed depth required is read on the abscissa by interpolation between the parameters that enclose the adjusted K_Ga value.

The packed depth just determined applies for 2-in. plastic Super Intalox® packing. For other types or sizes of tower packings, this depth should be multiplied by the ratio: K_Ga for 2-in. plastic Super Intalox® packing to K_Ga value for the packing selected as given in Table 2-3. This procedure is shown in detail in the example problem at the end of this chapter.

If the packed depth just determined is excessive, the designer should increase the liquid rate and/or select a different tower packing. If the packed depth required still is too high, either the removal efficiency required must be reduced or two scrubbers should be operated in series.

After the initial design is fixed, the pressure drop should be calculated using Figure 1-15 or Figure 1-16. The operating pressure drop should not exceed 0.60 in. H_2O/ft when water is used as the scrubbing liquid. When other liquids are used, the pressure drop normally is a maximum of 0.40 in. H_2O/ft if the liquid specific gravity is at least 0.80. Some liquids containing dissolved salts or solid particulates tend to foam. This foaming of the liquid phase will be greater when the fume scrubber is operated at high pressure drops. For such foaming systems, the scrubber should be designed to produce a maximum pressure drop of 0.35 in H_2O/ft of packed depth. If the calculated pressure drop for the scrubber exceeds the allowable value, then the design procedure must be repeated using a larger diameter column or a different tower packing.

NOx REMOVAL

A special design procedure is necessary for fume scrubbers intended to remove NOx from gas streams. The contaminant usually is a mixture of NO, NO_2 together with its dimer N_2O_4, and N_2O_5. NO is a relatively insoluble gas. It must be oxidized to NO_2 before it becomes soluble in water and allows effective absorption. The N_2O_5 is readily soluble in water to produce a nitric acid solution.

When NO_2 is dissolved in water, two thirds of the mols react with water to form nitric acid. However, the other one third of the mols are desorbed into the gas stream as NO:

$$3NO_2 + H_2O = 2HNO_3 + NO \qquad (2\text{-}24)$$

The by-product NO then must be oxidized to NO_2 for it to be reabsorbed. Because this oxidation reaction in the gas phase is time dependent, NO_2 removal efficiency usually is limited to about 80% in a single fume scrubber when water is the scrubbing liquid.

When sodium hydroxide solutions are used for scrubbing NO_2, the resultant reaction produces equal mols of sodium nitrate and sodium nitrite:

$$2NO_2 + 2Na\,OH = Na\,NO_3 + Na\,NO_2 + H_2O \qquad (2\text{-}25)$$

The NO_2 first must be absorbed by the water into the liquid film before it can react with the caustic. In such a liquid phase two competing reactions take place: NO_2 with water and NO_2 with NaOH. If the NaOH concentration in the liquid film is deficient, NO gas is released back into the gas phase in accordance with Equation 2-24. The diffusion rate of NaOH into the liquid film is a function of the liquid-phase solution concentration. For this system, 3 normal (12 wt%) NaOH seems to provide optimum absorption efficiency. Higher solution concentrations are less effective because the associated greater liquid viscosity retards the diffusion rate of the NaOH as well as the products of reaction.

NO_2 removal efficiency, as defined by Equation 2-23, can be related to the gas retention time (i.e., the depth of the packed bed divided by the superficial gas velocity). Empirically, suitable designs for such scrubbers employing water as the liquid phase are produced using:

$$\ln\left[\frac{y_o}{y_i}\right] = -0.734 \ln\left[\frac{Z}{V}\right] - 0.141 \qquad (2\text{-}26)$$

This relationship seems to apply as long as the NO_2 concentration in the exit gas (y_o) is not less than 200 ppm by volume. Such scrubbers usually use a 1-in. or 1½-in. size tower packing and employ a liquid irrigation rate of at least 4 gpm/ft².

Where an NaOH solution is used as the scrubbing liquid, the removal efficiency for NO_2 is substantially increased as compared to water scrubbing according to:

$$\ln \left[\frac{y_o}{y_i}\right] = -0.736 \frac{Z}{V} - 0.130 \qquad (2\text{-}27)$$

Normally, these scrubbers are operated in a batch mode with respect to the liquid phase. A 12 wt% NaOH solution will be charged to the system and recirculated until there is 2 wt% free NaOH remaining. Equation 2-27 gives the average removal efficiency over one liquid batch. Initially the NO_2 removal efficiency is higher, then efficiency deteriorates as the free NaOH concentration becomes lower. Such scrubbers usually use a 2-in. size packing and a liquid recirculation rate of about 6 gpm/ft².

Usually the gas stream entering the scrubber contains other oxides of nitrogen in addition to NO_2. Any residual NO in the gas stream leaving the scrubber tends to oxidize on mixing with the outside air. A colorless exit stack cannot be assured when scrubbing NOx contaminants.

ODOR CONTROL

Some contaminants in a gas stream are neither chemical pollutants nor objectionable particulates. They are malodorous materials that are considered a nuisance if vented into the atmosphere. The maximum desired atmospheric level of a malodorous substance is defined as that concentration just below the threshold of detection by 50% of an odor panel. Table 2-6 gives this detection limit for many common malodorous substances [3]. Note that many substances can be sensed by the olfactory nerves at levels below one part per billion. For instance, hydrogen sulfide can be detected to one fifth of one ppb, while butyric acid (the principal odor from rancid butter) can be detected to one half of one ppb.

Countercurrently operated packed scrubbers are one method for controlling malodorous emissions. A wet scrubber absorbs the malodorous material into the liquid phase; however, many of these substances have limited solubility in water. If the scrubber operates with a once-through water flow, the effluent liquid may be a source of water pollution as the

Table 2 – 6
Odor Threshold of Common Materials

Chemical Compound	50% Threshold (ppb by vol)
Acetaldehyde	210
Acetic acid	210
Acrolein	100
Aniline	1000
Benzyl chloride	10
Benzyl sulfide	2.1
Butyric acid	0.5
Carbon disulfide	100
Chloral	47
p-Cresol	0.5
Dimethyl amine	21
Dimethyl sulfide	1
Diphenyl sulfide	2.1
Ethyl acrylate	0.1
Ethyl mercaptan	0.5
Formaldehyde	1000
Hydrogen sulfide	0.2
Methyl mercaptan	1
Methyl methacrylate	210
Monochlorbenzene	210
Nitrobenzene	4.7
Phenol	21
Phosgene	470
Pyridine	10
Styrene	47
Sulfur dioxide	470
Toluene diisocyanate	210
Trimethyl amine	0.2

malodorous substance in the effluent liquid is desorbed into the surrounding atmosphere. If the scrubbing liquid is recirculated over the scrubber packing, the exit-gas stream is limited to a contaminant concentration in equilibrium with this entering liquid.

For effective odor control, normally there is a chemically reactive compound added to the scrubbing liquid that converts the absorbed contaminant into a less objectionable substance. Hydrogen sulfide, for instance, can be absorbed by a solution of sodium hydroxide in which it is quite soluble. This is due to a chemical reaction with the absorbed solute that forms a stable sulfide. There are only a few inorganic odorous substances, such as sulfur dioxide, hydrogen chloride, nitric oxide, hydrogen sulfide, hydrogen cyanide, ozone, chlorine, and ammonia. Removing such contaminants by absorption has been practiced for some time; however, it is becoming increasingly difficult to dispose of the spent scrubbing liquid. In large-capacity systems, for economical reasons, the reactive absorbant may be regenerated. Thus, H_2S absorbed into an alkaline solution can be oxidized to elemental sulfur. Then, the sulfur can be recovered and the scrubbing liquid recycled.

Removal of organic odors is a much more complex problem. Wet scrubbing using a combination of absorbant and oxidant has successfully reduced such odors. The malodorous substance first is absorbed into the liquid phase; then the oxidant converts the absorbed contaminant to less odorous substance. This sequence eliminates the normal Henry's Law vapor pressure that would be exhibited if the malodorous material simply were absorbed into water. Because these oxidants represent an operating expense, this type of system usually is applied to gas streams from which massive concentrations of organic materials previously have been eliminated. The four most popular oxidants used in the liquid phase are potassium permanganate, sodium hypochlorite, hydrogen peroxide, and chlorine dioxide. The operation of such scrubbers requires careful control of the oxidant concentration as well as the solution pH. Degradation products also must be purged from the solution to prevent their buildup.

Table 2-7 gives some successful applications of this technique as applied to a variety of industrial odors. Such scrubber designs normally

Table 2 – 7
Typical Odor Control Applications

Industry	Contaminant	Absorbant	Oxidant
Brass Foundry	phenol formaldehyde	Na_2CO_3 solution	$KMnO_4$
Varnish Plant	alkyd resin	NaOH solution	$KMnO_4$
Iron Foundry	amines	$NaHSO_4$ solution	$KMnO_4$
Silver Plating	cyanides	NaOH solution	NaOCl
Food Processing	vegetable oil	$Na_2B_4O_7$ solution	$KMnO_4$
Pulp Mill	organic sulfides	H_2SO_4 solution	ClO_2
Hardboard	linseed oil	NaOH solution	$KMnO_4$
Rendering	ham fat	NaOH solution	NaOCl

use a small-size plastic packing, such as 1-in. Super Intalox® packing. This type of packing presents a large surface area for malodorous material absorption and provides a high liquid residence time for oxidation of the absorbed contaminant. Typically, the tower diameter is selected to produce a superficial air velocity from 4.5 fps to 6.0 fps. The liquid circulation rate usually will be 17 to 22 gpm per 1,000 cfm of air flow. Packed-bed depth normally varies from 6 ft to 8 ft. An effective entrainment eliminator should be installed in the top of the scrubber to prevent the loss of costly chemical solution in the outlet-gas stream.

EXAMPLE PROBLEM

A wastewater treatment unit is ventilated at an air flow of 25,800 cfm. This air is scrubbed at atmospheric pressure and a temperature of 65°F. The inlet-air stream contains 50 ppm by volume H_2S that is to be absorbed with a recirculated caustic soda solution containing an average of 4 wt% NaOH. The exhausted air is to contain a time weighted average of 2 ppm by volume maximum H_2S concentration. A scrubber design is needed that does not require more than 4-in. H_2O total pressure drop.

For such a large size scrubber, a liquid circulation rate of 6 gpm/ft^2 has been selected. To keep the scrubber shell height reasonable, a 1^1/$_2$-in. size plastic Pall ring packing will be used. From Table 2-2, the base K_Ga value for this absorption system is 4.4 lb-mol/h·ft^3·atm. This K_Ga value must be adjusted for the higher liquid circulation rate based on the factors from Table 2-4:

$$K_Ga = \frac{1.14}{1.00}(4.4) = 5.0 \text{ lb-mol/h·ft}^3\text{·atm}$$

Because this is a liquid-film-controlled system, the small gas rate effect is not significant in these graphical calculations. Using Figure 2-2, the packed depth required for 96% H_2S removal at a gas rate of 5.0 fps is 30.2 ft for 2-in. plastic Super Intalox® packing. For the 1^1/$_2$-in. plastic Pall rings, the bed depth can be corrected by factors taken from Table 2-3:

$$Z = \frac{1.00}{1.19}(30.2) = 25.4 \text{ ft}$$

At 5.0 fps gas rate, the scrubber cross-sectional area required is 86.0 ft^2 so a 10-ft 6-in. ID tower will be specified. At 6 gpm/ft^2 liquid irrigation rate, the recirculated caustic solution flow is 520 gpm.

Next the pressure drop through the packed bed selected is checked. Gas density is 0.0757 lb/ft³ and the liquid density is 65.2 lb/ft³. The flow parameter is:

$$X = \frac{272,000}{117,200} \left[\frac{0.0757}{65.2} \right]^{0.5} = 0.0791$$

The gas mass velocity in a 10-ft 6-in. ID tower is 1,350 lb/ft²·h which gives a C_s value of 0.169 fps. With a liquid viscosity of 1.3 cps, the ordinate value for Figure 1-16 is 1.08. From this figure, the pressure drop is 0.32 in. H_2O/ft for 1½-in. plastic Pall rings. The pressure drop through the 25.4 ft packed depth is 8.1 in. H_2O total.

This pressure drop exceeds the allowable value, therefore the gas rate will be lowered to 3.5 fps. Referring to Figure 2-1, the packed depth required is 21.2 ft of 2-in. plastic Super Intalox® packing at a gas rate of 3.5 fps. A 17.8-ft depth of 1½-in. plastic Pall rings will be used based on the adjustment of packed depth from Table 2-3.

The air flow still will be 117,200 lb/h, but the liquid circulation rate increases to 740 gpm. This maintains the 6.0 gpm/ft² irrigation rate for a column diameter that has now been increased to 12-ft 6-in. ID. The new flow parameter is:

$$X = \frac{387,000}{117,200} \left[\frac{0.0757}{65.2} \right]^{0.5} = 0.113$$

The gas mass velocity has now been reduced to 955 lb/ft²·h, giving a C_s of 0.119 fps. The ordinate value for Figure 1-16 is 0.76 which gives a pressure drop of 0.15 in. H_2O/ft. The pressure drop through a 17.8-ft bed of 1½-in. plastic Pall rings would be only 2.7 in. H_2O total.

Because the pressure drop is lower than necessary, the column diameter can be reduced slightly. The final design for this scrubber specifies a 12-ft 0-in. ID tower with a 19.4-ft deep bed of 1½-in. plastic Pall rings. The liquid circulation rate is 680 gpm and the pressure drop through the scrubber only is 3.5 in. H_2O total. This means that the tower internals can have a pressure drop of 0.5 in. H_2O and the scrubber will still meet the original specifications.

NOTATION

A	Column cross-sectional area (ft²)
a	Interfacial area (ft²/ft³)

E	Efficiency (%)
g	Gravitational constant (ft/s^2)
Gm	Gas phase flow (lb-mol/h)
H	Henry's Law constant (atm/mol fraction)
KE	Kinetic energy (ft-lb)
$K_G a$	Overall gas-phase mass transfer coefficient (lb-mol/ h $\cdot$ ft^3 $\cdot$ atm)
k_G	Gas-film mass transfer coefficient (lb-mol/h $\cdot$ ft^2 $\cdot$ atm)
$K_L a$	Overall liquid-phase mass transfer coefficient (lb-mol/ h $\cdot$ ft^3 $\cdot$ mol/mol)
k_L	Liquid-film mass transfer coefficient (lb-mol/h $\cdot$ ft^2 $\cdot$ mol/mol)
m	Slope of equilibrium curve
N	Solute transferred (lb-mol/h)
P	Total system pressure (atm)
p	Partial pressure in gas phase (atm)
p$'$	Partial pressure of solute in gas film (atm)
p*	Vapor pressure of solute (atm)
V	Superficial gas velocity (fps)
w	Mass (lb)
x	Mol fraction in liquid phase
x*	Equilibrium mol fraction in liquid phase
x$'$	Mol fraction in liquid film
y	Mol fraction in gas phase
y*	Equilibrium mol fraction in gas phase
y$'$	Mol fraction in gas film
y_i	Mol fraction solute in inlet gas
y_o	Mol fraction solute in outlet gas
Z	Packed depth (ft)
Δp_{LM}	ln mean pressure driving force (atm)

REFERENCES

1. Eckert, J. S., and Strigle, R. F., *Journal of the Air Pollution Control Association*, Vol. 24, No. 10, 1974.
2. *1983 Equipment Volume*, "Industrial Gas Cleaning and Air Pollution Control," Chap. 11, American Society of Heating, Refrigerating, and Air-Conditioning Engineers.
3. Eckert, J. S., and Strigle, R. F., "Removal of Odors from Plant Exhaust," Air Pollution Control Association, East Central Section Meeting, Sept. 1973.

3

GAS ABSORPTION

In order to illustrate the usage of packed columns in absorption operations, it is necessary to refer to mass transfer theory. The initial part of this chapter has been devoted to a review of the fundamental principles of mass transfer that need to be understood to design absorption and stripping columns.

Absorption refers to the physical transfer of a solute from the gas phase to the liquid phase. Generally, the solute enters the column in a gas which is either insoluble or only slightly soluble in the liquid phase. While some of the liquid phase may be vaporized into the gas phase, this is incidental to the absorption operation.

The absorbed solute may form a simple solution in the liquid phase or it may react chemically with a component in the liquid phase. If the concentration of solute in the liquid phase is small and the solute forms a simple solution, Henry's Law applies:

$$p^* = Hx \qquad (3\text{-}1)$$

The partial pressure of solute in the gas phase is a function of the gas composition:

$$p = yP \qquad (3\text{-}2)$$

Combining these Equations 3-1 and 3-2 we obtain:

$$y^* = \frac{Hx}{P} \qquad (3\text{-}3)$$

for the vapor-phase concentration in equilibrium with the liquid phase. Absorption will take place whenever the partial pressure of solute in the vapor phase (Equation 3-2) exceeds the vapor pressure of solute above the liquid phase (Equation 3-1).

As the temperature of the liquid phase increases toward its boiling point, its vapor pressure approaches the system pressure. Thus, at the liquid-phase boiling temperature, the solubility of the solute is reduced toward zero. The vapor pressure of the solute gas also increases with increasing temperature. Therefore, the Henry's Law constant increases with increasing liquid-phase temperature. As shown by Equation 3-3, at a constant gas-phase composition and pressure, the solubility of a solute in the liquid phase is inversely proportional to the value of the Henry's Law constant.

Equation 3-1 permits calculation of the vapor pressure of the solute only for low concentrations of the solute in the liquid phase. The value of H must be modified in order that Equation 3-1 can be used at higher concentrations of solute in the liquid phase. Also when the system pressure exceeds 150 psia, a correction for the effect of pressure may be required.

TWO-FILM THEORY

The two-film theory still is widely employed to explain mass transfer operations. The boundary between the gas phase and the liquid phase is presumed to consist of a gas film adjacent to a liquid film. Flow in both of these films is assumed to be laminar or stagnant. The main-body gas phase as well as the main-body liquid phase are assumed to be completely mixed in turbulent flow so that no concentration gradient exists in the main body of either phase. Further, the solute concentration in the gas film at the interface is assumed to be in equilibrium with the solute concentration in the liquid film at the interface and there is no resistance to mass transfer across the interface. There is a solute concentration gradient across both the gas film and the liquid film.

Absorption has been considered through an analogy to heat transfer wherein the flow of heat is equal to the product of a heat transfer coefficient, a transfer surface area, and a driving force. Thus the total mass transferred per unit time from the main-body gas phase through the gas film is indicated by this equation:

$$N = AZk_Ga(p - p')$$

(3-4)

The driving force $(p - p')$ at any point is the difference between the partial pressure of solute in the main-body gas phase and that in the gas film at the interface. The interfacial area is the actual mass transfer area between liquid and gas phases. This area is not necessarily the same as the geometrical surface area of the tower packing. The product of a and AZ represents the total interfacial area within the entire packed bed.

Similarly, the solute transferred per unit of time through the liquid film to the main-body liquid phase is given by this expression:

$$N = AZk_La(x' - x) \qquad (3\text{-}5)$$

The driving force $(x' - x)$ at any point is the difference between mol fraction of solute in the liquid film at the interface and that in the main-body liquid phase. The values of p' (in Equation 3-4) and x' (in Equation 3-5) are difficult to determine in practical cases. Also, the interfacial area (a) may vary with the flow rates of the two phases; therefore, overall terms have been adopted for calculative purposes.

The driving force for absorption involving highly soluble solutes usually is considered in terms of the partial pressure of solute in the vapor phase minus the vapor pressure of solute above the liquid phase. In other words, the calculation involves the solute concentrations in the main-body gas phase and in the main-body liquid phase rather than the solute concentrations at the interface. Thus the driving force is $p - p^*$ or $p - Hx$ where Henry's Law is applicable. The greater this driving force, the faster will be the rate of mass transfer if there are no other influences. The effect of the value of H on the overall mass transfer coefficient will be discussed later and is given by Equations 3-11 and 3-12.

The interfacial area is combined with the gas-phase mass transfer coefficient to produce an overall volumetric coefficient (K_Ga). The volume of tower packing required is AZ; thus the overall mass transfer analogous equation for the gas phase is:

$$N = AZK_Ga(p - p^*) \qquad (3\text{-}6)$$

The driving force for stripping operations involving slightly soluble solutes is considered in terms of liquid-phase composition minus the composition of a liquid in equilibrium with the gas phase. Thus the driving force is $x - x^*$ or $x - p/H$ where Henry's Law applies. For practical purposes, again we have resorted to overall terms. The overall liquid-phase mass transfer coefficient in volumetric terms (K_La) is represented by the equation:

$$N = AZK_La(x - x^*) \qquad (3\text{-}7)$$

GAS-FILM MASS TRANSFER COEFFICIENT

In absorption operations, the gas-film mass transfer coefficient from Equation 3-4 is:

$$k_G = \frac{N}{aAZ(p - p')} \qquad (3\text{-}8)$$

The gas-film mass transfer coefficient (k_G) does not change greatly with temperature. Initially k_G was believed to be related to the gas-phase Schmidt number to the -0.67 power [1]. This dimensionless number is:

$$Sc = \frac{u'}{\rho D} \qquad (3\text{-}9)$$

Due to the fact that mass transfer in packed beds is not totally controlled by molecular diffusion, the exponent for the Schmidt number later was changed to -0.5 [2]. Since the gas is in turbulent flow in a bed of modern packing, the exponent for the Schmidt number may be lower than this latter value.

The gas-film mass transfer coefficient, however, is significantly influenced by the pressure. It has been reported that the mass transfer coefficient is a function of the partial pressure of solute in the gas phase raised to the -0.32 power [3]. Thus at twice the absolute system pressure, the rate of mass transfer is increased only by 80%; however, the pressure difference driving force will increase in direct proportion to the system pressure at the constant gas-phase composition. For many absorption systems (such as those following Henry's Law), increasing the pressure will increase the solubility of the solute in the liquid phase.

LIQUID-FILM MASS TRANSFER COEFFICIENT

Likewise, the liquid-film mass transfer coefficient taken from Equation 3-5 is:

$$k_L = \frac{N}{aAZ(x' - x)} \qquad (3\text{-}10)$$

The liquid-film mass transfer coefficient (k_L) is markedly affected by temperature. Several investigators have proposed that this coefficient is proportional to the liquid-phase diffusivity to the 0.5 power [4 and 5].

Other investigators have reported this coefficient to be related to the liquid-phase Schmidt number to the -0.5 power [6 and 7]. This mass transfer coefficient increases as the temperature increases, probably as a result of reduced liquid viscosity and increased diffusivity.

It is expected that a change in system pressure, and therefore the partial pressure of the solute, should have little effect on the liquid-phase coefficient. Although the solubility in the liquid phase is reduced with temperature increase, and the Henry's Law constant is greater, the liquid-film coefficient (k_L) may increase rapidly with temperature. Thus, there may exist an optimum temperature for a particular absorption system which is not the lowest temperature where solubility of the absorbed solute is greatest in the liquid phase.

OVERALL MASS TRANSFER COEFFICIENTS

The overall gas-phase mass transfer coefficient is related to the individual film coefficients in the following manner:

$$\frac{1}{K_GaP} = \frac{1}{k_GaP} + \frac{m}{k_La} \tag{3-11}$$

For systems following Henry's Law, the value of the slope of the equilibrium curve (m) equals the value of H.

The reciprocal of the individual film mass transfer coefficient is the resistance to mass transfer exhibited by that film. The absorption is considered to be liquid-film controlled when its mass transfer coefficient (k_L) is small compared to the gas-film mass transfer coefficient (k_G) or when m is large. The absorption is considered to be gas-film controlled when its mass transfer coefficient (k_G) is small compared to the liquid-film mass transfer coefficient (k_L) or when m is small. Some examples of typical absorption systems indicating the controlling phase resistance are shown in Table 3-1.

In systems which are gas-film controlled, the solute either will be highly soluble in the liquid phase or will react rapidly with a component in the liquid phase. In liquid-film-controlled systems, the solute either has a low solubility in the liquid phase or reacts with a component in the liquid phase at a slow rate. In some cases, depending on the value of m, one may approximate the overall coefficient by neglecting the smaller resistance to mass transfer. In reality this is an extremely simplifying assumption since the percentage of gas and liquid-film control varies with the concentration of solute as well as the physical properties which change the solubility of the solute in the liquid phase.

Table 3 – 1
Typical Absorption Operations

Solute	Absorbant Liquid	Controlling Phase
Oxygen	Water	Liquid
Chlorine	Water	Liquid
Carbon Dioxide	Water	Liquid
Carbon Dioxide	4% NaOH	Liquid
Carbon Dioxide	12% MEA	Liquid
Water Vapor	Water	Gas
Water Vapor	93% H$_2$SO$_4$	Gas
Ammonia	Water	Gas
Ammonia	10% H$_2$SO$_4$	Gas
Sulfur Dioxide	4% NaOH	Gas
Hydrogen Chloride	Water	Gas
Chlorine	5% NaOH	Gas
Sulfur Trioxide	98% H$_2$SO$_4$	Gas

In stripping operations, we can relate the overall liquid-phase mass transfer coefficient to the individual film coefficients as follows:

$$\left(\frac{1}{K_L a} = \frac{1}{m k_G a P} + \frac{1}{k_L a} \right) \tag{3-12}$$

Thus, if m is very large (the solute has low solubility in the liquid phase), the overall $K_L a$ is substantially the same as the liquid-film coefficient $k_L a$.

The interfacial area (a) should not be confused with the geometric surface area of the tower packing. Shulman, et al., demonstrated that the interfacial area is not directly related to the wetted area [8]. The increase in overall mass transfer coefficient for ceramic Intalox® saddles compared to ceramic Raschig rings could, at least in part, be attributed to increased surface area per unit volume. However, metal Pall rings show a substantial increase in mass transfer coefficient compared to metal Raschig rings yet both packings have the same surface area for the same size packing. Modern tower packing shapes tend to be permeable so that the gas and liquid can flow through the center of the packing element as well as around the shape. The increased mass transfer rates associated with these packings are due in part to increased interstitial transfer within the internal void.

For absorption operations it is customary to use K_Ga values since we usually are concerned about the composition of the gas phase. The overall mass transfer coefficients in absorption are considered to be a function of the gas and liquid flow rates:

$$K_Ga = \psi L^b G^c \tag{3-13}$$

In liquid-film-controlled systems, the value of K_Ga primarily is a function of the liquid flow rate. For most random dumped tower packings, the value of the exponent b in Equation 3-13 lies between 0.22 and 0.38; the exact value is characteristic of the type of packing employed. If data on the particular packing are not readily available, it is suggested that this exponent be assumed as 0.30 for preliminary designs. In such liquid-film-controlled systems there is a very small effect of gas rate. The value of the exponent c in Equation 3-13 normally is only 0.06 to 0.08. Thus if a standard K_Ga value for such a system is determined to be 6.0 lb-mol/h $\cdot$ ft^3 $\cdot$ atm at a liquid rate of 5,000 lb/ft^2 $\cdot$ h, the K_Ga value for this same tower packing at a liquid rate of 20,000 lb/ft^2 $\cdot$ h would be about 9.1 lb-mol/h $\cdot$ ft^3 $\cdot$ atm.

In gas-film-controlled absorption systems, the value of K_Ga is a function of both the liquid and the gas flow rates. The value of the exponent b for the effect of liquid flow rate in Equation 3-13 is the same for gas-film-controlled systems as for liquid-film-controlled systems. However, the value of the exponent c for the effect of gas flow rate in Equation 3-13 for a gas-film-controlled system has increased to between 0.67 and 0.80. Therefore, if the foregoing system were gas-film-controlled and the gas rate was increased from 900 lb/ft^2 $\cdot$ h to 1,200 lb/ft^2 $\cdot$ h along with the preceding liquid rate increase, the new K_Ga would have a value between 11.0 and 11.4 lb-mol/h $\cdot$ ft^3 $\cdot$ atm. In gas-film-controlled systems, the value of K_Ga is much greater than in liquid-film-controlled systems. This is because the liquid-film resistance reduces the value of the overall coefficient in liquid-film-controlled systems while it has only a small effect on this value in gas-film-controlled systems.

The pressure driving force difference must be determined at the bottom of the packed bed (Δp_B) as well as at the top of the packed bed (Δp_T) in an absorber. For a gas stream containing a low concentration of solute, L/G is almost constant and the operating line of the absorber is straight. Also, if there is negligible heat of solution in the liquid phase, the value of H or m may be constant. Under these conditions the pressure difference driving force is the logarithmic mean average of the driving forces at the bottom and top of the packed bed.

$$\Delta p_{LM} = \frac{\Delta p_B - \Delta p_T}{\ln(\Delta p_B/\Delta p_T)} \tag{3-14}$$

The volume of tower packing required for the absorber can be calculated as follows:

$$AZ = \frac{N}{K_G a \; \Delta p_{LM}} \tag{3-15}$$

DESIGN THEORY

From a knowledge of the overall mass transfer coefficient, one might assume the design of a packed column was straightforward. This simple approach to design as described in Equation 3-15 provides a quick method for specifying industrial absorption columns; however, there are several drawbacks to this procedure. For instance, the rate of mass transfer will decrease significantly as the concentration of solute approaches the solubility limit. Secondly, some systems change from gas-film control to liquid-film control. These changes can occur as a result of a change in liquid-phase properties, solute concentration in the liquid, or pH of the liquid phase. Third, there is an important difference between the heat transfer and mass transfer analogies. The temperature difference driving forces lend themselves to a logarithmic average since sensible heat transfer usually means a straight operating line and a straight equilibrium curve. The terminal temperature differences usually have values which differ by less than ten-fold. However, the driving forces in mass transfer may exhibit terminal partial pressure differences that vary by 100 or 1,000 times. Obviously it is unlikely that the operating line and particularly the equilibrium curve is linear over such wide concentration ranges; therefore, a logarithmic mean average is not truly representative of the driving force in typical absorption operations.

SIMPLIFIED DESIGN PROCEDURES

Kremser generally is credited with development of a procedure for calculation using the absorption factor [9]. However, this method does not estimate vapor and liquid compositions or temperature profiles in the column [10]. It assumes a straight operating line and an equilibrium curve of constant slope. The slope of the equilibrium curve is represented by the equilibrium ratio (K) which is the ratio of the mol fraction of solute in the vapor phase to mol fraction of solute in the liquid phase (Equation 3-22). The absorption factor A^* is the ratio of the slope of the operating line to the slope of the equilibrium curve.

$$A^* = \frac{Lm}{KGm} \tag{3-16}$$

The absorption factor can be used to calculate around each theoretical stage by the following equation:

$$y_n = \frac{y_{n+1} + A^*Kx_{n-1}}{1 + A^*} \tag{3-17}$$

Once the number of theoretical stages has been determined, it is necessary to estimate stage efficiency in order to calculate the packed depth required.

In an attempt to obtain more consistency with mass transfer theory, the transfer unit concept has been proposed. The number of gas-phase transfer units (N_{OG}) can be calculated by the Souders and Brown procedure using the absorption factor [11]. This equation assumes linear, although not parallel, operating line and equilibrium curve.

$$N_{OG} = \frac{\ln \left[\frac{y_i - Kx_i}{y_o - Kx_i} \left(1 - \frac{1}{A^*} \right) + \frac{1}{A^*} \right]}{\ln A^*} \tag{3-18}$$

In order to do a preliminary absorber design, the Colburn correlation shown in Figure 3-1 can be used [12]. To determine the number of gas-phase transfer units, it merely is necessary to calculate the ratio of inlet to outlet gas compositions $(y_i - Kx_i)/(y_o - Kx_i)$ and the absorption factor from Equation 3-16.

Once the number of transfer units has been calculated, the height of a transfer unit must be determined to ascertain the packed depth required. The height of a transfer unit is that depth of packing which produces a change in composition equal to the mass transfer driving force causing that change. The overall volumetric mass transfer coefficient and height of a transfer unit are related as follows:

$$H_{OG} = \frac{Gm}{K_GaAP} \tag{3-19}$$

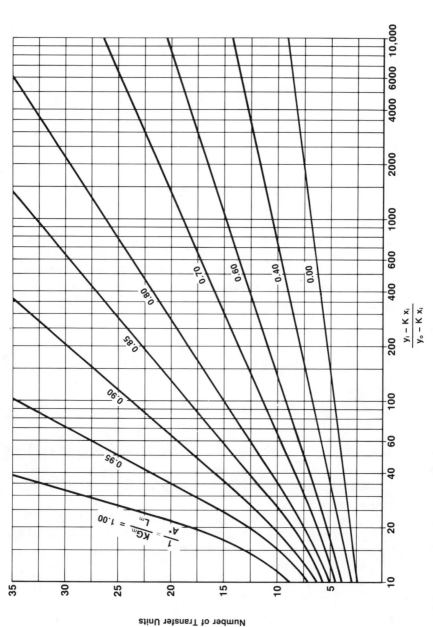

Figure 3-1. Colburn correlation for absorber design. (From Colburn [12]. Reprinted with permission from *Industrial and Engineering Chemistry*, Vol. 33, 1941, pg. 459, American Chemical Society.)

$$H_{OL} = \frac{Lm}{K_L aA} \tag{3-20}$$

The height of a transfer unit varies inversely with the value of the overall mass transfer coefficient.

GENERAL DESIGN CONCEPT

Unfortunately, many commercially important absorption operations do not follow Henry's Law for equilibrium values and do not operate at constant gas rates or liquid rates. The concentration of solute in the entering gas stream may represent a significantly large percentage of that stream; so that after absorption of solute, the exit gas flow rate is reduced. Likewise the liquid rate leaving the tower exceeds the entering liquid rate by the amount of solute absorbed. This statement assumes no vaporization of the solvent and zero solubility of the inert gas phase in the solvent. Equation 3-21 gives the mass balance across such an absorber:

$$y_i G_i + x_i L_i = y_o G_o + x_o L_o \tag{3-21}$$

This equation applies regardless of whether the equilibrium curve and operating line are straight. Rather than use an overall mass transfer coefficient analysis of the absorption operation, we can consider it as a series of theoretical stages. Such a theoretical stage is visualized as a mass transfer stage where the liquid and gas are in equilibrium with each other leaving the stage. The equilibrium ratio for that stage is defined as the slope of the equilibrium curve:

$$K = \frac{y_n}{x_n} \tag{3-22}$$

For any theoretical stage n, the material balance becomes

$$y_{n+1} G_{n+1} + x_{n-1} L_{n-1} = y_n G_n + x_n L_n \tag{3-23}$$

where $n + 1$ is the theoretical stage below and $n - 1$ is the theoretical stage above. Over the entire column for any theoretical stage Equation 3-23 becomes:

$$y_i G_i + x_i L_i = y_n G_n + x_n L_n \tag{3-24}$$

This equation can be rearranged as follows:

$$y_i = x_n \frac{L_n}{G_i} + y_n \frac{G_n}{G_i} - x_i \frac{L_i}{G_i} \tag{3-25}$$

if the solute transferred per theoretical stage is small compared to total gas and liquid flows, then:

$$\frac{G_n}{G_{n+1}} \cong 1.0 \tag{3-26}$$

and

$$\frac{L_{n-1}}{L_n} \cong 1.0 \tag{3-27}$$

In this event Equation 3-25 for absorption of solute from a lean entering gas stream becomes approximately:

$$y_i = x_n \frac{L_n}{G_n} + y_n - x_i \frac{L_i}{G_i} \tag{3-28}$$

Equation 3-28 represents a straight operating line with a slope of L_n/G_n and an intercept of $y_i + x_i(L_i/G_i)$. An overall equation for the entire column permits calculation of the outlet gas composition (y_o) as follows:

$$y_o = y_i + x_i \frac{L_i}{G_i} - x_o \frac{L_n}{G_n} \tag{3-29}$$

In those cases in which the solute constitutes a large percentage of the inlet gas stream, the gas flow rate will decrease from the bottom to the top of the absorber. In other cases, when dealing with a highly soluble solute, it may be desired to produce a concentrated solution of solute leaving the absorber. In this latter case, inlet solvent flow will be restricted by the material balance, and the liquid rate will increase from the top to the bottom of the absorber.

The example problem in Chapter 1 represents a case of a rich inlet gas stream containing 7.3 mol % solute. The gas flow rate is reduced from an inlet flow of 241,600 lb/h to an exit flow of 219,820 lb/h due to solute absorption. The 30 wt% DEA flow rate likewise is increased from an inlet liquid flow of 504,200 lb/h to an outlet liquid flow of 525,980 lb/h.

In order to simplify a calculation of the number of theoretical stages required for systems with a rich gas stream, we can replace the usual abscissa value of mol fraction solute in the liquid phase with a value which shows mol CO_2 per mol DEA. The flow of DEA through the absorber is constant since this solvent is not volatile at the operating temperature. The usual ordinate value of mol fraction solute in the gas phase can be replaced with a value which represents mol CO_2 per mol inert gas. The inert gas flow is almost constant, increasing only by the small amount of water evaporated.

On such a plot, the abscissa value at the bottom of the absorber is 0.45 mol CO_2 per mol DEA and the ordinate value is 0.07875 mol CO_2 per mol inert gas. At the top of the absorber the abscissa value is 0.10 mol CO_2 per mol DEA and the ordinate value is 0.00503 mol CO_2 per mol inert gas. The slope of the operating line varies from 0.2080 mol DEA per mol inert gas at the bottom of the tower to 0.2074 mol DEA per mol of inert gas at the top of the tower. The operating line, therefore, essentially is straight. The equilibrium curve can be constructed on such a plot from data on the vapor pressures of CO_2 above 30 wt% DEA solutions. A correction should be made for any change in temperature of the liquid due to the heat released by the solute and sensible heat absorbed by the gas. The number of theoretical stages required then can be stepped-off in the usual manner.

The number of theoretical stages for systems with nonlinear operating or equilibrium lines can be calculated by the methods described in Chapter 6. The relationship between HETP and H_{OG} is given by Equation 6-16.

CHOICE OF SOLVENT

In absorption operations the inlet gas flow rate, solute concentration, and operating pressure are known as is the desired solute concentration in the outlet gas stream. The solvent liquid may be low cost (such as water) and, therefore, used on a once-through basis when gas purification rather than solute recovery is required. On the other hand, the solvent may be expensive, thus it must be recycled through a regenerator. This especially is the case where solute recovery is the goal. Since the outlet gas stream will be saturated with solvent vapor, the cost of solvent losses by evaporation should be evaluated. Additionally, the solvent selected should be chemically stable, noncorrosive, nontoxic, nonpolluting, and of low flammability.

The designer first must select the solvent liquid to be used and then specify its circulation rate. The greater the solubility of solute in the solvent, the lower will be the necessary liquid rate. The economic optimum design results from a balance between the solvent circulation rate and the depth of packing in the absorber.

SELECTION OF COLUMN DIAMETER

Once the solvent rate is fixed, the designer can proceed to calculate the column diameter. The column cross-sectional area usually is specified by the pressure drop produced as a result of the design gas and liquid flow rates. Absorbers normally are specified to give a pressure drop between 0.10 to 0.40 in. H_2O/ft of packed depth. In nonfoaming systems, the design pressure drop usually is between 0.25 and 0.40 in. H_2O/ft. For systems which tend to foam moderately, the design pressure drop should be reduced to a maximum of 0.25 in. H_2O/ft at the point of greatest loading. Such a design will avoid imparting energy from the gas stream to the liquid phase which can promote additional foaming.

Table 3 – 2
Maximum Recommended Liquid Loading

Packing Size (in.)	Liquid Rate (gpm/ft²)
¾	25
1	40
1½	55
2	70
3½	125

Since high liquid flow rates frequently are encountered in absorption operations, the size of packing should be chosen as shown in Table 3-2 to avoid hydraulic overload. These liquid rates apply to mobile liquids and should be reduced at higher liquid viscosities as discussed in Chapter 1. At very high L/G ratios (exceeding 20) the calculated pressure drop still may fall within the above allowable design limits; however, in these situations, the gas rate should not exceed 85% of the rate which would give a pressure drop of 1.5 in. H_2O/ft from the generalized correlation as shown in Figure 1-15 or Figure 1-16.

In some cases, the solute is absorbed from the gas stream to produce a specific liquid effluent concentration, such as for an HCl absorber. In this case the liquid flow rate is fixed by the mass balance. Such operations may exhibit a very low L/G ratio (less than 1.2). In these cases, it usually is advisable to use a larger size packing (such as 1½- or 2-in. size) in order to reduce column diameter and thus increase the liquid irrigation rate. However, such a design may increase the packed depth required. The gas velocity at the top of the column should be kept low enough to avoid entrainment of liquid which would represent loss of solvent and contamination of the outlet gas stream. The maximum capacity as limited by liquid entrainment is discussed in Chapter 6.

PHYSICAL ABSORPTION

After the column diameter and packing size have been selected, the required packed depth must be specified. This calculation requires a knowledge of the equilibrium values for the system involved. First, we will consider a system which uses a pure physical solvent in which there is a low heat of solution of the solute, such as the absorption of CO_2 into Selexol® solvent (trademark Norton Chemical Process Products). This small heat release plus the high liquid-to-solute ratio means that the liquid temperature changes very little in the absorber. In such a system, the Henry's Law constant can be used to provide the equilibrium relationship. The inlet gas composition is known and the desired outlet gas concentration is specified. The liquid circulation rate normally is fixed so that the equilibrium partial pressure of solute above the effluent liquid is about 80% of the partial pressure of solute in the entering gas stream. Assuming that the solvent is recirculated, the regenerated solvent feed to the absorber must have an equilibrium partial pressure of solute less than the specified partial pressure of solute in the exit-gas stream. Since driving forces at the top of the absorber may be quite small, in order to avoid excessive packed depths, the solvent should be regenerated so that the equilibrium partial pressure of solute above the lean solvent is no more than 50% of the solute partial pressure specified for the exit-gas stream.

Although acid gases may have a high solubility in Selexol® solvent, this system is considered liquid-film controlled. Absorption is limited by diffusion in the liquid phase due to the high viscosity of Selexol® solvent; therefore, liquid properties are important in determining the mass transfer rate. The height of a liquid-phase transfer unit increases with increasing liquid viscosity and with increasing Henry's Law constant. Within a given type of packing, at high liquid rates which completely wet the packing surface, the height of a liquid-phase transfer unit varies only to about the 0.33 power of packing size.

SOLVENT ABSORPTION

Next, we will consider a system which uses a solvent into which the solute vapor is condensed. This operation will release a significant quantity of heat, which in turn will raise the solvent temperature as it flows down the absorption column. In this case, the effect of temperature on the equilibrium ratio (K) must be allowed for in the calculations. The solubility of solute normally will decrease with increasing solvent temperature (the K value will increase). To obtain high solute removal from the gas stream, a large solvent flow rate can be used in order to limit the temperature rise. If solvent flow is to be kept low, the heated liquid phase must be removed from the column, cooled externally, then returned to the absorber.

In the recovery of light hydrocarbons by use of an absorption oil as the solvent, no chemical reactions occur and the liquid phase is an ideal solution for practical purposes. Fortunately, in a refinery gas absorber the K values usually are available for all major components of the gas stream. The heat load imparted to the solvent primarily represents the latent heat of vaporization of the absorbed light hydrocarbons. In addition, there may be a sensible heat load due to the temperature difference between the entering gas stream and the solvent feed.

Usually the solvent temperature will be reduced as low as practical before entering the absorber in order to provide the greatest possible hydrocarbon removal from the gas stream. As hydrocarbon is absorbed in the top of the column, the liquid temperature increases as does the K value. As hydrocarbon is absorbed in the bottom of the column, the mol fraction and the partial pressure of solute in the gas phase decrease. In order to avoid an equilibrium pinch in the center of the absorber, the partially enriched solvent is collected on a trap tray and withdrawn from the column. This liquid is cooled in an external heat exchanger and returned to the absorber below the trap tray. Normally a sufficient solvent feed rate is used so that only a single liquid removal and cooling operation is required.

The calculation of such a column must be done by an iterative procedure around each theoretical stage until the mass balance, heat balance, and equilibrium ratios are satisfied simultaneously. By working down from the top of the absorber, the optimum liquid withdrawal point can be located. Next the cooled solvent return temperature can be fixed by working from the bottom up to the liquid withdrawal point. This system usually is considered to be liquid-film controlled; however, in operations at very high pressures and with low concentrations of solute in the gas phase, the gas-film resistance also can become significant.

GAS DEHYDRATION

As another case of absorption, we will consider the drying of an insoluble gas by contact with a dehydrating liquid. Due to the high heat of vaporization of water plus its high heat of solution in the dehydrating liquid, there can be a large heat load imparted to the liquid phase. As the dehydrating liquid is diluted by the condensed water and as the liquid temperature increases, the vapor pressure of water above the liquid phase will increase. Usually a high liquid circulation rate is used in each stage of drying to minimize both the temperature rise and the dilution of the liquid dehydrating agent. When the amount of water vapor to be removed is large, a number of towers each recycling cooled liquid may be operated in series.

In the drying of chlorine, the hot cell gas typically is cooled to about 60° to 65°F before entering the first drying tower. The inlet gas stream at atmospheric pressure will contain 2 mol % maximum water vapor. Usually three drying towers in series will produce an exit chlorine gas containing no more than 40 mol ppm water vapor. Since only 20 lb of 98 wt% sulfuric acid is consumed per ton of dry chlorine, each column must be recirculated to provide a liquid rate of 4 to 5 gpm/ft^2 of cross-sectional area. The first tower and the third tower (with respect to gas flow) normally will use coolers on the recirculated acid stream to keep the outlet acid from each tower to 95°F maximum temperature.

The three towers usually are sized to a common diameter which will give a pressure drop of 0.10 to 0.15 in. H$_2$O/ft of packed depth since the overall pressure drop desired for the entire drying system is only 4 to 5 in. H$_2$O. This process largely is gas-film controlled as expected. It is desirable to keep the packed depth in each of the three columns the same. To accomplish this configuration, an iterative design procedure is necessary. The driving force for mass transfer is the difference between the partial pressure of water vapor in the gas stream and the vapor pressure of water above the liquid phase. Because of the high liquid flow rate, as a first approximation the acid concentration and temperature in each tower can be assumed constant in order to establish the amount of water vapor removed in each column and thereby the acid concentration.

When super-dry chlorine (having a maximum water content of 10 mol ppm) is required, a fourth drying tower is utilized. This column removes very little water vapor so that the liquid recirculated will be about 96 wt% sulfuric acid. Because of the high liquid-phase viscosity (greater than 15 cps), the absorption in this tower will be substantially liquid-film controlled.

SULFURIC ACID MANUFACTURE

The production of sulfuric acid utilizes some of the largest diameter packed towers in chemical plant process trains. Column diameters up to 30 ft have been used for both the drying tower and the SO$_3$ absorber. However, since the middle 1960s, with the acceptance of newer tower packings and advanced design procedures, column diameters seldom approach this size in modern plants. In a sulfur-burning plant, the hot gas stream entering the SO_3 absorber usually contains 8 to 10 mol % SO_3 which must be almost completely absorbed so the gas leaving the tower will contain only 30 to 40 mol ppm SO_3. The SO_3 is absorbed into 98 wt% sulfuric acid in which it is highly soluble. The acid enters the absorber at a temperature of 170° to 180°F and leaves the column 50° to 60°F hotter. This temperature rise in the acid is due both to the heat of solution of SO_3 and the sensible heat removed by cooling the inlet gas stream. The large heat of formation of H_2SO_4 is not released in the absorption column, but in the subsequent water dilution tank and removed in acid coolers.

This system is almost a pure gas-film-controlled absorption. The sum of the exponents b and c in Equation 3-13 is greater than unity. Thus an increase in gas flow rate at constant gas composition will increase the mols of SO_3 to be absorbed in direct proportion. By holding a constant liquid to gas ratio while increasing flow rates, the overall mass transfer coefficient will increase even faster than the quantity of SO_3 to be absorbed.

The design of the absorber first involves fixing the diameter so that the exit gas stream velocity is not so high as to entrain liquid sulfuric acid out of the column. The use of a design pressure drop of 0.25 to 0.30 in. H_2O/ft at the bottom of the absorber is common practice. This pressure drop may double in 9 to 10 years of operation due to an accumulation of sulfation products in the packed bed. To avoid blockage of the packed bed, a 2-in. or 3-in. size ceramic packing normally is specified. As a result of the use of modern tower packings as well as the development of improved packing support systems and liquid distributor designs, the superficial gas velocity within the column has been increased almost two-fold from designs common in the late 1950s.

The design of the SO_3 absorber is relatively straightforward for the packed depth required. The driving force for mass transfer is the difference between the partial pressure of SO_3 in the gas stream and the vapor pressure of SO_3 above the sulfuric acid. The overall mass transfer coefficients are very high, in the order of 18 lb mol/h $\cdot$ ft³ $\cdot$ atm for 2-in. ceramic Intalox® saddles at a liquid rate of 7.5 gpm/ft² and a gas rate of 1,200 lb/ft² $\cdot$ h. This high value for K_Ga indicates that there is very little liquid-film resistance.

Because of the materials of construction necessary to resist corrosion, the uniformity of gas and liquid distribution may be less than current best practice. The designer should allow for this situation in specifying the packed depth which may be up to 50% greater than the theoretical depth required.

ABSORPTION WITH CHEMICAL REACTION

Many absorption operations of great commercial importance involve a reaction between the solute and a component present in the liquid phase. Of course, the solute first must be dissolved into the liquid phase before a reaction can take place. As an example, organic sulfides are easily oxidized, however they are not removed from pulp mill vent gases by contact with aqueous solutions of oxidizing agents simply because of the very low solubility of these sulfides in water.

Chemical reactions in the liquid phase are either reversible or irreversible. Typical reversible reactions are involved in the absorption of H_2S into ethanolamines or the absorption of CO_2 into alkali carbonate solutions. These reversible reactions permit the resultant solution to be regenerated so that the solute can be recovered in a concentrated form. Some irreversible reactions are the absorption of NH_3 into dilute acids and the absorption of CO_2 into alkaline hydroxides. The solute in such absorptions is so tightly bound in the reaction product that there is no appreciable vapor pressure of solute above the liquid phase. Under these conditions regeneration of the solute is not possible and the reacting component in the liquid is consumed.

The absorption of CO_2 into sodium hydroxide solutions has been used to characterize the relative performance of tower packings. Most of the available data are based on atmospheric pressure operation in which the inlet gas phase contains 1 mol % CO_2 in air and the gas mass flow rate is constant at a superficial velocity of 2.0 to 3.5 fps. The liquid phase is one normal aqueous sodium hydroxide at a temperature of 75°F. The conversion to soda ash is kept low (25%) to ensure the availability of sufficient free hydroxyl ions so as to provide an excess over that required for combining with the absorbed CO_2.

In this system the reaction of hydrolyzed CO_2 with hydroxyl ions is moderately rapid and the partial pressure of CO_2 in equilibrium with the bulk liquid is zero for practical purposes. The effect of the liquid-phase reaction is to reduce substantially the liquid-film resistance since the distance the absorbed solute must diffuse is only about 10% of that customary for a simple physical absorption. The liquid-film mass transfer coefficient is a function of liquid flow rate [4]. The liquid-film mass transfer coefficient is constant at any fixed percentage carbonation and almost independent of gas flow rate below the loading region. This system, therefore, is used to measure the relative interfacial area for different packings as influenced by the liquid flow rate.

Tables 3-3, 3-4, and 3-5 show the overall K_Ga values obtained for this system at a liquid rate of 10 gpm/ft^2 and a gas rate of 3.5 fps with differ-

Table 3 – 3
Overall Mass Transfer Coefficient
CO_2/NaOH System
Metal Tower Packings

Packing	K_Ga (lb-mol/h · ft³ · atm)
#25 IMTP® Packing	3.42
#40 IMTP® Packing	2.86
#50 IMTP® Packing	2.44
#70 IMTP® Packing	1.74
1 in. Pall Rings	3.10
1½ in. Pall Rings	2.58
2 in. Pall Rings	2.18
3½ in. Pall Rings	1.28
#1 Hy-Pak® Packing	2.89
#1½ Hy-Pak® Packing	2.42
#2 Hy-Pak® Packing	2.06
#3 Hy-Pak® Packing	1.45

Table 3 – 4
Overall Mass Transfer Coefficient
CO_2/NaOH System
Plastic Tower Packings

Packing	K_Ga (lb-mol/h · ft³ · atm)
#1 Super Intalox® Packing	2.80
#2 Super Intalox® Packing	1.92
#3 Super Intalox® Packing	1.23
1 in. Pall Rings	2.64
1½ in. Pall Rings	2.25
2 in. Pall Rings	2.09
3½ in. Pall Rings	1.23

ent sizes and types of metal, plastic, and ceramic packings. These overall mass transfer coefficients are calculated from the following equation:

$$K_Ga = \frac{y_iG_i - y_oG_o}{AZ\,\Delta p_{LM}} \qquad (3\text{-}30)$$

Table 3 – 5
Overall Mass Transfer Coefficient
CO₂/NaOH System
Ceramic Tower Packings

Packing	K_Ga (lb-mol/h · ft³ · atm)
1 in. Intalox® Saddles	2.82
1½ in. Intalox® Saddles	2.27
2 in. Intalox® Saddles	1.88
3 in. Intalox® Saddles	1.11
1 in. Raschig Rings	2.31
1½ in. Raschig Rings	1.92
2 in. Raschig Rings	1.63
3 in. Raschig Rings	1.02

The logarithmic mean partial pressure driving force is:

$$\Delta p_{LM} = \frac{P(y_i - y_o)}{\ln(y_i/y_o)} \tag{3-31}$$

In Equation 3-31 no vapor pressure of CO_2 is assumed above the liquid phase.

In this system the K_Ga will increase with liquid rate in accordance with Equation 3-13. However, the K_Ga value reaches a maximum value, as the liquid rate is increased at constant gas rate, when a pressure drop of about 0.75 in. H_2O/ft is achieved. This increase in K_Ga value primarily is due to variation of the interfacial area with liquid rate because of an increase in liquid holdup. This effect is verified by data on oxygen desorption as well as by data on CO_2 absorption [13, 14]. However, liquid entrainment makes absorption measurements invalid at liquid rates above those listed in Table 3-2.

AMINE SYSTEMS

One of the most widely used commercial absorption processes is the removal of CO_2 or H_2S from a gas stream by contacting it with a solution of monoethanolamine or diethanolamine. Both of these solutions are alkaline and combine chemically with one-half mol of acid gas per mol of amine. Although there exists a chemical combination, still even at equilibrium, the acid gas exhibits a vapor pressure above the solution.

Since this vapor pressure of the absorbed acid gas increases rapidly with temperature increase, it is possible to regenerate the rich amine solution by stripping the heated solvent.

In general, about three normal (18 wt%) MEA solutions have been used as solvents for acid gases. It is desirable to operate with a high solution strength so as to reduce the liquid circulation requirement. However, the vapor pressure of CO_2 above the rich solution at constant CO_2/MEA ratio increases with increasing MEA concentration. Also, the boiling point for regeneration increases at higher MEA concentrations which greatly increases the rate of corrosion of common metals. Because of the higher vapor pressures of CO_2 produced at elevated temperatures, regeneration of the rich amine solution at several atmospheres pressure would be more easily accomplished; however actual regenerator pressures in many cases are kept about 10 psig in order to minimize corrosion. Further, MEA tends to degrade as the temperature increases, which incurs the expense of replacement of this solvent and removal of the degradation products.

Recently, higher strength amine solutions, about five normal MEA concentration, have been used in conjunction with proprietary stabilizer systems. These systems also contain special chemical agents to inhibit corrosion of metals.

The basic equipment arrangement for an amine acid gas removal system is shown in Figure 3-2. It consists of an absorber in which cooled lean solvent flows downward in contact with the upwardly flowing gas to be treated. Before leaving the absorber, the purified gas may be washed with water to recover any vaporized MEA. The rich solvent at the bottom of the absorber is in contact with the entering gas stream thus providing the greatest mass transfer driving force. Due to the heat of solution and heat of reaction of the acid gas with the amine, the rich liquid effluent will be at a higher temperature than the lean liquid feed unless cooled by the gas stream. The rich liquid flows through a heat exchanger where it is heated by the regenerator bottoms liquid. The hot rich amine is fed to the top of a reboiled stripping column. The overhead stripped acid gas is cooled to remove water vapor and the condensate is returned to the system to maintain the water balance. The stripped hot lean bottoms solution first is cooled against the rich stripper feed liquid and then against cooling water before being returned to the top of the absorber. If the gas stream to be treated contains condensable hydrocarbon vapors, the lean solvent temperature should be above the dew point temperature of these vapors in order to prevent condensation of an immiscible hydrocarbon liquid which promotes foaming of the liquid phase in the absorber.

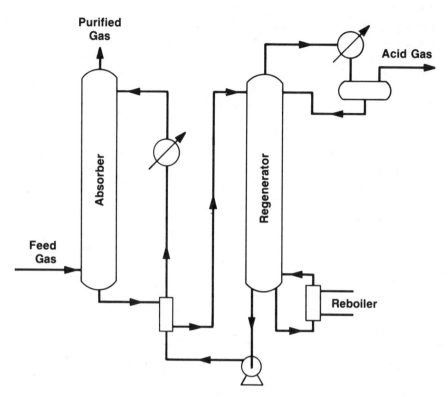

Figure 3-2. Typical amine gas treatment system.

Amines are considered to be moderately foaming systems in absorbers; therefore, the absorber diameter is specified so that the pressure drop for the packed bed does not exceed 0.25 in. H_2O/ft at the point of greatest loading. The pressure drop is restricted to avoid the gas phase doing excessive work on the liquid phase which would produce a greater degree of foaming by the amine solution. There will be a different tower diameter required for different size tower packings. Generally, as absorber operating pressure increases, the size of packing used is increased. Since the thickness of the vessel shell is a function of operating pressure and diameter, at high pressures it usually is less expensive to increase the packed height as a result of the use of larger size packing rather than to increase the diameter and therefore the shell thickness.

The gas flow rate and inlet composition are known and the outlet gas composition is specified for the absorber. Normally the lean solvent feed will contain 0.12 to 0.15 mol of CO_2 per mol MEA. This will allow absorption of 0.30 to 0.35 mol of CO_2 per mol of MEA in the lean solvent feed. The solvent flow rate now can be fixed from the material balance.

The effects of liquid and gas flow rates for this absorption are given by Equation 3-13 using the exponents applicable to liquid-film-controlled systems. Since one normal sodium hydroxide for the standard test system has been replaced with a three normal MEA solution as the liquid phase, the values of the overall mass transfer coefficients will be twice those shown for the standard system in Tables 3-3, 3-4, and 3-5 for lean solvent containing 0.15 mol CO_2 per mol MEA. The values shown in these tables are based on a liquid rate of 10 gpm/ft² and a gas capacity factor (F_s) of 0.93 lb$^{0.5}$/ft$^{0.5} \cdot$ s.

The K_Ga values taken from these tables are for a solvent temperature of 75°F. They will increase by 40% at a liquid temperature of 100°F and by 90% at 125°F. These K_Ga values apply for a partial pressure of CO_2 in the gas stream of 0.01 atm. The K_Ga is reduced as the partial pressure of solute in the gas stream increases. These K_Ga values would be reduced by 75% at a CO_2 partial pressure of 1 atm and by 90% at 20 atm partial pressure. Of course, the driving force for mass transfer is increased at the higher partial pressure. Although the solubility of CO_2 in the liquid phase would be expected to increase at higher pressures, the mass transfer coefficient is restricted by diffusion of the reactive amine.

The K_Ga value decreases as the ratio of mol acid gas per mol MEA in the solvent increases. As compared to lean solvent containing 0.15 mol CO_2 per mol MEA, the K_Ga value will be reduced by 40% for solvent containing 0.31 mol CO_2 per mol MEA and by 70% for 0.43 mol CO_2 per mol MEA in the solvent.

Increasing the concentration of MEA in the solvent normally would be expected to increase the K_Ga value because of the increased diffusion of reactive amine into the liquid film. However, increasing the MEA concentration also increases the viscosity of the liquid phase which reduces the rate of diffusion. The K_Ga value shows an overall decrease of 5% for a one normal increase in the MEA concentration above three normal.

The driving force for mass transfer is the difference between the partial pressure of CO_2 in the gas phase and the vapor pressure of CO_2 above the liquid phase. A mass and heat balance across the absorber will fix the outlet rich solvent temperature and composition enabling the vapor pressure of CO_2 above the effluent liquid to be determined. For purposes of initial heat balance calculations, the exit gas stream temperature can be assumed to be the same as the inlet lean solvent temperature.

Usually both the equilibrium line and the operating line for such an absorption operation are curved; still it is normal practice to use a logarithmic mean average of the partial-pressure difference driving forces at the top and bottom of the absorber as the overall driving force. The mass transfer coefficients are corrected empirically, as has been described, from the values obtained for the standard test system. To accommodate the use of the logarithmic average overall driving force, a logarithmic average of the K_Ga values at the top and bottom of the absorber is used as the overall mass transfer coefficient. The packed depth required then can be calculated from Equation 3-15.

When H_2S is the solute to be removed from the gas stream, the design of an amine system is similar to that just described for CO_2 absorption. However, the K_Ga value for CO_2 absorption into MEA is only about 40% of the K_Ga value for H_2S absorption into the same MEA solution. The K_Ga value for H_2S absorption is influenced by the same variables in the same manner as for CO_2 absorption with the exception of the temperature influence. The K_Ga for H_2S absorption decreases with increasing solvent temperature probably because of reduced H_2S solubility in the liquid phase. The K_Ga value applicable at 75°F will be reduced by 20% at 100°F and will be reduced by 25% at 115°F solvent temperature.

Diethanolamine solutions find wide use in treating sulfur-bearing gas streams. This is because MEA forms a nonregenerable stable chemical compound with carbonyl sulfide and carbon disulfide. In the past, usually a 2.5 normal (26 wt%) DEA solution has been used as a solvent for H_2S in treating natural gas and refinery gas streams. Newer, proprietary stabilized solvent systems have been reported to contain up to 5.5 normal DEA concentrations.

Again the design of the treating system is similar to that using an MEA solvent. However, the K_Ga value for absorption into a DEA solvent is only 50% to 60% of that for an MEA solution of the same normality. Because of the lower vapor pressure of DEA solutions, a water wash normally is not required at the top of the absorber.

HOT CARBONATE SYSTEMS

Another very widely used commercial absorption process involves the removal of CO_2 or H_2S by contacting the gas stream with a hot potassium carbonate solution. This process was developed to operate at a constant liquid temperature, thereby eliminating the heat required to raise the temperature of an amine solution to permit regeneration. Absorption and release of acid gases using this process depend largely on the difference in operating pressure in the absorber compared to the pressure in the regenerator. Normally the hot carbonate process is useful only when the partial pressure of the acid gas in the gas stream to be treated is at least 18 psi. Since the solvent is an aqueous inorganic salt solution, hydrocarbon solubility is very low. This process is widely used to purify high pressure natural gas as there is no loss of fuel gas by coabsorption with the acid gas.

The absorbed CO_2 reacts with the alkaline solvent as follows:

$$K_2CO_3 + CO_2 + H_2O = 2\ KHCO_3 \tag{3-32}$$

When H_2S is absorbed the reaction is:

$$K_2CO_3 + H_2S = KHCO_3 + KHS \tag{3-33}$$

Although the first hydrogen ionization constant for H_2CO_3 is more than six times that for H_2S, nevertheless CO_2 is absorbed into an alkaline carbonate solution at a slower rate than H_2S. Note that Equation 3-32 shows a mol of water in the reaction while Equation 3-33 shows the acid gas reacting directly with the carbonate. It is believed that the absorbed CO_2 first reacts with water to form H_2CO_3 which subsequently combines with the alkaline carbonate. Thus, the overall rate of absorption is controlled by the relatively slow chemical reaction between CO_2 and water. Much effort has been devoted to the development of catalysts which promote the rate of hydrolysis of CO_2. Proprietary hot carbonate systems using such promoters develop overall mass transfer coefficients for CO_2 absorption, which typically are 2.5 to 3 times those exhibited by unpromoted hot carbonate systems.

The basic arrangement of a hot carbonate acid gas removal system is shown in Figure 3-3. It consists of an absorber in which hot lean solvent flows downward contacting the upwardly flowing gas stream to be purified. The rich solution from the bottom of the absorber flows through a pressure reduction valve into the top of the regenerator where the solution flashes at the lower regenerator operating pressure. The overhead vapor stream from the regenerator is cooled to condense water vapor. This condensate is used to wash the outlet gas free of entrained K_2CO_3. The regenerator is reboiled to provide steam to strip the acid gas from the solvent. The lean bottoms from the regenerator is returned by means of high pressure pumps to the top of the absorber as feed. Because the solvent is circulated hot, the sensible heating load required by an amine system is eliminated; however the reboiler on the regenerator still must provide the heat of solution and the heat of reaction of the solute with the carbonate.

Although this process originally was developed using a 40 wt% K_2CO_3 solution strength, most commercial processes use a 24 to 30 wt%

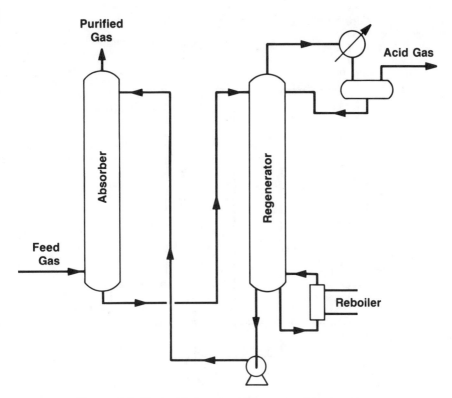

Figure 3-3. Typical hot carbonate gas treatment system.

solution. Solvent concentrations greater than 30 wt% K_2CO_3 are avoided because of the possibility of $KHCO_3$ precipitation. The rich solution from the absorber is up to 80% converted to bicarbonate by CO_2 absorption. The rich solution CO_2 concentration, of course, is limited by the equilibrium between the partial pressure of CO_2 in the inlet gas stream and the vapor pressure of CO_2 above the rich solvent. The lean solution normally is regenerated so that it contains no less than 20% of the carbonate in the form of bicarbonate. This lean solvent strength will give an equilibrium concentration of about 2,000 mol ppm CO_2 in the gas leaving an absorber operating at a pressure of 300 psia [15]. Regeneration of the solvent to a lower bicarbonate content would require considerably more stripping steam and thus a greater reboiler duty.

To reduce the CO_2 content of the absorber exit gas stream, the majority of the lean solvent can be fed to the absorber to irrigate the second packed bed down from the top. A portion of the lean solvent will be cooled to about 190°F and fed to the top of the absorber as shown in

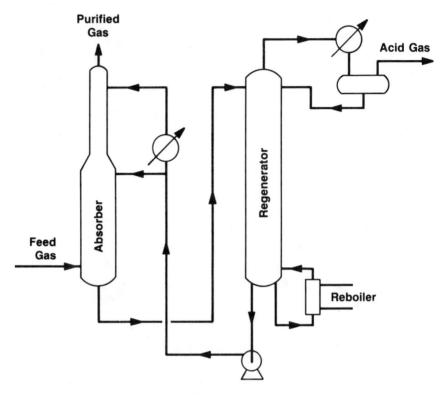

Figure 3-4. Modified hot carbonate gas treatment system.

Figure 3-4. The cooler solvent in contact with the exit gas stream at the top of the absorber has a lower equilibrium vapor pressure of CO_2. However, this modification does add a sensible heat load to the system which increases the regenerator reboiler duty somewhat.

In an effort to produce a low CO_2 content in the absorber exit gas as well as to minimize energy consumption, a split stream process has been developed. As Figure 3-5 illustrates, the rich solvent flows downward through about 70% of the total packed depth in the regenerator at which point it is intercepted by a trap tray. The majority of the solvent, which has been partially regenerated, is withdrawn at that level. The balance of the solvent continues down the column where it now is stripped with three to four times the pounds of steam per gallon of solvent as the ratio in the upper part of the column. The resultant very lean solvent from the bottom of the regenerator is cooled and fed to the top of the absorber. The partially stripped solvent which had been withdrawn from the side of the regenerator is fed to the absorber about half-way down the total packed depth. This arrangement will permit reducing the CO_2 content of the exit gas to 1,000 mol ppm for an absorber operating at a pressure of 400 psia.

A hot carbonate absorber is considered to be a slightly foaming system. The diameter of the column and the packing size should be selected so that the design pressure drop is restricted to about 0.30 in. H_2O/ft at the point of maximum loading. In such systems, liquid loadings tend to be very high, so that the packing size should be selected to accommodate the irrigation rate in accordance with the recommendations in Table 3-2. In a split-stream system (Figure 3-5), because the liquid flow is lower in the upper section and since the gas flow has been reduced by absorption of some of the solute, the upper section of the absorber may be of a smaller diameter than the lower section.

The inlet gas flow rate and composition will be known. The absorber exit gas composition will be related to the bicarbonate content and tem-

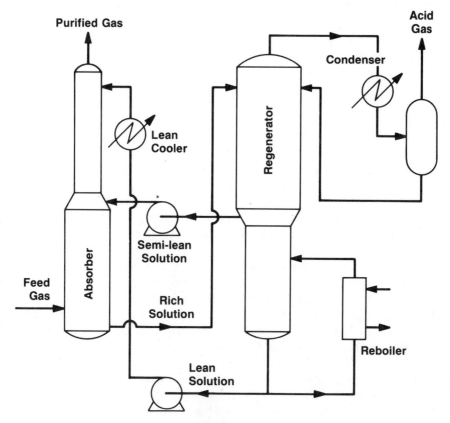

Figure 3-5. Split-stream hot carbonate gas treatment system.

perature of the lean solvent. The rich liquid composition leaving the absorber will be related to the partial pressure of acid gas in the inlet gas stream. Once these terminal stream compositions have been determined, then a mass balance will be used to set the solvent flow rate.

The effects of liquid and gas flow rates for this process are given by Equation 3-13 using the exponents for liquid-film-controlled systems. For an unpromoted 25 wt% K_2CO_3 solution at a liquid rate of 40 gpm/ ft^2 with a gas capacity factor (F_s) of 0.93 $lb^{0.5}/ft^{0.5} \cdot s$, industrial experience indicates that the overall K_Ga values will be approximately 17% of the values for the standard CO_2/NaOH system given in Tables 3-3, 3-4, and 3-5. These values apply for 20% conversion to bicarbonate in the solvent at a temperature of 235°F. The K_Ga value decreases as the percent conversion to bicarbonate increases. At 50% conversion to $KHCO_3$ the K_Ga value is reduced by 35%, and at 80% conversion by 65% compared to the above values for 20% conversion.

These K_Ga values also apply for a CO_2 partial pressure of 1.3 atm in the gas stream. At higher CO_2 partial pressures, the K_Ga value will be lower. At 2.6 atm CO_2 partial pressure the K_Ga value is 25% lower, and at 3.7 atm CO_2 partial pressure the K_Ga is reduced by 40%. However, the driving force for mass transfer increases at higher CO_2 partial pressures. Although, at a CO_2 partial pressure of 0.7 atm, the K_Ga value will increase by 20%, normally the hot carbonate process is not useful at such low pressures.

The hot carbonate system has been promoted with organic materials which not only increase the rate of CO_2 hydrolysis, but also alter the equilibrium to lower the CO_2 vapor pressure above the lean solvent. Since this process operates at a continuous high temperature, organic materials may degenerate to produce corrosive by-products; therefore, a corrosion inhibitor usually is used in combination with the organic promoter. When H_2S is being absorbed, oxidative-type inhibitors must be avoided because of the possible production of solid sulfur in the solution.

The calculation of packed depth required is similar to the procedure used for an amine absorber. The number of mols of acid gas to be absorbed is calculated by material balance from the gas flow rate and the concentrations of solute in the inlet and outlet gas streams. The liquid flow rate is fixed by mass balance which depends on carbonate strength, the degree of regeneration, and the extent of carbonation of the solvent. The driving force is considered to be the logarithmic mean average of the solute partial-pressure differences at the top and bottom of the absorber. The design overall mass transfer coefficient is the logarithmic average of the coefficients for the terminal ends of the absorber, or section between feeds for split-stream operations. Because of some inconsistencies in the data, it is suggested that individual K_Ga values not exceed those applicable to a partial pressure for CO_2 of 0.7 atm. The packed depth required then can be calculated from Equation 3-15.

Because the bulk of the solvent is recirculated without cooling, there is only a small sensible heat load. The heat of reaction with K_2CO_3 is only 280 Btu/lb of CO_2 absorbed. This is one-third the heat of reaction of CO_2 with MEA; therefore, the heat load on a hot carbonate system per pound of CO_2 absorbed and regenerated is lower than for an amine solvent system.

Generally, the hot carbonate process is much less corrosive to common metals than amine solvent systems. Potassium carbonate is a very stable compound which is not degraded at the usual high operating temperatures or by oxidizing agents. Hot carbonate systems, therefore, are used to remove CO_2 from recycle gas streams in organic oxidation reactions.

When H_2S is to be removed from the gas stream, the mass transfer coefficient for this absorption is only slightly higher than for CO_2 absorption [16]. This is due to the high temperature of the recirculated solvent, as a colder carbonate solution would absorb H_2S much more rapidly than CO_2. Since CO_2 is a stronger acid than H_2S, it is more securely bound in the alkaline solvent; therefore, because of the higher vapor pressure of H_2S above the carbonate solution, it is more readily regenerated than is CO_2. The hot carbonate process is capable of treating natural gas to meet pipeline specifications of 0.25 grains H_2S per 100 std ft^3 of gas. Also, this process can be expected to remove carbonyl sulfide from the gas stream. It is believed that the hot alkaline solution hydrolyzes the COS to H_2S and CO_2, which subsequently are absorbed.

EXAMPLE PROBLEM

A 7-ft 0-in. ID CO_2 absorber in an ammonia plant presently is equipped with 20 valve trays on 24-in. spacing. The gas to the absorber is 79,400 lb/h at 130°F with a density of 0.792 lb/ft^3. The inlet gas contains 18.2 mol % CO_2 which must be reduced down to 90 mol ppm CO_2 in the outlet gas stream. The absorber operates at a top pressure of 325 psia. The liquid feed is 30.2 wt% monoethanolamine solution at a temperature of 110°F. This lean solution flow is 575,000 lb/h which contains 0.12 mol CO_2 per mol MEA. It is desired to increase the rates by 35%, which the present trays will not accommodate. Can the existing column handle these higher rates with tower packing?

By material balance, there are 994.2 lb-mol/h of CO_2 present in the inlet gas and 0.4 lb-mol/h of CO_2 present in the outlet gas; thus 993.8 lb-mol/h of CO_2 is absorbed. The rich liquid flow is 618,700 lb/h containing 0.47 mol CO_2 per mol MEA. This rich liquid has a density of 65.7 lb/ft^3 and a viscosity of 1.1 cps.

First we will determine whether #2 Hy-Pak® packing could be used with respect to the capacity of the packing and then with respect to its absorption efficiency. The point of greatest loading normally is at the bottom of an absorber. The flow parameter here from Figure 1-15 is:

$$X = \frac{618,700}{79,400} \left[\frac{0.792}{65.7}\right]^{0.5} = 0.856$$

The inlet gas mass velocity is 0.573 lb/ft$^2 \cdot$ s. The ordinate value for the present flow is:

$$Y = \frac{(0.573)^2(26)(1.04)^{0.10}}{32.2(0.792)(65.7 - 0.792)} = 0.00518$$

Thus the pressure drop at the bottom of the absorber for #2 Hy-Pak® packing would be 0.081 in. H$_2$O/ft at the present flow rates.

If the gas and liquid rates are increased by 1.35 times, then at the bottom of the absorber the flow parameter still will be X = 0.856.

However, the ordinate value will increase to:

$$Y = \frac{(0.774)^2(26)(1.04)^{0.10}}{32.2(0.792)(65.7 - 0.792)} = 0.00945$$

From Figure 1-15 the pressure drop for #2 Hy-Pak® packing now has increased to 0.23 in. H$_2$O/ft. Thus the #2 Hy-Pak® packing can handle the increased hydraulic flows without exceeding a pressure drop of 0.25 in. H$_2$O/ft that is the maximum design basis for amine absorbers which are considered moderately foaming systems.

Next, we will check the operation at increased rates to determine the depth of packing required. From Table 3-3, the standard K_Ga value for #2 Hy-Pak® packing is 2.06 lb-mol/h $\cdot$ ft$^3 \cdot$ atm. For a 5 normal MEA solution, the base K_Ga value would be 3.71 lb-mol/h $\cdot$ ft$^3 \cdot$ atm. This K_Ga value must be modified for the gas and liquid flow rates, the liquid temperature, the CO_2 partial pressure, and mol of CO_2 per mol MEA in the solvent both at the bottom of the column as well as the top of the column.

The 35% increased flow rates will require that 1,342 lb-mol/h of CO_2 is absorbed. The CO_2 concentration in the inlet and outlet gas streams, as well as the CO_2 concentration in the inlet and outlet MEA solutions, will be the same as at the original lower rates. The logarithmic mean partial-pressure driving force also will be unchanged.

The partial pressure of CO_2 at the bottom of the column is 4.025 atm while at the top of the column it is 0.00199 atm. After reduction of these values by the equilibrium partial pressure of CO_2 above the MEA solutions, the logarithmic mean-pressure driving force is 0.522 atm. The logarithmic mean average of the modified K_Ga value is 2.33 lb-mol/ $h \cdot ft^3 \cdot atm$ at flow rates 135% of present rates.

The packed depth required can be calculated from Equation 3-15:

$$Z = \frac{1,342}{38.5(2.33)(0.522)} = 28.7 \text{ ft}$$

Since there is 38 ft of vertical height available from the bottom tray to the top tray, #2 Hy-Pak® packing can handle the absorption requirement at the desired higher flow rates.

In summary, the 20 trays can be replaced with a 31.5 ft deep bed of #2 Hy-Pak® packing utilizing only 16 tray spaces to facilitate optimum use of the existing tray support rings. This revamped column will accommodate a 35% increase in gas and liquid flow rates while providing the same CO_2 removal efficiency as the present trays.

NOTATION

A	Column cross-sectional area (ft^2)
A*	Absorption factor
a	Interfacial area (ft^2/ft^3)
D	Diffusivity (ft^2/h)
F_s	Vapor capacity factor ($lb^{0.5}/ft^{0.5} \cdot s$)
G	Gas mass velocity ($lb/ft^2 \cdot h$)
G_i	Inlet gas flow (lb-mol/h)
Gm	Gas phase flow (lb-mol/h)
G_o	Outlet gas flow (lb-mol/h)
H	Henry's Law constant (atm/mol fraction)
HETP	Height equivalent to a theoretical stage (ft)
H_{OG}	Overall height of gas transfer unit (ft)
H_{OL}	Overall height of liquid transfer unit (ft)
K	Equilibrium ratio
K_Ga	Overall gas-phase mass transfer coefficient (lb-mol/h $\cdot ft^3 \cdot$ atm)
K_La	Overall liquid-phase mass transfer coefficient (lb-mol/ $h \cdot ft^3 \cdot$ mol/mol)

k_G Gas-film mass transfer coefficient (lb-mol/h $\cdot$ ft^2 $\cdot$ atm)
k_L Liquid-film mass transfer coefficient (lb-mol/h $\cdot$ ft^2 $\cdot$ mol/mol)
L   Liquid mass velocity (lb/ft^2 $\cdot$ h)
L_i Inlet liquid flow (lb-mol/h)
Lm   Liquid phase flow (lb-mol/h)
L_o Outlet liquid flow (lb-mol/h)
m   Slope of equilibrium curve
N   Solute transferred (lb-mol/h)
N_{OG} Number of overall gas transfer units
n   Stage number
P   Total system pressure (atm)
p   Partial pressure in gas phase (atm)
p^* Vapor pressure of solute (atm)
p' Partial pressure of solute in gas film (atm)
Sc   Schmidt number
u' Viscosity (lb/ft $\cdot$ h)
x   Mol fraction in liquid phase
x^* Equilibrium mol fraction in liquid phase
x' Mol fraction in liquid film
x_i Mol fraction solute in inlet liquid
x_o Mol fraction solute in outlet liquid
y   Mol fraction in gas phase
y^* Equilibrium mol fraction in gas phase
y_i Mol fraction solute in inlet gas
y_o Mol fraction solute in outlet gas
Z   Packed depth (ft)
Δp_{LM} ln mean pressure driving force (atm)
Δp_B Partial pressure difference at bottom (atm)
Δp_T Partial pressure difference at top (atm)
ψ Proportionality constant
ρ Density (lb/ft^3)

REFERENCES

1. Chilton, T. H., and Colburn, A. P., *Industrial and Engineering Chemistry,* Vol. 26, 1934, p. 1183.
2. Cornell, D., Knapp, W. G., and Fair, J. R., *Chemical Engineering Progress,* Vol. 56, No. 7, 1960, p. 68.
3. Eckert, J. S., *Canadian Gas Journal,* March–April 1972, p. 2.
4. Sherwood, T. K., and Holloway, F. A. L., *Transactions of American Institute of Chemical Engineers,* Vol. 36, 1940, p. 39.

5. Huckabay, H. K., and Garrison, R. L., *Hydrocarbon Processing*, Vol. 48, No. 6, 1969, p. 153.
6. Onda, K., Takeuchi, H., and Okumoto, Y., *Journal of Chemical Engineering, Japan*, Vol. 1, 1968, p. 56.
7. Bolles, W. L., and Fair, J. R., *Chemical Engineering*, Vol. 89, No. 14, 1982, p. 109.
8. Shulman, H. L., Press, S., and Whitehouse, W. G., *American Institute of Chemical Engineers Journal*, Vol. 6, No. 1, 1960, p. 174.
9. Kremser, A., *National Petroleum News*, Vol. 22, No. 21, 1930, p 45.
10. Maddox, R. N., *Process Engineer's Absorption Pocket Handbook*, Gulf Publishing, 1985, p. 2.
11. Souders, M., and Brown, G. G., *Industrial and Engineering Chemistry*, Vol. 24, 1932, p. 519.
12. Colburn, A. P., *Industrial and Engineering Chemistry*, Vol. 33, 1941, p. 459.
13. Yoshida, F., and Konayagi, T., *Industrial and Engineering Chemistry*, Vol. 50, No. 3, 1958, p. 365.
14. Shulman, H. L., et al., *American Institute of Chemical Engineers Journal*, Vol. 1, No. 2, 1955, p. 259.
15. Bocard, J. P., and Mayland, B. J., *Hydrocarbon Processing*, Vol. 41, No. 4, 1962, p. 128.
16. Kohl, A. L., and Riesenfeld, F. C., "Gas Purification," McGraw Hill, 1960, p. 145.

4

LIQUID STRIPPING

Stripping is a mass transfer operation that involves the transfer of a solute from the liquid phase to the gas phase. This operation may use an insoluble inert gas phase or a gas that is only slightly soluble in the liquid phase. Some of the liquid solvent also may be evaporated into the gas phase; however, this is incidental to the stripping operation. The stripping operation also may use a saturated vapor, such as steam, as the gas phase that will be totally or partially condensed into the liquid phase. This condensate need not be soluble in the liquid phase. Finally, the gas phase can be generated by reboiling the solvent liquid. In any case, the solute must be more volatile than the solvent for a successful stripping operation.

In the most simple case, the entering liquid is a solution of solute in the liquid phase that follows Henry's Law. The vapor pressure of solute above the liquid phase is given by:

$$p^* = Hx \tag{4-1}$$

The partial pressure of solute in the vapor phase is a function of the composition:

$$p = yP \tag{4-2}$$

Stripping of solute will continue as long as the vapor pressure of solute above the liquid phase exceeds the partial pressure of solute in the gas phase.

Solute solubility in the liquid phase is inversely proportional to the value of the Henry's Law constant. From Equation 4-1, anything that increases the H value will enhance the stripping operation. Because the

Henry's Law constant increases with temperature, a commonly utilized stripping method involves heating the liquid phase.

It is convenient to use liquid-phase concentrations in calculations involving stripping of solute from a solvent. The driving force for stripping operations is the difference between the solute concentration in the main-body liquid phase and that of the liquid film at the interface between the gas and liquid phases. The driving force is:

$$\Delta x = x - x' \tag{4-3}$$

The mass transferred per unit time is expressed by:

$$N = AZ\, k_L a\, (x - x') \tag{4-4}$$

The interfacial area (a) is not the geometric surface area of the packing, but it is the mass transfer area between the gas and liquid phases. Thus the product of a and AZ represents the total interfacial area within the entire packed bed. As stated in Chapter 3, the a and x' values are very difficult to evaluate in commercial operations. Overall terms, therefore, have been utilized. The interfacial area is combined with the liquid-phase mass transfer coefficient to produce an overall volumetric coefficient $(K_L a)$.

To facilitate the calculation, the overall driving force is based on the liquid-phase and gas-phase compositions. For systems following Henry's Law, as given in Table 4-1, Equation 4-3 can be written [1]:

$$\Delta x = x - \frac{yP}{H} \tag{4-5}$$

Or, when Henry's Law does not apply to the system, the equilibrium ratio (K) can be used to express the overall driving force:

$$K = \frac{y}{x} \tag{4-6}$$

This equilibrium ratio is a function of temperature, pressure, and composition, even in a simple hydrocarbon system [2]. Thus Equation 4-3 can be written as:

$$\Delta x = x - \frac{y}{K} \tag{4-7}$$

Table 4 - 1
Solubilities of Organic Compounds in Water

Compound	H @ 68°F (atm/mol fraction)	H @ 77°F (atm/mol fraction)
Benzene	240	
Carbon Tetrachloride	1,290	
Chloroform	170	
1, 4 Dichlorbenzene	190	
Methyl Chloride	480	
1, 2, 4 Trimethyl Benzene		353
Toluene		340
Vinyl Chloride	355,000	

The mass transfer equation, in overall terms, becomes:

$$\overset{\checkmark}{N} = AZ\ K_{L}a\ \Delta x_{LM} \tag{4-8}$$

The compositional overall driving force is the logarithmic mean average of the driving forces at the bottom and top of the packed bed:

$$\Delta x_{LM} = \frac{\Delta x_T - \Delta x_B}{\ln(\Delta x_T/\Delta x_B)} \tag{4-9}$$

Equation 4-9 assumes a straight operating line and equilibrium curve. This is valid for systems where the solute mass transferred is small compared with the liquid and gas mass flows and the value of H or K is independent of solute concentration in the liquid phase.

DESIGN THEORY

The overall liquid-phase mass transfer coefficient is related to the individual gas and liquid-film mass transfer coefficients as:

$$\frac{1}{K_La} = \frac{1}{mk_Ga P} + \frac{1}{k_La} \tag{4-10}$$

where m is the slope of the equilibrium curve. For systems that obey Henry's Law, m is equal to H/P.

The Henry's Law constant, as given in Table 4-2, usually is applied to slightly soluble gases such as aqueous solutions of oxygen, chlorine, carbon monoxide, hydrogen, ethylene, hydrogen sulfide, methane, nitrogen and carbon dioxide [3]. For solutes of greater solubility, such as C-3 and C-4 hydrocarbons dissolved in light naphtha, the operating line slope (m) equals the equilibrium ratio (K). This ratio (K) generally is applicable to ideal liquid-phase solutions at pressures up to about 10 atm.

Overall mass transfer coefficients show similar variations with gas and liquid flow rates as in absorption (see Chapter 3). The effects of temperature and pressure are expected to be the same for the gas-film and liquid-film mass transfer coefficients as in absorption operations. Because liquid-film mass transfer coefficients, as well as the Henry's Law constant, increase with rising temperature, stripping is facilitated by heating the liquid phase.

The stripping factor can be used to calculate the number of theoretical stages in a stripping operation in a manner analogous to the use of the absorption factor in absorption processes as described in Chapter 3. The stripping factor is the ratio of the equilibrium curve slope to the operating line slope:

$$S^* = \frac{KG_m}{L_m} \qquad (4\text{-}11)$$

The stripping factor is the reciprocal of the absorption factor described in Chapter 3.

Table 4 - 2
Solubilities of Gases in Water

Compound	H @ 50°F (atm/mol fraction)	H @ 68°F (atm/mol fraction)
Acetylene	960	1,210
Carbonyl Sulfide	1,480	2,190
Ethane	18,900	26,300
Ethylene	7,680	10,200
Hydrogen	63,600	68,300
Hydrogen Sulfide	367	483
Methane	29,700	37,600
Nitrogen	66,800	80,400
Oxygen	32,700	40,100
Ozone	2,480	3,760
Propylene	4,460	

Source: International Critical Tables [3].

The Colburn correlation, shown in Figure 4-1, can be used to determine the number of liquid-phase transfer units, (N_{OL}) [4]. For this calculation, it is first necessary to calculate the abscissa value

$$\frac{x_i - y_i/K}{x_o - y_i/K}$$

and secondly the stripping factor from Equation 4-11. These calculations assume that the equilibrium curve and the operating line are linear, although not necessarily parallel.

COLUMN DIAMETER SELECTION

In stripping operations the inlet liquid flow rate, inlet solute concentration, and column operating pressure are known while the desired solute concentration in the outlet liquid stream will be specified. The solvent liquid may be low cost or a waste product that will be stripped on a once-through basis. On the other hand, if the solvent is expensive, it will be recycled through an absorber. This latter type of operation usually is the case when solute recovery is the primary purpose of the operation. The designer first must select the stripping gas to be used, then determine its flow rate. The greater the solubility of solute in the solvent, the larger will be the required stripping gas flow. Solutes that are highly soluble in the liquid phase exhibit low H or K values, thus gas-phase concentrations of solute are low. Because the outlet gas stream will be saturated with solvent liquid, the gas stream usually is cooled to condense the solvent vapor if the solvent is costly. In any event, this condensate may be used as reflux to a wash section above the stripper feed.

After the stripping gas flow rate is determined, the designer can calculate the column diameter needed and then the packed depth. The column cross-sectional area usually is set to produce a pressure drop between 0.15 to 0.50 in. H_2O/ft of packed depth at the point of maximum loading. For systems that are known to foam, the design pressure drop should not exceed 0.25 in. H_2O/ft in operations using inert gas stripping. Where steam or reboiled solvent vapor is the stripping gas, the design pressure drop can be a maximum of 0.30 in. H_2O/ft for a moderately foaming liquid.

Usually liquid irrigation rates in strippers are only about 60% of those in companion absorbers. In single-pass strippers, the liquid irrigation rate should not exceed the values shown in Table 3-2 to avoid aspiration

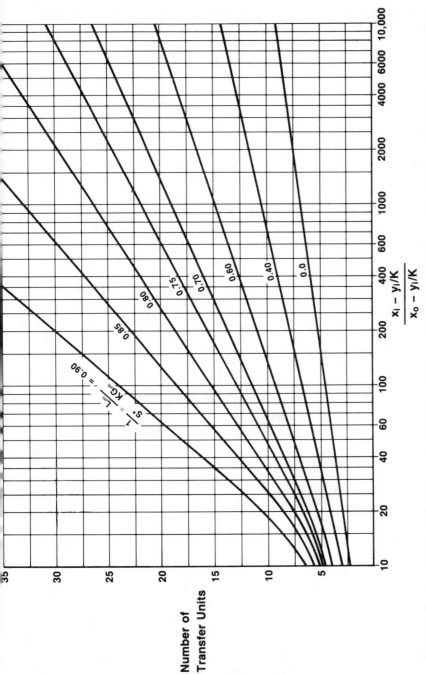

Figure 4-1. Colburn correlation for stripper design. (From Colburn [4]. Reprinted with permission from *Industrial and Engineering Chemistry*, American Chemical Society, Vol. 33, 1941, pg. 459.)

of the gas phase down the column with the liquid. Such a gas recycle increases the solute concentration in the gas stream entering the packed bed and reduces the mass transfer driving force at the column bottom. These liquid rates in Table 3-2 apply to mobile liquids. For liquids with viscosities of 50 cps or greater, 1½-in. or larger-size packings normally should be specified.

WATER DEAERATION

A common stripping operation that obeys Henry's Law is illustrated by the removal of dissolved oxygen from water. This can be accomplished by stripping the water with steam, a method commonly used for boiler feed-water treatment. The Henry's Law constant for this system is 75% greater at 212°F water temperature than at 68°F, and results in increased vapor pressure of oxygen above the liquid. In addition, the pure steam stripping vapor contains no oxygen. Therefore, the maximum possible driving force for mass transfer is available at the column bottom.

Frequently, it is not desirable to have boiling water as effluent from the deaeration column. Normally it is not cost effective to use the large flow of inert gas required for stripping oxygen down to the desired low concentration in the effluent liquid. Under these conditions, vacuum deaeration usually is utilized.

When water is fed into a column under vacuum, a portion of the liquid will flash to vapor. The resultant water then drops in temperature until its vapor pressure, plus those of the dissolved gases, equals the column pressure. The vapor pressure exerted by the dissolved air in water is so small that it can be neglected for practical purposes. Thus at a column pressure of 15 mm Hg absolute, the water will flash and be cooled to a temperature of 63.5°F. At this lower temperature, the Henry's Law constant for dissolved oxygen is reduced by only 7% as compared to water at 70°F.

The partial pressure of oxygen in the gas phase is the product of a larger mol fraction (y) and a lower total system pressure. The actual stripping gas in this operation is water vapor. Because the water flashes to the lower temperature in one equilibrium stage, there is very little stripping vapor available in the lower part of the column. Even if the liquid and vapor were to reach equilibrium at the column bottom, the amount of stripped oxygen is so small that there is almost no upward movement of the vapor phase. The high liquid flow used in these deaerators tends to drag the small vapor phase out of the vacuum column where the oxygen is reabsorbed quickly.

If a second-stage column is operated in series with the first column, but at a lower absolute pressure, additional flashed water vapor is generated for stripping the oxygen to a lower concentration. Thus in a second-stage deaerator, operated at 10 mm Hg absolute pressure, the water flashes further and is cooled to a temperature of 52.2°F. This additional water vapor will serve to sweep the stripped oxygen out of the packed bed.

A small amount of inert gas added to the bottom of the vacuum column causes a substantial reduction in the effluent water oxygen content. Thus, the use of 0.24 scf of methane per 100 gallons of water can reduce the effluent oxygen content by an additional 66% [5]. Adding a small amount of steam per gallon of water is even more effective in reducing the oxygen content, compared to straight vacuum deaeration. The steam both heats the water at the interface to reduce oxygen solubility and acts as a stripping vapor.

A vacuum deaerator diameter typically is specified to give a liquid irrigation rate of about 40 gpm/ft^2 of column cross-sectional area. Originally, vacuum deaerators used ceramic packing and operated at lower liquid rates. However, most modern columns utilize 2-in. or larger-size plastic packings with a packed bed typically 7 ft to 16 ft deep.

This operation is so highly liquid-film controlled that the gas-film resistance, for practical purposes, can be neglected. Therefore, the number of transfer units required is:

$$N_{OL} = \ln\left[\frac{x_i}{x_o}\right] \tag{4-12}$$

The overall height of a liquid-film transfer unit (H_{OL}) is a function of the liquid flow rate and the temperature. The H_{OL} for #2 plastic Super Intalox® packing is 2.3 ft at a liquid rate of 40 gpm/ft^2 and temperature of 68°F. The H_{OL} increases as the water temperature is lowered. At 53°F water temperature, the H_{OL} is 9% greater than at 68°F, while at 41°F it is 17% greater. The H_{OL} increases as the 0.38 power of the liquid irrigation rate. At a liquid rate of 26 gpm/ft^2, the H_{OL} is reduced by 15% compared to the value at 40 gpm/ft^2.

The total packed depth required is:

$$Z = N_{OL}H_{OL} \tag{4-13}$$

In some cases a 3-in.- or 3½-in.-size plastic packing is specified. The H_{OL} for this larger size packing will be about 3.1 ft at 40 gpm/ft^2 liquid rate and 68°F.

WATER STRIPPING

Another common stripping problem is the removal of chlorinated hydrocarbons for the purification of well water. Table 4-3 lists some of the commonly found well water contaminants. Also shown are the concentrations of these chlorinated hydrocarbons typically present. The Henry's Law constant for these chlorinated hydrocarbons in water at 68°F is given in this table [6].

Table 4 - 3
Typical Well Water Contaminants

Compound	Concentration (ug/1)	H @ 68°F (atm/mol fraction)
1, 1 Dichlorethane	50	250
1, 1, 1 Trichlorethane	190	400
cis 1, 2 Dichlorethylene	270	360
Trichlorethylene	60	550
Perchlorethylene	110	1100

Source: Kavanaugh [6]. Reprinted from *Journal of American Water Works Association*, Vol. 72, No. 12 (December 1980) by permission. Copyright © 1980, American Water Works Association.

Chlorinated hydrocarbons are stripped using atmospheric air that is assumed to contain practically no chlorinated hydrocarbons. This operation is the exact opposite of a gas scrubbing process for air pollution control as described in Chapter 2. This stripping is made possible because of the low solubility (high value of Henry's Law constant) of these chlorinated hydrocarbons.

Stripping columns for this process typically have diameters that give a liquid irrigation rate between 20 and 40 gpm/ft^2. An 8-ft diameter tower would handle a liquid flow of about 1,500 gpm, for example. Usually 200 to 600 scfm of stripping air is used per 100 gpm of water. The resulting superficial gas velocity is about 1 to 3 fps.

The number of liquid transfer units required is calculated from Equation 4-14 using the stripping factor:

$$N_{OL} = \frac{S^*}{S^* - 1} \ln \left[\frac{\frac{x_i}{x_o}(S^* - 1) + 1}{S^*} \right] \qquad (4\text{-}14)$$

This equation assumes that the stripping gas contains negligible solute. Because Henry's Law can be used, the stripping factor in Equation 4-11 can be rewritten:

$$S^* = \frac{HG_m}{PL_m}$$ (4-15)

If 98% removal efficiency is required $x_i/x_o = 50$. Thus, this stripper would require 4.0 to 5.3 transfer units, depending on the particular chlorinated hydrocarbon, to provide 98% removal of each individual chlorinated hydrocarbon in Table 4-3. If 4,500 scfm of stripping air is used in the 8-ft ID tower for stripping 1,500 gpm of water, an overall removal of 98% of the total chlorinated hydrocarbons will require 4.4 liquid transfer units.

The overall height of a liquid transfer unit (H_{OL}) is 4.8 ft for 2-in. plastic Super Intalox® packing at a liquid rate of 30 gpm/ft^2 and a water temperature of 68°F. This system is highly liquid-film controlled because the slope of the equilibrium curve is much greater than the slope of the operating line. The column, therefore, would require a packed depth of 21-ft for #2 plastic Super Intalox® packing to strip 98% of the total chlorinated hydrocarbons from the entering well water.

Typically in such columns only one packed bed is used with a maximum depth of 30 ft. At liquid rates greater than 37 gpm/ft^2 or when using more than 500 scfm of air per 100 gpm of water, a 3-in.- or 3½-in.-size packing normally will be selected. The H_{OL} for this larger packing is 30% greater than that for a 2-in. size of the same type of packing. At liquid rates less than 23 gpm/ft^2, or when using less than 300 scfm of air per 100 gpm of water, a 1-in.-size packing usually will be specified. The H_{OL} for this size will be about 20% less than that for a 2-in.-size packing.

If the water temperature is reduced to 55°F, the Henry's Law constant will be 30% lower than at 68°F. This will increase the number of transfer units required for the same percentage contaminant stripping.

If 99% contaminant removal is necessary, the number of transfer units required will be 18% greater than for 98% removal. On the other hand, if 95% contaminant removal is satisfactory, the number of transfer units required will be reduced 23% compared to 98% removal efficiency.

AMINE REGENERATION

One of the most common stripping operations is the regeneration of an amine solution that has been used to absorb CO_2 or H_2S. Typically, a 3-normal monoethanolamine solution containing 0.42 to 0.50 mol CO_2 per mol MEA will be fed to the stripper. The rich solvent is preheated to a temperature of 190° to 210°F by heat exchange against the hot, lean stripper bottoms liquid. The stripper typically operates at a top pressure not greater than 10 psig and the overhead vapor will contain about 27 mol% CO_2 with the balance being water vapor. The stripped vapor passes through a condenser to reduce the water vapor content. Then the condensate is returned to the column to irrigate a wash bed at the top of the stripper to prevent loss of MEA vapor in the overhead gas stream.

The stripper is heated by a reboiler that typically requires 0.9 to 1.1 lb of heating steam per gallon of solvent to be regenerated. Lean solvent leaves the stripper bottom at a temperature of 235° to 245°F and contains 0.12 to 0.15 mol CO_2 per mol MEA. Reboiler energy must be sufficient to provide: 820 Btu/lb of CO_2 heat of reaction with MEA, the sensible heat load to raise the solvent temperature, and the steam present in the overhead vapor.

Amines are considered moderately foaming systems; therefore, the column diameter is specified to limit the pressure drop to 0.30 in. H_2O/ ft of packed depth at the point of greatest loading.

The complex of CO_2 and MEA must be chemically decomposed in the stripper. The rate of this decomposition reaction is increased by raising the stripper temperature. However, the MEA itself tends to decompose thermally producing by-products that are corrosive to common metals. Regeneration temperatures, therefore, usually are limited to a maximum of 250°F. If the overhead CO_2 gas is used in the process rather than vented, a compressor may be used to increase the CO_2 pressure. This can be a lower-cost alternative to raising the stripper pressure and requiring nickel alloy construction for the column and internals.

Because CO_2 release is a function of the decomposition rate of the CO_2/MEA complex, it is necessary to provide sufficient liquid residence time in the stripper. A column for this reaction normally has tower packing no larger than 2-in. size and operates at a pressure drop of no less than 0.10 in. H_2O/ft. Maximum liquid irrigation rate typically is 30 gpm/ft^2.

The vapor pressure of CO_2 above the MEA solvent varies with the molar ratio of CO_2 to MEA, as well as with the temperature. The equilibrium curve representing this stripping operation is a plot of the mol fraction of CO_2 in the vapor in equilibrium with the liquid phase. The operating line on this same plot is determined by a heat and material balance. The number of liquid-phase transfer units (N_{OL}) usually varies from five to nine, depending on the ratio of mols of liquid to mols of stripping vapor. The lower the steam consumption per gallon of solvent, the greater the number of liquid-phase transfer units required. However, because of the equilibrium curve shape, use of a larger number of transfer units does not substantially reduce reboiler duty [7].

Because of the liquid-phase reaction to liberate CO_2, this stripping operation is highly liquid-film controlled. For practical purposes, the gas-film resistance can be neglected. The H_{OL} for $1\frac{1}{2}$-in. ceramic Intalox® saddle packing is 3.1 ft at a liquid rate of 10 gpm/ft². If the liquid rate is raised 25 gpm/ft², the H_{OL} increases to 4.1 ft for the same packing. Thus the K_La value for regeneration is increasing as the 0.7 power of the liquid flow rate. However, in absorption the K_Ga value increases only as about the 0.3 power of the liquid rate.

The mass transfer rate is influenced significantly by the operating temperature. This is, in large part, due to the effect of temperature on the decomposition rate of the CO_2/MEA complex. The K_La value will, therefore, increase about 11% for each 10°F rise in liquid temperature. This temperature effect on the K_La value in the regenerator is similar to the effect of temperature on the K_Ga value in the absorber.

Because of the volatility of MEA, a wash bed, packed 4 ft to 6 ft deep, usually is installed above the feed point. This bed is irrigated with condensate and the liquid rate is low, therefore a smaller size packing than used in the stripping bed may be selected.

The stripping of diethanolamine solutions is similar to MEA regeneration. In this case, although the heat of reaction of CO_2 with DEA is 20% lower than with MEA, the regeneration still requires 1.0 to 1.2 lb of steam per gallon of solvent regenerated. The 2.5-normal solution of DEA typically used requires a higher solvent flow rate for the same acid gas absorption than 3-normal MEA solvent.

DEA solutions are utilized when a sulfur-bearing gas stream is being purified because MEA forms nonregenerable compounds with COS and CS_2. The DEA system should be followed by a caustic wash if 10 ppm or less COS concentration is specified in the purified gas stream. Even though H_2S is absorbed faster than CO_2, the equilibrium favors stripping of H_2S more rapidly than CO_2 because CO_2 forms a stable complex with the amine solvent.

Although the rate of absorption of CO_2 and H_2S into a DEA solvent is less than into an MEA solvent, the DEA solution is somewhat easier to strip than an MEA solution. Usually the same H_{OL} value is used to design DEA strippers as is used for the design of MEA strippers. The DEA solvent, however, can be regenerated to a lower acid gas concentration, about 0.07 mol CO_2 per mol DEA, than is typical for an MEA solvent. Because of the low vapor pressure of DEA, a wash bed may not be required at the top of the stripper.

DEA solutions degrade thermally in the operation. Purification of a small sidestream of DEA solvent by vacuum distillation formerly was employed. Currently, decomposition products are deactivated by the addition of an alkali carbonate to the solvent. In addition, a small sidestream liquid flow continuously is passed through an activated carbon filter. The filter adsorbs degradation products as well as dissolved hydro-carbons that may promote foaming.

HOT CARBONATE REGENERATION

Another widely used stripping operation is the regeneration of a rich potassium carbonate solution from an absorber which removes H_2S or CO_2 from a gas stream. This process typically uses a 25 wt% K_2CO_3 aqueous solution that enters the stripper 70% to 80% converted to bi-carbonate. The liquid feed comes from the absorber bottom at a temper-ature of about 240°F and at a high pressure.

The stripper usually operates at a top pressure of about 25 psia, there-fore the liquid feed undergoes a large flash on entering this column. The rich liquid throttle valve should be located as close to the stripper feed inlet nozzle as possible. Sometimes this high-pressure rich liquid is passed through a power recovery turbine that drives the lean carbonate booster pump to reduce the plant energy consumption. The feed liquid in the fully flashed condition may have a velocity of 100 to 150 fps through the regenerator feed nozzle. Special design of the feed liquid dis-tributor in the regenerator is required to dissipate this energy.

The CO_2 is stripped from rich solvent by a combination of flashing and steam stripping. As much as 40% to 60% of the total CO_2 stripped can be released during the flashing operation. The overhead vapor from the stripper usually contains about 18 mol % CO_2; the balance is steam. The vapor passes through a condenser to reduce the water vapor con-tent. The condensate returns to the system to maintain the water bal-ance. This condensate usually irrigates a wash section at the top of the stripper to prevent loss of K_2CO_3 by entrainment in the vapor stream.

The stripping steam required is provided by a reboiler that is heated with steam or with hot process gas feed to the absorber. The lean solution leaves the regenerator at about the same temperature as the feed-liquid temperature. This lean solution still is 20% to 25% converted to bicar-bonate. Because the solvent is circulated hot through the system, there is very little sensible heat load. The reboiler must supply enough energy to provide the 270 Btu/lb of CO_2 heat of reaction with the K_2CO_3, plus the heat to vaporize the water contained in the overhead gas stream. Regen-eration usually requires about 0.6 lb of steam per gallon of solvent. If regeneration of the lean solvent is carried out to less than 20% bicarbon-ate content, the stripping steam requirement increases considerably. In systems where a portion of the lean solvent is cooled before it returns to the absorber (see Figure 3-4) an additional sensible heat load is added to the reboiler duty.

Hot carbonate systems are considered slightly foaming, therefore the stripper diameter should be selected to give a pressure drop no higher than 0.40 in. H_2O/ft of packed depth at the point of maximum loading. In a split-stream system (Figure 3-5), a smaller packing can be specified for the bottom bed than is used in the upper section of the regenerator or the bottom section can be of a smaller diameter. This is possible because the liquid rate is much lower in the bottom bed after withdrawal of the semi-lean solution. For mechanical reasons, the regenerator usually has the same diameter throughout the entire column height. In hot carbonate systems, the liquid loading can be very high. Therefore packing size should be selected in accordance with the recommendations in Table 3-2. Any vapor that is aspirated in the liquid phase and carried to the bottom of the column results in a stripping efficiency loss.

The regeneration of a hot carbonate solution requires reversal of Equation 4-16 or 4-17:

$$K_2CO_3 + CO_2 + H_2O = 2KHCO_3 \tag{4-16}$$

$$K_2CO_3 + H_2S = KHCO_3 + KHS \tag{4-17}$$

Because acid gas release is a function of the $KHCO_3$ decomposition rate, sufficient liquid residence time must be provided in the packed bed. The regenerator packing usually is no larger than the 2-in. size and the pressure drop at minimum loading is at least 0.15 in. H_2O/ft of packed depth. Where a high turndown ratio is necessary for processing the gas stream in the absorber, the solvent circulation rate should be reduced to not less than 50% of design flow. This is recommended even though the gas flow to the absorber is less than one-half the design rate.

The solvent flow rate and composition of rich and lean solutions are known from the absorber design or operation. Because regeneration normally is carried out at an absolute pressure of less than 2 atm, the boiling temperature for the lean solvent is only 230° to 250°F. The stripper usually is designed on the basis of an overall liquid-phase mass transfer coefficient (K_La) because this operation is substantially liquid-film controlled. Data released by Norton Company in 1968 demonstrated that the K_La for steam stripping K_2CO_3 solutions increases as the liquid rate to the 0.90 power [8]. Thus the K_La at 22 gpm/ft^2 is 50% greater than at 14 gpm/ft^2 liquid rate. The number of mols of CO_2 to be stripped, however, is 57% greater at the higher liquid flow rate. Higher liquid irrigation rates, therefore, require slightly greater packed depths to regenerate the solvent to the same lean solution concentration.

The K_La also is a function of the percentage conversion to bicarbonate as shown in Figure 4-2. At 60% conversion, the K_La is 33% lower than

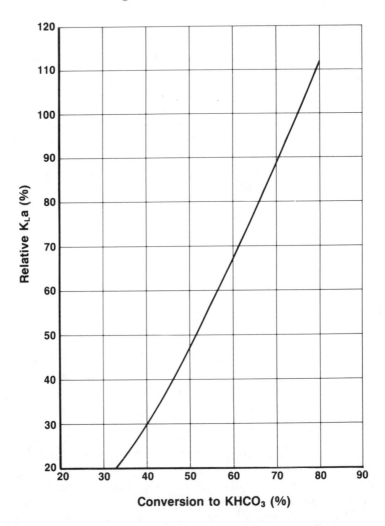

Figure 4-2. Relative K_La for 20% K_2CO_3 regeneration.

at 75% bicarbonate; while at 40% bicarbonate the K_La is 70% lower. The K_La used to calculate the packed depth required is the logarithmic average of the K_La values at the top and bottom of the stripper.

The K_La value for stripping CO_2 at a liquid rate of 20 gpm/ft^2 for a solution of 75% conversion to bicarbonate is 37 to 43 lb-mol/h·ft^3·mol/ mol for 2-in. ceramic Intalox® saddles, #2 Hy-Pak® packing, or 2-in. metal Pall rings. The K_La value for 2-in.-size packings is about 60% of K_La for 1-in.-size packings of the same type.

The mol fraction CO_2 in the lean solvent normally will be 0.008 to 0.010 for a 25% wt% K_2CO_3 solution. The CO_2 content in the vapor from the reboiler fixes the equilibrium liquid-phase solute concentration from the K value. This value can be calculated from the data compiled by Bocard and Mayland for the vapor pressure of CO_2 above hot carbonate solutions as a function of K_2CO_3 concentration, CO_2 absorbed, and the temperature [9]. Solute concentration in the solution leaving the packing is one theoretical stage richer than the lean solvent when the regenerator is heated by a reboiler. Thus, the driving force (Δx_B) is determined for the bottom of the packed bed. From a mass balance, the concentration of CO_2 in the vapor phase at the stripping section top can be calculated. Again the K value can be used to fix the equilibrium solute concentration above the feed liquid. The actual rich solution contains 0.028 to 0.033 mol fraction CO_2. The driving force (Δx_T) at the stripping section top is determined from the liquid composition, after the flash of the rich liquid feed. The overall driving force used in the calculation of the packed depth is the logarithmic mean average of the driving forces at the bottom and top of the stripper or between liquid draws for split-stream operation.

The mols of CO_2 to be stripped can be calculated from a mass balance on the solvent. Then, the total packed depth can be determined from Equation 4-8. Each packed bed normally is a maximum of 30 ft depth when using metal or ceramic packings. With polypropylene packing, the maximum suggested bed depth is 24 ft because of the possibility of creep at elevated temperatures. If the operating temperature is 245°F or greater, the polypropylene packing should be glass-reinforced to reduce the creep rate.

Hot carbonate systems are widely used for treating high-pressure natural gas to remove H_2S down to 4 mol ppm to meet pipeline requirements. The H_2S has a higher vapor pressure above the carbonate solution than CO_2, thus it is more readily stripped from the solvent. This occurs because CO_2 forms a stronger acid which is more tightly held in the alkaline solvent.

Generally it is uneconomical to regenerate a solvent with a bicarbonate content so low that it permits reduction of the CO_2 in the absorber outlet gas below 1,500 mol ppm for a typical hot carbonate system (shown in Figure 3-3). Although some promoted systems claim to be able to purify gas down to 500 mol ppm CO_2 content, the steam required for regeneration of the solvent may be up to 30% greater than with the higher CO_2 content in the treated gas stream.

When organic promoters are used with this system, the process licensor usually supplies a corrosion inhibitor as part of the package. The corrosion inhibitor is present only in the liquid phase because it is not

volatile. Severe carbon steel corrosion due to the wet CO_2 has been experienced in the vapor phase areas. The use of austenitic stainless steels
therefore is common practice at the top of the regenerator column in
these cases.

EXAMPLE PROBLEM

It is desired to air strip the chlorinated hydrocarbons from 1,730 gpm
of water at 61°F. This water has as the principal contaminant 520 micro-
grams/liter of trichlorethylene. The effluent water is to contain no more
than 9 microgram/liter of TCE.

As an initial estimate, an 8-ft 6-in. ID column packed with #2 plastic
Super Intalox® packing will be selected, which gives a liquid rate of 30.5
gpm/ft². The blower specified provides 7,000 cfm of air at 60°F to strip
the water. This is about 400 cfm per 100 gpm of water. Water flow is
48,040 lb-mol/h and the air flow is 1,109 lb-mol/h. From Table 4-3, the
Henry's Law constant for TCE above water corrected to 61°F is 480
atm/mol fraction.

The stripping factor is calculated from Equation 4-15:

$$S^* = \frac{480(1,109)}{1(48,040)} = 11.1$$

The number of liquid transfer units is calculated from Equation 4-14.
However, first it is necessary to determine the ratio of x_i/x_o to give the
required removal efficiency. This ratio can be expressed in consistent
convenient units of ug/1:

$$\frac{x_i}{x_o} = \frac{520}{9} = 57.8$$

The number of transfer units is:

$$N_{OL} = \frac{11.1}{10.1} \ln \left[\frac{57.8(10.1) + 1.0}{11.1} \right] = 4.36$$

The overall height of a liquid-phase transfer unit for #2 plastic Super
Intalox® packing at a liquid rate of 30.5 gpm/ft² and 61°F is 5.0 ft.
Thus, 4.36 transfer units require a packed depth of 22 ft.

Next the hydraulic loading should be checked. The air density is
0.0765 lb/ft³ and the water density is 62.4 lb/ft³.

The flow parameter for Figure 1-16 is:

$$X = \frac{15,260}{566}\left[\frac{0.0765}{62.4}\right]^{0.5} = 0.944$$

The C_s for an 8-ft 6-in. ID tower is 0.0720 fps. The ordinate value is:

$$Y = (0.0720)(28)^{0.5}(1.11)^{0.05} = 0.383$$

The pressure drop is only 0.07 in. H_2O/ft of packed depth. Thus, the overall packing pressure drop is only 1.5 in. H_2O. The blower should be specified to deliver a positive pressure of 2.0 in. water gauge at the inlet to the column.

Because of the very low power requirement for an 8-ft 6-in. ID column, a smaller column is calculated as an alternate to reduce capital investment. A 7-ft 6-in. ID column could be used to give a water flow rate of 39.2 gpm/ft². To keep the packing height from increasing substantially, the air flow rate is increased to 8,600 cfm, which is equivalent to almost 500 cfm per 100 gpm of water. The air flow now is 1,363 lb-mol/h so that the stripping factor becomes:

$$S^* = \frac{480(1,363)}{1(48,040)} = 13.6$$

The number of transfer units is now reduced to:

$$N_{OL} = \frac{13.6}{12.6}\ln\left[\frac{57.8(12.6) + 1.0}{13.6}\right] = 4.30$$

The overall height of a liquid phase transfer unit for #2 plastic Super Intalox® packing at a liquid rate of 39.2 gpm/ft² has increased to 5.5 ft. Thus, 4.30 transfer units would require a 24-ft packed bed depth. In Figure 1-16, the flow parameter is:

$$X = \frac{19,600}{894}\left[\frac{0.0765}{62.4}\right]^{0.5} = 0.768$$

The C_s for a 7-ft 6-in. ID tower is 0.114 fps. The ordinate value is:

$$Y = 0.114(28)^{0.5}(1.11)^{0.05} = 0.606$$

The pressure drop now increases to 0.29 in. H_2O/ft of packed depth. The overall pressure drop through the packed bed is 7.0 in. H_2O. The alternate blower must deliver a positive pressure of 7.5 in. water gauge at the column inlet.

The alternate design reduces the column shell and internals cost by over 12%. However, the blower horsepower required is several times as great because of the larger air flow rate and much higher pressure drop for this design.

NOTATION

A	Column cross-section area (ft^2)
a	Interfacial area (ft^2/ft^3)
G_m	Gas phase flow (lb-mol/h)
H	Henry's Law constant (atm/mol fraction)
H_{OL}	Overall height of liquid transfer unit (ft)
K	Equilibrium ratio
K_La	Overall liquid-phase mass transfer coefficient (lb-mol/$h \cdot ft^3 \cdot$mol/mol)
k_G	Gas-film mass transfer coefficient (lb-mol/$h \cdot ft^2 \cdot$atm)
k_L	Liquid-film mass transfer coefficient (lb-mol/$h \cdot ft^2 \cdot$mol/mol)
L_m	Liquid phase flow (lb-mol/h)
m	Slope of equilibrium curve
N	Solute transferred (lb-mol/h)
N_{OL}	Number of overall liquid transfer units
P	Total system pressure (atm)
p	Partial pressure in gas phase (atm)
p^*	Vapor pressure of solute (atm)
S^*	Stripping factor
x	Mol fraction in liquid phase
x'	Mol fraction in liquid film
x_i	Mol fraction of solute in inlet liquid
x_o	Mol fraction of solute in outlet liquid
y	Mol fraction in gas phase
y_i	Mol fraction of solute in inlet gas
y_o	Mol fraction of solute in outlet gas
Z	Packed depth (ft)
Δp	Partial pressure difference (atm)
Δx	Mol fraction difference in liquid
Δx_B	Mol fraction difference at bottom
Δx_{LM}	ln mean mol fraction driving force
Δx_T	Mol fraction difference at top

REFERENCES

1. Landolt-Boernstein, *Zahlenwerte und Funktionen ous Physik, Vol. 4,* Part 4, Band c, Springer-Verlag 1976.
2. Maddox, R. N., *Process Engineer's Absorption Pocket Handbook,* Gulf Publishing, 1985, p. 9.
3. *International Critical Tables,* Vol. 3, McGraw-Hill, 1928, p. 256.
4. Colburn, A. P., *Industrial and Engineering Chemistry,* Vol. 33, 1941, p. 459.
5. Frank, W. J., "Efficient Removal of Oxygen in Waterflood by Vacuum Deaeration," American Institute of Mining Metallurgical and Petroleum Engineers, Paper SPE-4064, 1972.
6. Kavanaugh, M. C., and Trussell, R. R., *Journal of American Water Works Association,* Vol. 72, No. 12, 1980, p. 684.
7. Kohl, A. L., and Riesenfeld, F. C., *Gas Purification,* McGraw-Hill, Chap. 2, 1960, pp. 56–60. (See also Kohl and Riesenfeld, *Gas Purification,* 4th Ed., Gulf Publishing Company, Houston, 1985.)
8. Eckert J. S., Foote, E., and Walter, L., "Technical Data Related to Tower Packing," Norton Company, 1968, GR-274A Rev. 1.
9. Bocard, J. P., and Mayland, B. J., *Hydrocarbon Processing,* Vol. 41, No. 4, 1962, p. 128.

5

HEAT TRANSFER

This chapter discusses the very complex phenomenon of combined heat and mass transfer. In some cases, these two transfer operations may take place in opposite directions across the interface between phases. At times, the mass transfer may involve more than one component. Methods for design of such columns will be developed despite the absence of rigorous theory for many of these engineering applications. This chapter deals with these complicated situations through empirical adjustments to heat transfer coefficients, based upon extensive practical experience.

There are many situations where a tubular heat exchanger is not efficient or desirable. The packed tower as a heat transfer device presents some very important advantages when heat is transferred between a gas or vapor phase and a liquid phase which are mutually insoluble. While most other equipment offered for this service imposes some sort of surface between two fluids exchanging heat, in the packed tower heat is transferred by intimate contact between the fluids. Thus, there is no reduction in the heat transfer rate because of fouling or scaling. Conventional tubular heat exchangers may have corrosion of the metal tube or deposits may form on the tube surface. Both factors lower the heat transfer rate. Therefore, higher heat transfer coefficients are obtained in packed columns, leading to closer temperature approaches between the two fluids and considerably reduced initial equipment cost. In addition, the high pressure drop through the tubular equipment, which may be detrimental to the process, is avoided.

Although heat transfer is the primary purpose in such direct contact operations, in most of these cases, exchange of mass between fluids occurs simultaneously. However, heat transfer can occur without appreciable mass transfer, as when a cold gas is heated by a very high-boiling liquid. Nevertheless, the design of many direct-contact heat transfer col-

110

umns requires consideration of the variables affecting both mass and heat flow. It had been proposed that the ratio of the heat transfer rate to the mass transfer rate would equal the gas-phase humid heat capacity. The ratio of heat transfer coefficient to the product of mass transfer coefficient and gas-phase humid heat capacity then should be unity. While this relationship seems to hold for an air/water system, it does not apply to many organic vapors. Walker et al. show this ratio to be about 1.8 for many organic solvent vapors in air [1].

Heat transfer from gas phase to liquid phase takes place by convection. The mass transfer coefficient is based on diffusion of the liquid vapor through a non-diffusing gas film and the rate of heat transfer through the gas phase, as well as heat conduction through the films. At high liquid and gas rates, the ratio of the heat transfer rate to the mass transfer rate is constant. At high flow rates (liquid rates of 4 gpm/ft² or greater) the heat transfer area is the same as the mass transfer area. At low flow rates (a liquid rate of 0.5 gpm/ft² or lower) the heat transfer area approaches twice the mass transfer area.

WATER COOLING THEORY

In heat transfer applications, either the liquid stream or the gas stream can be cooled. The most common application, in which the liquid stream is cooled, is a water cooling tower. Although there is sensible heat transfer between the warmer water and the cooler air, in this device, the warm water is primarily cooled by evaporation of some of the water into the air stream. Both the heat and mass are transferred in the same direction—from the water to the air stream. Exit air from the water cooling tower may be assumed to be saturated with water vapor. Exit air enthalpy can be obtained from a psychrometric table. The inlet air condition usually is defined by the dry-bulb and wet-bulb temperatures. For practical design purposes, the inlet air is assumed to be saturated with water at the wet-bulb temperature because the enthalpy of this air is sufficiently close to the theoretically accurate adiabatic saturation temperature.

Inlet water temperature is known and the desired exit water temperature is specified. Normally, the exit water temperature is at least 6°F warmer than the inlet air wet-bulb temperature.

The heat transferred into the air stream is:

$$Q = G_d(H_o - H_i) \tag{5-1}$$

The outlet water flow is the inlet flow less the water evaporated into the air stream. This evaporation is:

$$W = G_d(h_o - h_i) \tag{5-2}$$

The heat transferred out of the water is:

$$Q = L_w Cpt_i - Cpt_o[L_w - G_d(h_o - h_i)] \tag{5-3}$$

which can be written as:

$$Q = L_w Cpt_i - L_w Cpt_o + G_d Cpt_o(h_o - h_i) \tag{5-4}$$

This equation can be simplified to:

$$Q = L_w Cp(t_i - t_o) + G_d Cpt_o(h_o - h_i) \tag{5-5}$$

The second term on the right in Equation 5-5 is small in comparison to the first term at moderate temperatures and can be neglected. Thus, by a combination of Equation 5-5 with Equation 5-1:

$$G_d(H_o - H_i) \cong L_w Cp(t_i - t_o) \tag{5-6}$$

Equation 5-6 can be rearranged to that of a straight line eliminating the Cp for water which equals 1 Btu/lb $\cdot$ °F:

$$H_o = \frac{L_w}{G_d}(t_i - t_o) + H_i \tag{5-7}$$

The exact solution of the equations which describe both the heat and mass transfer processes is rather complicated, although both must be considered as just described. However, for the most common case of an air/water system, the ratio of the heat transfer coefficient to the product of the mass transfer coefficient and gas-phase humid heat capacity is unity. In this case, both the heat and mass transfer processes are combined by simply using an enthalpy driving force. Equation 5-7 represents the operating line of a countercurrent flow water cooling tower. The equilibrium curve is a plot of the enthalpy of saturated air (in Btu/lb BDG) against the temperature of the water which is in thermal equilibrium with the air.

The driving force in this application is the enthalpy difference, not the temperature difference. This system is gas-film controlled because the diffusing water vapor is infinitely soluble in the liquid phase, and substantially at the same temperature. The resistance to sensible heat transfer in the water film is so small that it may be neglected. The number of transfer units can be obtained by integrating the area between the operating line and equilibrium curve with respect to the average driving force:

$$N_{OG} = \int_{H_i}^{H_o} \frac{dH_v}{H_v^* - H_v} \qquad (5\text{-}8)$$

In Figure 5-1, AB is the equilibrium curve and CD is the operating line of the water cooling tower. Point C represents the temperature of the entering water (t_i) and the enthalpy of the saturated air leaving (H_o). Point D represents the desired temperature of the water leaving (t_o) and the enthalpy of the entering air (H_i) at wet-bulb temperature.

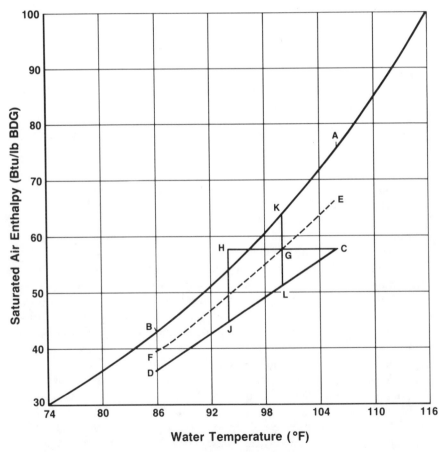

Figure 5-1. Water cooling operation.

The air flow rate must be sufficient so that the slope of the operating line L_w/G_d is low enough to avoid pinching off against the equilibrium curve. This can occur because the equilibrium curve AB has a convex curvature toward the operating line CD. Typically L_w/G_d varies from 0.9 to 1.4 for normal water cooling ranges of 10°F to 30°F.

For this gas-film-controlled system, the rate of mass transfer is proportional to gas rate to approximately the 0.8 power. This is similar to data on the isothermal evaporation of pure liquids from a pipe wall into a turbulent air stream. There, Gilliland and Sherwood showed that the mass transfer rate is proportional to the gas mass velocity to the 0.83 power [2]. For systems evaporating water into an air stream, the effect of the liquid rate is similar to that for absorption. Water flow typically affects the mass transfer rate as the liquid rate to about the 0.3 power. The effect of gas rate on mass transfer in humidification, however, is greater than for mass transfer in absorption operations.

COOLING TOWER DESIGN

The number of transfer units (N_{OG}) can be determined by graphical integration. Line EF in Figure 5-1 is constructed as the locus of points equal to 0.5 [$H_v^* + H_v$]. Horizontal line CH intersects line EF at point G so that CG = GH. Vertical line HJ intersects line CD at point J. Vertical line KL through point G intersects curve AB at point K and line CD at point L. By the theory of similar triangles, HJ = KL. Because KL represents the average enthalpy driving force for water temperatures from point C to point J, HJ represents a change of air enthalpy equal to the average driving force. Therefore, CHJ represents one transfer unit. This process is repeated until a one transfer unit step gives a lower value of water temperature than represented by point D. The last step then is considered a fractional transfer unit.

In practice, the movement of the air stream through the tower can be a substantial operating cost. Cooling towers either use natural draft or a propeller-type fan to move the air stream. The total pressure drop through a forced-draft column, therefore, is limited to about 0.33 in. of water. The use of a random dumped tower packing is not customary in water cooling towers. Because of the pressure drop available, the maximum packed depth for large size plastic packings is under 6 ft.

While this packed depth provides a sufficient number of transfer units to cool the water as specified, such a short column may produce another problem. A short water cooling tower would discharge the humid air only 15 ft to 18 ft above the air intake. During periods of atmospheric inversion, the humid air may be recirculated back into the cooling tower air inlet. This occurrence would prevent the tower from cooling the wa-

Table 5 – 1
Height of a Gas-Phase Transfer Unit (in.) for Water Cooling

Packing	Size (in.)			
	1	1½	2	3 or 3½
Ceramic Intalox® Saddles	16	20	24	34
Plastic Super Intalox® Saddles	16	—	23	34
Plastic Pall Rings	17	20	22	34
Metal Pall Rings	14	17	21	31
Metal Hy-Pak® Packing	15	18	22	29
Intalox® Metal Tower Packing	14	16	19	26

ter to the desired temperature. To avoid this problem, a short cooling tower needs a tall discharge stack for the humid air.

Table 5-1 gives the height of a gas-phase transfer unit for common dumped tower packings in water cooling applications. These heights were determined with packed depths providing at least three transfer units. In the design of columns with fewer transfer units, 9 in. to 12 in. of additional height over that calculated is recommended to allow for completion of liquid and gas distribution.

In addition, these depths apply to packed beds with uniform liquid and gas distribution similar to that utilized in distillation columns. In many designs of commercial cooling towers, distribution is of substantially lower quality. Thus, the packed depth specified must make allowance for these less efficient distributor designs. For large size tower packings, the value of H_{OG} may be 20% to 40% greater than that from Table 5-1 when commercial liquid distributors are used.

COOLING TOWER FILL

Most industrial water cooling towers are equipped with a *fill* which is much less efficient than random dumped tower packing with respect to mass transfer. For example, splash grids of wood or plastic construction are arranged so that the falling liquid must contact alternate rows of grids. All the grids in a row run in the same direction, although alternate rows may be oppositely inclined. Such a fill commonly may be 25 ft to 30 ft in depth. Therefore, the grids must be arranged to provide a high open area for gas flow to minimize pressure drop. Some newer plastic grids are contoured to encourage more streamlined air flow with reduced pressure drop.

A newer fill material for mechanical draft towers consists of vacuum-formed plastic sheets installed as vertical modules to minimize pressure drop. Arranging the sheets close together provides a relatively large surface area for mass transfer. Such a fill provides a pressure drop per transfer unit of height similar to random dumped packings, although the transfer unit height for such a fill may be twice that developed by the more efficient random dumped tower packing.

Some cooling towers operate with natural draft. This is possible because the warmer humid air inside the tower is less dense than the colder, drier outside air. Many such towers are hyperbolic, and may require an overall height of 220 ft. The fill used in such a column must be quite open to avoid any significant pressure drop. Such fill can have a tee- or vee-shaped cross section molded from perforated plastic sheets. Corrugated sheets made of asbestos and cement are popular in large natural draft towers. A ceramic cellular block that is stacked into the tower also is used. These fills, however, provide a small interfacial area per cubic foot so mass transfer is rather low per unit of packed depth.

GAS QUENCH TOWERS

When the gas stream is cooled, one of three different types of operation usually will take place:

1. Gas cooling with liquid vaporization.
2. Gas cooling with total condensation.
3. Gas cooling with partial condensation.

An example of Type 1 operation is a hot gas quench tower using water as the liquid coolant. In this application, sensible heat is transferred from a hot gas stream to the cooler water. As the liquid temperature increases, water is vaporized into the gas stream, which raises its humidity. Thus, mass transfer is in the opposite direction to heat transfer.

The exit gas from the quench tower is assumed to be saturated with water vapor. The desired exit gas temperature usually is specified and the inlet water temperature is known. Normally, the exit gas temperature is at least 3°F higher than the inlet water temperature. The inlet gas enthalpy must be calculated from gas temperature, heat capacity, and humidity. The heat capacity of common dry diatomic gases at atmospheric pressure and temperatures from 80° to 180°F is approximately 7 Btu/lb-mol · °F. The inlet gas stream temperature should be converted to its adiabatic temperature (that saturated gas stream temperature having the same enthalpy as the inlet gas). The entering hot gas stream is saturated quickly with water vapor and cools to its adiabatic saturation temperature.

If the exit water temperature is more than 20°F cooler than the inlet adiabatic gas temperature, a fog may be produced. This occurs because the inlet gas is cooled at a faster rate by sensible heat transfer than dehumidified by mass transfer. As a result, the gas is chilled below ~s dew point temperature. The resultant fog is of such small particle size that it is carried out of the quench tower with the exit gas stream. To prevent this occurrence, water flow to the quench tower should be reduced to raise the exit liquid temperature.

QUENCH TOWER DESIGN

Figure 5-2 illustrates the operation of a hot gas quenching column with water as the coolant. Line OP is the operating line of the quench

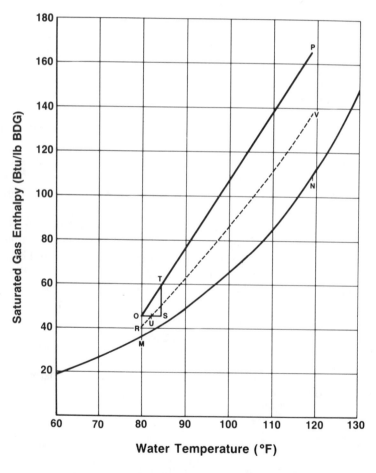

Figure 5-2. Gas quenching operation.

column. If the amount of water evaporated is negligible, compared to the total water flow, the equation of this line is:

$$G_d(H_i - H_o) = L_w Cp(t_o - t_i) \tag{5-9}$$

Equation 5-9 can be rearranged to that of a straight line, eliminating the Cp for water which equals 1 Btu/lb·°F:

$$H_o = H_i - \frac{L_w}{G_d}(t_o - t_i) \tag{5-10}$$

The equilibrium curve MN is obtained in the same manner as for Figure 5-1. Point P represents the inlet gas enthalpy (H_i) and the outlet water temperature (t_o) while point O represents the enthalpy of the saturated outlet gas (H_o) and the temperature of the inlet water (t_i). Line RV is the locus of points equal to 0.5 ($H_v^* + H_v$). OS is a horizontal line intersecting line RV at U so that OU = SU. As in Figure 5-1, TS is an enthalpy change equal to the average driving force from a water temperature at point O to point T. Therefore, OST represents one transfer unit.

The cooling water rate must be large enough so the operating line slope L_w/G_d is sufficient to avoid intersection of the operating line with the equilibrium curve before the inlet gas enthalpy is reached. For gas cooling, the equilibrium curve has a concave curvature away from the operating line. For quenching flue gas from the combustion of natural gas at atmospheric pressure L_w/G_d varies from 2 to 7.

Using a logarithmic mean enthalpy driving force, based on terminal column conditions, is not recommended when calculating gas-quenching operations. Such a procedure usually produces a substantial column over design because the true enthalpy driving force is greater than the average of the terminal driving forces. This is due to the concave equilibrium curve.

TOTAL CONDENSER THEORY

In a Type 2 operation, the gas phase is a totally condensible vapor. Usually the coolant liquid is of the same composition as the condensate. Thus, from a mass balance standpoint:

$$L_o' = L_i' + G_i' \tag{5-11}$$

The heat transferred in to the liquid phase is:

$$Q = L_o'Cpt_o - L_i'Cpt_i \qquad (5\text{-}12)$$

Therefore, combining Equations 5-11 and 5-12:

$$Q = L_i'Cpt_o + G_i'Cpt_o - L_i'Cpt_i \qquad (5\text{-}13)$$

Equation 5-13 is simplified to:

$$Q = L_i'Cp(t_o - t_i) + G_i'Cpt_o \qquad (5\text{-}14)$$

The heat transferred from the vapor phase is:

$$Q = G_i'\Delta H + G_i'Cpv(T_i - t_o) \qquad (5\text{-}15)$$

or the heat load is:

$$Q = G_i'[\Delta H + Cpv(T_i - t_o)] \qquad (5\text{-}16)$$

These total condensers are designed on a heat transfer basis using the relationship:

$$Q = U_v AZ\Delta T_{LM} \qquad (5\text{-}17)$$

Temperature differences are calculated as if a surface condenser were being used. If a single-component vapor is condensing at a constant pressure, the temperature difference at the liquid coolant inlet is $T_i - t_i$. Similarly, the temperature difference at the liquid coolant outlet is $T_i - t_o$. This is true because the vapor temperature remains constant from the first drop of condensate to the last drop. Thus, the logarithmic mean temperature driving force is:

$$\Delta T_{LM} = \frac{(T_i - t_i) - (T_i - t_o)}{\ln\left[\dfrac{(T_i - t_i)}{(T_i - t_o)}\right]} \qquad (5\text{-}18)$$

This can be simplified to:

$$\Delta T_{LM} = \frac{t_o - t_i}{\ln\left[\dfrac{(T_i - t_i)}{(T_i - t_o)}\right]} \qquad (5\text{-}19)$$

The volume of tower packing required from Equation 5-17 is:

$$AZ = \frac{Q}{U_v \Delta T_{LM}} \qquad (5\text{-}20)$$

A volumetric heat transfer coefficient (U_v) is utilized in Equation 5-20. Normally, heat transfer coefficients are used with the rate of heat flow expressed per unit temperature difference per unit area. However, in direct-contact heat transfer, the conventional heat transfer coefficient must be multiplied by the interfacial area between gas and liquid to obtain a volumetric coefficient. The interfacial area is not always the geometric surface area of the tower packing. To simplify the calculation, this interfacial area term is combined with the conventional heat transfer coefficient. This produces a volumetric coefficient for heat transfer in a manner analogous to the use of a mass transfer coefficient in absorption.

TOTAL CONDENSER DESIGN

The volumetric heat transfer coefficient primarily is a function of the liquid-phase properties. In particular, this coefficient depends on the volumetric liquid irrigation rate and the liquid viscosity. The heat transfer coefficient varies as:

$$Uv \propto \left[\frac{L_i'}{\rho_L u' A} \right]^{0.33} \qquad (5\text{-}21)$$

This variation with liquid rate is similar to the effect on the mass transfer coefficient in absorption operations.

There are no concentration differences across either the gas film or the liquid film for a single component vapor. The main resistance to condensation is the thermal gradient across the liquid film. Thus, the heat transfer coefficient is primarily a function of the thermal conductivity of the liquid, similar to the performance of vertical condenser tubes as described by Nusselt [3]. The thermal conductivity of most liquids decreases with temperature increase, however some liquids exhibit a maximum value of thermal conductivity at a particular temperature [4].

The volumetric heat transfer coefficients are very high for Type 2 operations because there is little or no gas-film resistance, due to the absence of an inert gas phase. Values from 500 to 1,300 Btu/h · ft^3 · °F have been obtained for #50 IMTP® packing with organic liquids having a thermal conductivity of 0.08 Btu-ft/h · ft^2 · °F.

Packed beds find application as total condensers at the top of distillation columns. In such services, the tower packing produces a low pressure drop that especially is desirable in high vacuum services. The arrangement of the packed condenser system consists of a liquid collector plate at the bottom to permit removal of the liquid from the column. Above this collector is a support plate and the packed bed which is irrigated by a liquid distributor using a portion of the condensate that is recycled after being cooled in an external heat exchanger. The organic vapor losses thus are limited to the vapor pressure above the cooled irrigating liquid.

Some liquids become extremely viscous when cooled. In such cases, the heat transfer coefficient should be calculated separately for the top and bottom of the packed bed. If the cool liquid at the top of the bed has a viscosity of 35 cps and the warm liquid at the bottom of the bed has a viscosity of only 1.3 cps, the heat transfer coefficient at the top of the bed is only one-third that at the bottom of the bed, before allowing for variations in liquid flow rate and thermal conductivity. In such cases, it may be desirable to utilize a primary lower condenser packed bed operating at a higher liquid inlet temperature and, therefore, a lower liquid viscosity and a higher heat transfer coefficient. Above this bed would be a secondary condenser packed bed, operating at a lower liquid inlet temperature, to minimize vent loss of organic vapor. With this arrangement, the primary condenser could handle about 80% of the total heat load and the secondary condenser the small balance of the condensing duty. Such an arrangement could require 15% less total packed depth to condense the same amount of inlet vapor as a single bed.

CHLORINE GAS COOLING

Type 3 operations involve some of the most common uses of packed beds. In such operations, a part of the inlet gas stream is condensed and the balance of the gas stream merely lowered in temperature. This type of operation is complicated from a theoretical standpoint. For mixtures of gases and vapors, other than air and water, the ratio of the heat transfer coefficient to the product of the mass transfer coefficient and the gas phase humid head capacity no longer may be unity.

First, applications will be considered where a condensible vapor is present in an inert, noncondensible gas. An example of this situation is cooling a chlorine cell gas with water to condense the majority of the gas stream water vapor content. The simplified design method described here is based on a large bank of practical experience with the particular system discussed. Thus, an empirical adjustment of the heat transfer coefficients provides a suitable design basis to overcome the lack of precise theory.

The total enthalpy of the inlet gas as Btu/lb-mol BDG can be calculated from the water vapor content and the heat capacity of the inert gas. Because water vapor is being condensed throughout the packed bed, the exit gas is saturated with the water. Since the condensate is of the same composition as the irrigating liquid, specifying the inlet liquid temperature usually fixes the exit gas temperature within a narrow range. Thus, the exit gas enthalpy can also be calculated.

The total heat transferred is:

$$Q = G_d(H_i - H_o) \tag{5-22}$$

Using Equation 5-20 to calculate the necessary packing volume requires a corrected heat transfer coefficient (U_v). The temperature differences then can be used as driving forces as with sensible heat transfer. If such an adjustment is not made, the amount of packed depth required will be overestimated. Equation 5-23 gives a method for calculating the adjusted heat transfer coefficient for 2-in. plastic Pall rings. This equation applies to dehumidification of an inert gas by direct contact with water at atmospheric pressure. The equation is based on data by Eckert et al. for a saturated inlet gas at temperatures from 110° to 150°F [5].

$$U_v = 13.8H_M^{0.57} \tag{5-23}$$

For 2-in. ceramic Intalox® saddles, the coefficient in this equation is reduced from 13.8 to 11.6. The heat transfer coefficient at the bottom of the bed should be calculated separately from the coefficient at the top of the packed bed. The arithmetic average coefficient then can be used to calculate the packed volume required. Equation 5-23 allows for the mass transfer of vapor because the gas phase enthalpy is, in large part, determined by the water vapor content of the gas stream. This empirical equation provides an easy method for a cooling column design.

The heat transfer coefficient is a function of vapor and liquid flow rates. The volumetric heat transfer coefficient value from Equation 5-23 is based on a vapor capacity factor (F_s) of 1.27 $lb^{0.5}/ft^{0.5} \cdot s$ and a water rate of 3,000 $lb/ft^2 \cdot h$. Even though theory suggests that the heat transfer coefficient varies as the 0.83 power of the gas rate, Nemunaitis and Eckert report that the coefficient varies as the first power of F_s for the dehumidification of air [6]. The same authors also state that the coefficient varies as the 0.68 power of the liquid rate. Thus, if the liquid-to-gas ratio is held constant, the heat transfer coefficient increases faster than the hydraulic loading.

Later work by Strigle and Foote indicated that the heat transfer coefficient varied as the 0.76 power of the vapor capacity factor [7]. This same work also showed that the heat transfer coefficient was a function of the 0.40 power of the liquid flow rate. The effect of liquid rate subsequently has been verified in industrial operations. These later tests were conducted using 2-in. metal Pall rings, 2-in. plastic Pall rings, and #2 Hy-Pak® packing. In this same series of tests, 3-in. or 3½-in. packing of the same type gave a heat transfer coefficient 12% to 15% lower than the 2-in. size.

The heat transfer coefficients have been determined by the cited investigators at atmospheric pressure. Industrial experience indicates that this coefficient increases at higher operating pressures to a greater extent than those merely due to the effect of gas density on the vapor capacity factor (F_s). At pressures above 1 atm, it is suggested that the heat transfer coefficient be increased by the 0.38 power of the operating pressure expressed in atmospheres.

The average temperature driving force for making this calculation is:

$$\Delta T_{LM} = \frac{(T_i - t_o) - (T_o - t_i)}{\ln \left[\frac{(T_i - t_o)}{(T_o - t_i)} \right]} \tag{5-24}$$

The inlet gas temperature (T_i) for use in Equation 5-24 is the adiabatic saturation temperature of this gas stream. The logarithmic average temperature driving force and the arithmetic average heat transfer coefficient, adjusted for hydraulic flow rates, permit calculation of the packed depth required from Equation 5-20.

Since the heat transfer coefficient (U_v) is a function of the vapor and liquid mass flow rates, it depends on column cross-sectional area. In this type of operation, the maximum vapor and liquid loadings occur at the bottom of the column. The diameter of the tower thus is fixed so that the pressure drop at the bottom of the packed bed does not exceed 0.40 in. H_2O/ft of packed depth.

VACUUM CRUDE STILLS

The second Type 3 application involves the condensation of a portion of the vapor stream by progressive cooling with condensate. An example of this situation occurs in a vacuum crude tower in petroleum refining (see Figure 5-3). In this operation, crude oil, from which lower-boiling components have been distilled at atmospheric pressure, is heated, then flashed under vacuum. The ascending vapor in the column is cooled by

Figure 5-3. Vacuum crude still: This 40-ft ID tower was revamped from trays to random packing.

means of a pumparound of condensate. This cooled liquid preferentially condenses the higher-boiling components from the vapor stream. Thus, the vapor ascends the column at its hydrocarbon dew point. Steam can be added to the furnace heating the reduced crude feed to decrease residence time and prevent coking. Steam also can be added to the bottom of the column to strip any remaining volatile components from the residue. A small quantity of inert gases, plus any added steam, leave the column top saturated with lower boiling hydrocarbons at the exit vapor temperature.

Columns typically have two pumparound condensing sections. In addition, there is a wash bed located above the flash zone that is irrigated with a small amount of condensate from the lower pumparound section. Tower packings now are being used in these towers because of the low pressure drop and high rates of heat transfer they provide. The traditional flash zone pressure of 50 mm to 80 mm Hg produced in a trayed column has been reduced to 20 mm to 35 mm Hg by the use of modern tower packings. The requirement for added steam to lower the hydrocarbon partial pressure needed for flashing the feed is greatly reduced. Thus, the cost of the added steam is much less, and the steam required to operate the vacuum jets is reduced because the quantity of inerts is smaller [8]. Also, the load on the water pollution control system is lower because there are fewer mols of hydrocarbon vapor leaving the column top to the barometric condensers.

Heat is recovered from each pumparound liquid stream to preheat the crude feed to the atmospheric still. Therefore, the temperature of the liquid return to the vacuum tower is fixed. As a result, the amount of heat removed in a pumparound bed is a function of the liquid circulation rate and the temperature of the liquid draw. This temperature is determined by the heat transfer coefficient developed by the tower packing used and depth of packing installed. The heat load is the difference in the total heat contents of the inlet and outlet vapor streams for the section. Two pumparound sections normally are used to maximize heat recovery since the vacuum gas oil products usually are combined and serve as feed for catalytic cracking.

The outlet vapor stream has much less mass than the inlet stream due to a large percentage of vapor condensation in the section. The heat load on the packed bed is greater than the heat removed by external pumparound liquid coolers since the net condensate normally is discharged from the system at the same temperature it is withdrawn from the column. The logarithmic mean temperature difference driving force is determined from Equation 5-24.

Pumparound sections usually contain from 4 ft to 9 ft of packed depth. The traditional method for calculating bed depth is by use of

Equation 5-20. This equation is a simplified representation of a complex group of heat and mass transfer processes. A considerable amount of industrial experience has led to development of satisfactory empirical equations for the calculation of overall heat transfer coefficients.

Because there are a great many organic compounds in crude oil, it is not possible to characterize this system precisely. Design procedures for such systems, therefore, have been developed empirically by packing manufacturers from operating data. Typically, an overall volumetric heat transfer coefficient is calculated from an equation such as:

$$U_v = d \left[\frac{G_i{}'}{1,000A\rho_G}\right]^{0.8} \left[\frac{L_i{}'}{1,000A}\right]^{0.4} \tag{5-25}$$

The exponent for the effect of vapor flow rate is the same as the theoretical value for a gas-film-controlled system, while the exponent for the effect of liquid rate is similar to that determined by Strigle and Foote [7].

In Equation 5-25, the inlet gas flow $(G_i{}')$ is the vapor rate to the bottom of the pumparound section and the inlet liquid flow $(L_i{}')$ is the pumparound return to the top of the bed. This equation applies where $G_i{}'/A$ is greater than 400 lb/ft$^2 \cdot$ h and $L_i{}'/A$ is not less than 500 lb/ft$^2 \cdot$ h. The constant d is a function of the packing type and size as well as the mean average boiling point of the condensate. In a typical light vacuum gas oil pumparound section, the value of d for #70 IMTP® packing is 21.9 as shown in Table 5-2. For 2-in. slotted ring packings, the value of d is 24.1; however, these packings have twice the pressure drop per foot of depth as #70 IMTP® packing. The 1½-in. slotted ring packings have a value for d of 25.8, but they likewise produce a 30% to 50% greater pressure drop than 2-in. slotted ring packings.

Table 5 - 2
Vacuum Crude Stills
Coefficient d for Heat Transfer Equation 5-25

Equivalent Packing Size (in.)	Slotted Ring Packings	IMTP® Packing
1½	25.8	27.7
2	24.1	25.8
3	20.6	21.9

The volumetric heat transfer coefficient for the light vacuum gas oil pumparound section is 25% to 30% greater than for the heavy vacuum gas oil pumparound. This is due to the influence of the higher condensate molecular weight in the lower pumparound section on the vapor density and the liquid-phase properties.

The volumetric heat transfer coefficients for #70 IMTP® packing are about 70% greater than those for grid structures that previously have been used to provide low pressure drop in some of these columns. The #40 size of IMTP® packing can provide over twice the volumetric heat transfer coefficient of grids under the same vapor and liquid flow rates. Normally, packings smaller than 1½-in. size are not used in heavy hydrocarbon service.

Unfortunately, the heat transfer coefficient is not completely independent of the packed depth. This occurs because the spray-type liquid distributor typically utilized in these towers also provides some amount of heat transfer. This results in proportionally better performance from short packed beds than from deeper beds. By correlating operating data from such towers, Graf reports that vapor-to-liquid temperature differences of 50°F are typical [9]. A deep packed bed is required to obtain a 20°F temperature difference between vapor and liquid streams. Figure 5-4 shows the effective packed depth as compared to an actual packed depth if each foot of bed depth greater than 4 ft were equally efficient.

Because of the high heat transfer rates available with packed beds, the packed depth calculated from Equation 5-20 can be quite short. Only a 6-in. to 9-in. design safety factor is applied to the calculated packed depth, after adjustment for the actual to effective depth is made, as shown in Figure 5-4. Because these vacuum towers normally are large in diameter, it is customary to install beds of not less than 16 packing diameters, or a 42-in. high minimum depth, in the heat transfer sections to ensure proper vapor and liquid contact.

The design of the vacuum crude tower many times involves only determining the packed depth in each section since the column already exists. In the case of a new installation, the column diameter must be fixed based on the pressure drop. Generally, the total pressure drop from column top to feed flash zone will be 10 mm to 15 mm Hg. The pressure drop will decrease significantly from the bottom to the top of each heat transfer section. The pressure drop actually may be somewhat higher at the top of the wash bed than at the bottom due to evaporation of part of the wash liquid.

As stated, Equation 5-25 has been developed empirically. It therefore should be applied only to columns operating under vacuum. Equations for calculating heat transfer coefficients at atmospheric or higher pressures indicate a greater effect of hydraulic loading. However, the actual heat transfer coefficient value may be considerably higher than for vacuum service at the same vapor capacity factor (F_s) and temperature driving force (ΔT_{LM}).

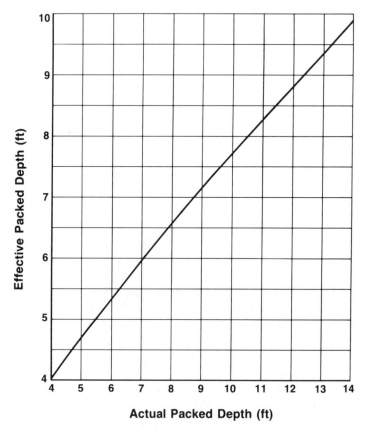

Figure 5-4. Performance of pumparound sections with spray distribution.

OLEFIN WATER QUENCH TOWER

A third Type 3 application involves the condensing of a portion of the vapor stream by progressively cooling it with a liquid that is of a different composition than the condensate. An example is the water quench tower in a naphtha-fed olefins plant. In this operation, the exit vapor from the oil quench tower is cooled further with recirculated water streams. In addition to condensing water vapor, these streams condense the higher hydrocarbons in the vapor stream. The inlet vapor typically has a water dew point of 180° to 195°F; however, the inlet vapor temperature usually is 30° to 40°F above the water dew point. This gas stream contains a complete range of hydrocarbons through C-9 aromatics. Normally the C-4 and lighter hydrocarbons pass through this tower uncondensed. Thus, the vapor stream ascends the column at the hydrocarbon dew point.

The entering vapor quickly is cooled to the adiabatic saturation temperature with respect to water. Thus, the vapor superheat, plus the heat of vaporization of the higher boiling hydrocarbons, is converted to heat of vaporization of water. The vapor then progresses up the column at the water dew point as well as the hydrocarbon dew point. The vapor leaving the quench tower normally is at a temperature about 8° to 14°F above the water feed temperature to the column top when trays are used.

The effluent liquid from the quench column flows to a decanter where the smaller hydrocarbon phase is separated from the larger water phase. The water phase, after removal of the amount of water condensed, is recycled through heat recovery systems before being returned to the quench column center. A minor portion of the recirculated water is cooled further before being returned to the column top. The heat load on the packed bed is greater than the heat load on the pumparound water coolers since both the hydrocarbon condensate and the water condensate discharge from the system at the liquid effluent temperature.

Normally, the column upper section uses 5 to 9 valve or sieve trays that are replaced with an 8-ft to 14-ft deep bed of #50 IMTP® packing. This packed depth permits cooling the outlet vapor to within a few degrees of the inlet water temperature. The vapor entering the upper section of the quench column normally is 10° to 20°F higher in temperature than the liquid leaving this section. The heat transfer coefficients in this section are high—U_v for #50 IMTP® packing is 35% greater than for valve trays on 24-in. spacing. The principal reason to install packing in this section is to reduce the pressure drop by 85% to 90%, as compared with valve or sieve trays in the same section. This results in an overall pressure drop reduction of 70% to 75% for the quench column, even when the angle trays are left in the bottom section. Thus, the resulting higher suction pressure reduces the compression ratio, and therefore the power requirement, on the first compression stage.

The lower sections of water quench towers typically employ baffle trays, splash decks, or angle trays. These devices have a very low efficiency so that 6 to 12 actual trays are installed. When this section is equipped with high capacity packing, the exit liquid temperature can be raised to within about 5°F of the inlet vapor adiabatic temperature. This can be done without increasing the pressure drop compared to the trays. Normally a 10 ft to 14 ft depth of #70 IMTP® packing is specified for the lower section. This provides at least 70% more theoretical stages than the trays that are replaced. The heat transfer coefficients in this section are very high. They can be up to 90% greater than those applicable to the upper section for the same tower packing, if there is a large mass of condensed hydrocarbon.

In revamping the water quench tower upper and lower sections, the column performance depends on the temperature approach between vapor and liquid at each end of the column. This is because the liquid from the upper section normally flows into the lower section of the tower, in addition to the mid-pumparound liquid return.

It is desirable to minimize the top pumparound return liquid flow to recover the greatest amount of the available heat. However, the top water flow must be sufficient to keep the operating line for this column section from pinching against the equilibrium curve and rapidly increasing the required number of theoretical stages. Otherwise, an attempt to raise the effluent liquid temperature to a maximum value for heat recovery purposes by reducing top water return flow may cause increased outlet vapor temperature from the column with the same top liquid feed temperature.

EXAMPLE PROBLEM

The gas steam leaves a first-stage compressor in an olefin plant at a pressure of 48 psia and a temperature of 196°F. The gas flow rate is 295,000 lb/h consisting of 240 lb-mol/h of water vapor and 10,000 lb-mol/h of hydrocarbon. The exit gas must be cooled to 97°F. Water to cool this gas steam is available to 90°F for use in a direct-contact gas cooler. The heated water effluent from this column should be at a temperature of about 130°F so that it can be returned to the center of the water quench tower. What will be the size of a packed interstage cooler and how much can it reduce the gas-side pressure drop of 4.0 psi through the present tube-and-shell heat exchangers?

The inlet gas stream contains 2.34 mol % water vapor and has a heat capacity of the hydrocarbon vapor of 0.434 Btu/lb·°F. The enthalpy of the inlet gas stream is 88.36 Btu/lb dry gas. Likewise, the enthalpy of the outlet gas stream at 97°F is 40.78 Btu/lb dry gas.

The inlet gas stream contains 0.0149 lb H_2O vapor/lb dry gas, while the outlet gas stream contains 0.0114 lb H_2O vapor/lb dry gas.

Water vapor content of gas in =

0.0149(290,675) = 4,331 lb/h

Water vapor content of gas out =

0.0114(290,595) = 3,313 lb/h

Water vapor condensed =

4,331 − 3,313 = 1,018 lb/h

In addition 80 lb/h of hydrocarbon will be condensed that will slightly reduce the dry gas flow leaving the column as just indicated.

The heat balance for the cooler is:

Heat content of gas in =

$88.36(290,675) = 25.684 \times 10^6$ Btu/h

Heat content of gas out =

$40.78(290,595) = 11.850 \times 10^6$ Btu/h

Cooling load =

$25.684 \times 10^6 − 11.850 \times 10^6 = 13.834 \times 10^6$ Btu/h

For a 40°F temperature rise in the cooling water, the inlet water feed rate is 345,700 lb/h.

The bottom of the column has a gas flow of 295,000 lb/h with a density of 0.196 lb/ft³ and a liquid flow of 346,798 lb/h with a density of 61.5 lb/ft³. The flow parameter for Figure 1-16 gives a value of 0.0664 at this point. A 9-ft 6-in. ID column is selected that produces a C_s of 0.333 fps at the bottom of the column. The ordinate on Figure 1-16 is 1.12 which gives a pressure drop of 0.34 in. H_2O/ft for #70 IMTP® packing. At the top of the column the gas flow rate is 293,902 lb/h with a density of 0.232 lb/ft³ and the liquid flow is 345,700 lb/h with a density of 62.1 lb/ft³. The flow parameter is 0.0719 and the C_s is 0.304 fps, giving a pressure drop of 0.28 in. H_2O/ft for #70 IMTP® packing at the top of the column. The average pressure drop through the #70 IMTP® packing is 0.31 in. H_2O/ft for a nonfoaming system.

Because only 0.03 wt% of the hydrocarbon entering the column condenses, the system can be treated as an inert gas dehumidification by use of Equation 5-23. For #70 IMTP® packing at this pressure, the value of the coefficient is 10.1. The average base heat transfer coefficient for this bed is 729 Btu/h · ft³ · °F.

The heat transfer coefficient must be adjusted for the effects of gas and liquid flow rates. This adjustment is made by taking U_v as a function of the vapor capacity factor (F_s) to the 0.8 power and the liquid mass flow rate to the 0.4 power. The adjusted average volumetric heat transfer coefficient is 1,530 Btu/h · ft³ · °F.

The inlet gas stream has a water dew point temperature of 105.5°F. However, because this gas is superheated, the adiabatic saturation temperature should be used to calculate the temperature driving force at the bottom of the column. The gas leaving the column is at the hydrocarbon and water dew point, therefore its temperature can be used to calculate the driving force at the top of the column. The temperature difference driving forces next are determined:

At top $\Delta T = 97 - 90 = 7.0°F$

At bottom $\Delta T = 138.3 - 130 = 8.3°F$

The ln mean temperature driving force for this column is therefore 7.63°F.

$$Z = \frac{13,834,000}{1530(70.88)(7.63)} = 16.7 \text{ ft}$$

To carry the 13.834×10^6 Btu/h heat load we will specify a packed depth of 17 ft in a 9-ft 6-in. ID column. This system is assumed to be slightly foaming because some insoluble hydrocarbon condenses into the water phase. After making allowance for an increase in pressure drop due to foaming plus the pressure drop through the column internals, the overall column pressure drop is expected to be only 0.30 psi. This is over a 90% reduction of the pressure drop, compared to the conventional tube-and-shell interstage cooler. The compression ratio on the second-stage compressor typically is reduced by about 8%.

NOTATION

A	Column cross-sectional area (ft^2)
BDG	Bone dry gas
Cp	Heat capacity of liquid $(\text{Btu/lb} \cdot °F)$
Cpv	Heat capacity of gas $(\text{Btu/lb} \cdot °F)$
F_s	Vapor capacity factor $(\text{lb}^{0.5}/\text{ft}^{0.5} \cdot \text{s})$
G_d	Bone dry gas flow (lb/h)
G_i'	Inlet gas flow (lb/h)
G_o'	Outlet gas flow (lb/h)
H_i	Inlet gas enthalpy (Btu/lb BDG)
H_o	Outlet gas enthalpy (Btu/lb BDG)
H_M	Molar gas enthalpy (Btu/lb-mol BDG)
H_{OG}	Overall height of a gas transfer unit (ft)

H_v Gas enthalpy (Btu/lb BDG)
H_v^* Equilibrium gas enthalpy (Btu/lb BDG)
h_i Inlet gas humidity (lb H_2O/lb BDG)
h_o Outlet gas humidity (lb H_2O/lb BDG)
L_i' Inlet liquid flow (lb/h)
L_o' Outlet liquid flow (lb/h)
L_w Inlet water flow (lb/h)
N_{OG} Number of overall gas transfer units
Q Heat transferred (Btu/h)
T_i Inlet gas temperature (°F)
T_o Outlet gas temperature (°F)
t_i Inlet liquid temperature (°F)
t_o Outlet liquid temperature (°F)
U_v Volumetric heat transfer coefficient (Btu/h $\cdot$ ft^3 $\cdot$ °F)
u' Viscosity (lb/ft $\cdot$ h)
W Water evaporated (lb/h)
Z Packed depth (ft)
ΔH Heat of vaporization (Btu/lb)
ΔT_{LM} ln mean temperature driving force (°F)
ρ_G Gas density (lb/ft^3)
ρ_L Liquid density (lb/ft^3)

REFERENCES

1. Walker, W. H., et al., *Principles of Chemical Engineering,* McGraw-Hill, 1937, Chap. 17.
2. Gilliland, E. R., and Sherwood, T. K., *Industrial Engineering Chemistry,* Vol. 26, 1934, p. 516.
3. Nusselt, W. Z., *Ver deut Ingeneurung,* Vol. 60., 1916, p. 541.
4. Perry, R. H., and Chilton, C. H., *Chemical Engineers' Handbook,* 5th ed. McGraw-Hill, 1973, p. 3-214.
5. Eckert, J. S., Foote, E. H., and Walter, L. F., "Technical Data Related to Tower Packing," Norton Company, 1968, GR-290 A, B, and C.
6. Nemunaitis, R. R., and Eckert, J. S., *Chemical Engineering Progress,* Vol. 71, No. 8, 1975, p. 60.
7. Strigle, R. F., and Foote, E. H., "Technical Data Related to Tower Packing," Norton Company, 1975, GR-303, 305, and 306.
8. Hainbach, J. J., and Rubero, P. A., *Oil and Gas Journal,* Vol. 76, No. 12, 1978, p. 72.
9. Graf, K., *Oil and Gas Journal,* Vol. 83, No. 20, 1985, p. 60.

6

ATMOSPHERIC DISTILLATION

Distillation is the most widely used method for separating mixtures of liquids in the chemical and hydrocarbon processing industries. Separation takes place because the vapor phase is of a different composition than the liquid phase.

Distillation operations will be classified on the basis of column operating pressure. This chapter is devoted to a discussion of the fundamental principles of distillation as applied to operations carried out at pressures close to atmospheric. The same principles also apply to distillations at very low or at high pressures, which are reviewed in detail in later chapters.

Pressure distillations normally use a top column pressure of 80 psia or greater. These high pressures produce a greater vapor density that may represent a significant percentage of the liquid density. The accompanying increase in boiling temperature not only lowers the liquid density, but also reduces the surface tension and the viscosity of the liquid phase. These factors complicate distillation column design and require somewhat modified design techniques. These procedural modifications are especially important as the critical region is approached. The design of such columns is discussed in detail in Chapter 8.

Vacuum distillations are those operating at pressures below atmospheric, usually not greater than 300 mm Hg top column pressure. The resultant lower boiling temperatures normally increase the relative volatility between components, therefore the ease of separation. At the same time, the associated higher liquid viscosities may reduce the efficiency of the distillation device. The pressure drop through such a column usually is an important design criterion. Vacuum column design is discussed in Chapter 7.

Generally the same factors that complicate the column design also reduce the economic viability of columns equipped with trays. This forms the basis for the increased acceptance of packed columns in vacuum or high-pressure distillation service. Although packed columns for atmospheric pressure distillations are not as widely used, their design will be discussed first. This design is relatively less complicated and provides an appropriate basis for the chapters on vacuum and pressure distillations.

IDEAL VAPOR/LIQUID EQUILIBRIUM SYSTEMS

According to Raoult's law, the equilibrium partial pressure of a component in the vapor phase is equal to the mol fraction of that component in the liquid phase multiplied by the vapor pressure of the pure component at the operating temperature. This law applies to an ideal system; one that has no interaction between components:

$$p = xp^* \tag{6-1}$$

Dalton's law states that the partial pressure of a component in the vapor phase equals the mol fraction of that component in the vapor times the system pressure:

$$p = yP \tag{6-2}$$

Combining these two equations gives an equilibrium relationship between the vapor-phase composition and liquid-phase composition for an ideal system:

$$\frac{y}{x} = \frac{p^*}{P} \tag{6-3}$$

Distillation separates two components because of the difference in the equilibrium relationships between the various components. The ratio of the equilibrium relationships between components A and C is termed the relative volatility of A to C:

$$\alpha_{AC} = \frac{y_A}{x_A} \frac{x_C}{y_C} \tag{6-4}$$

Relative volatility is a measure of the ease of separation of two components. The greater the value of α_{AC}, the more readily component A can be separated from component C. From Equation 6-3, for an ideal system the relative volatility is the ratio of the vapor pressures of the pure components A and C at the temperature of distillation:

$$\alpha_{AC} = \frac{p_A^*}{p_C^*} \qquad (6\text{-}5)$$

Boiling temperature is fixed by the column's operating pressure as well as by the liquid-phase composition. The vapor pressure for each component varies with the temperature at constant latent heat of vaporization in accordance with the Clapeyron equation:

$$\log p^* = b - \frac{j}{T} \qquad (6\text{-}6)$$

where b and j are constants. The use of Antoine's equation somewhat improves the accuracy of predicting vapor pressure:

$$\log p^* = b - \frac{j}{T + i} \qquad (6\text{-}7)$$

where i is an additional constant. The constants for Equation 6-6 or Equation 6-7 are determined experimentally for a particular component. An extensive table of Antoine constants is presented by Reid, et al. [1].

Because these constants differ for various compounds, the vapor pressures for different components usually do not change at the same rate with temperature variations. For an ideal system, the relative volatility between the two components, as expressed by Equation 6-5, varies with the boiling temperature. As an example, consider the separation of a system of toluene and ethyl benzene. Assume that the separation produces substantially pure toluene as distillate and equally pure ethyl benzene as bottoms. If the distillation column is operated at atmospheric pressure, the relative volatility between these two components is 2.1. If the distillation pressure is raised to 5 atmospheres absolute, the relative volatility is reduced to 1.8. However if the pressure of distillation is lowered to 200 mm Hg absolute, the relative volatility increases to 2.3. Thus, separation becomes easier as the column pressure is reduced.

The equilibrium ratio often is used in the calculation of hydrocarbon separations. It is the ratio of the vapor composition to the liquid composition with which it is in equilibrium:

$$K = \frac{y}{x} \qquad (6\text{-}8)$$

From Equation 6-3, for an ideal system:

$$K = \frac{p^*}{P} \tag{6-9}$$

There is an equilibrium ratio representing each component in the system. For light hydrocarbons the equilibrium ratio for any one component increases at higher temperatures and decreases at higher pressures. In addition, the value of K is altered by the other components present in the system as well as the concentration of the specified component in the liquid phase. The value of the equilibrium ratio usually decreases as the molecular weight increases for a homologous series of compounds. This is because the vapor pressure at any fixed temperature decreases as molecular weight increases.

As previously stated, the relative volatility of one component compared to another indicates the ease of separation of these components by distillation. The relative volatility of component A compared to component C also is expressed as a ratio of the equilibrium ratio for component A to the equilibrium ratio for component C:

$$\alpha_{AC} = \frac{K_A}{K_C} \tag{6-10}$$

The value of the relative volatility generally decreases as the pressure increases, as just illustrated for the system toluene and ethyl benzene. Thus, separation is greater per theoretical stage for a vacuum distillation than for a high-pressure distillation of the same mixture.

NONIDEAL VAPOR/LIQUID EQUILIBRIUM SYSTEMS

When the liquid phase is not ideal, the equilibrium ratio is modified by the activity coefficient (γ):

$$K = \gamma \, K' \tag{6-11}$$

where K' is the equilibrium ratio calculated from Equations 6-3 and 6-9. The liquid phase normally is ideal when all components are similar; such as a series of saturated aliphatic hydrocarbons. Nonideal liquids usually are mixtures of molecularly dissimilar components that associate in the liquid phase; such as methanol and benzene or acetone and chloroform. Hydrogen bonding often is a significant factor in nonideal liquid mixtures. Such systems can deviate substantially from Raoult's law (Equation 6-1). In all separations carried out by distillation, only a few systems are totally ideal. Many show a variation in relative volatility with liquid-phase composition other than that anticipated due to the change of boiling temperature with composition. One such system is propylene and propane at 17 atm pressure. In this system the relative volatility changes from 1.08 in the propylene-rich top of the column to 1.14 in the propane-rich bottom of the column.

The activity coefficient (γ) is a function of the temperature and composition of the liquid phase. If the volatilities of all components are increased, the deviation from ideal is considered positive ($\gamma > 1.0$). If the volatilities of all components are reduced, the deviation from ideal is considered negative ($\gamma < 1.0$). Van Laar developed a method to calculate the effect of liquid composition on liquid-phase activity coefficients for nonpolar, binary systems at a given temperature [2]. The constants for these equations are determined from experimental VLE data. This method applies to systems that show either positive or negative deviation from Raoult's law, but it will not predict curves exhibiting maximum or minimum values of γ. This method has been used on multicomponent mixtures by assuming a pseudobinary system of key components.

A better method of calculation for multicomponent mixtures has been developed by Wilson [3]. The binary parameters still must be determined from experimental VLE data. This method applies to mixtures of polar and nonpolar molecules, such as n-hexane and ethanol, that are strongly nonideal. Also this method has the ability to model nonideal systems even in dilute regions. However, this method does not predict curves exhibiting maximum or minimum values of γ nor will it predict immiscibility.

The UNIFAC model predicts liquid-phase activity coefficients for nonideal mixtures when no VLE data are available [4]. This model uses a group contribution method with about 50 identified functional groups. The liquid-phase activity coefficients are calculated from an equation by use of molecular configuration. The parameters calculated are independent of temperature. This method is restricted to systems in which all components are condensable. It is as accurate as the Wilson method, but has a more theoretical basis.

At pressures below 5.5 atm, the vapor phase normally may be considered ideal. In such a situation, Equations 6-2 and 6-8 apply. Certain systems, such as acetic acid and water, form dimers in the vapor phase. In these cases the degree of dimerization determines not only the VLE but the average molecular weight of the vapor. This, in turn, controls the gas density used in the hydraulic capacity calculations.

EQUILIBRIUM RELATIONSHIPS

Atmospheric distillations in this chapter are considered to be those distillations operating at top column pressures above 0.4 atm and less than 5.5 atm absolute. In this pressure range, the column pressure drop usually is small compared to the system pressure. Also the liquid surface tension is high enough to avoid capacity restrictions, which will be discussed in Chapter 8.

The feed composition and flow rate are known as is the specification for the top distillate and column bottoms. Normally the concentration of one heavy component, known as the heavy key, is specified in the distillate. Likewise, the concentration of one light component, known as the light key, is specified for the bottoms. Sometimes the percentage recovery of one of the feed components is the specification for either the distillate or the bottoms.

To calculate the vapor composition, it is necessary to develop an equilibrium relationship. For the distillation of an ideal binary system of components A and C the equilibrium relationship is given by:

$$y_A = \frac{\alpha_{AC}\, x_A}{1 + (\alpha_{AC} - 1)\, x_A} \tag{6-12}$$

This relationship is derived from the definition of relative volatility, as given in Equations 6-4 and 6-10.

Using Equation 6-12, a curve can be established that shows the relationship between the liquid composition and the equilibrium vapor composition at a constant relative volatility. Figure 6-1 shows curves at α

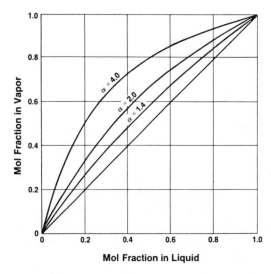

Figure 6-1. Vapor/liquid equilibrium relationship ideal system.

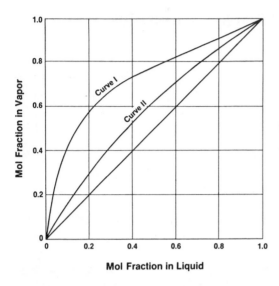

Figure 6-2. Vapor/liquid equilibrium relationship non-ideal system.

values of 1.4, 2.0, and 4.0 which represent separations of increasing ease. The equilibrium relationships between vapor and liquid compositions for some nonideal binary systems are shown in Figure 6-2. Curve I is a methanol/water system and Curve II is a water/acetic acid system. Note that these curves no longer are symmetrical like those in Figure 6-1.

Care must be taken in the selection of experimental vapor/liquid equilibrium data used in the calculations. These data should cover the range of compositions proposed for the column being designed. Extrapolation of VLE data, especially into high purity areas, can be a source of significant errors.

DETERMINATION OF THEORETICAL STAGES

The number of theoretical stages required for a given separation is calculated by one of the conventional methods. In many binary distillations, the molar flow rates of vapor and liquid are substantially constant. For systems in which the molar heats of vaporization and liquid heat capacities are almost the same and heat losses are negligible, Mc-Cabe and Thiele have developed a graphical method for determining the number of theoretical stages required [5]. Under these conditions, the operating line of the distillation column can be represented by a material balance equation. For a column with a total condenser, the overhead vapor and distillate are of the same composition. The operating line for the rectifying section must pass through the distillate composition. If a par-

tial condenser is used, the reflux composition will be a liquid in equilibrium with the condenser outlet vapor composition. A partial condenser
usually provides one additional theoretical stage. In this case the condenser outlet vapor constitutes at least some of the distillate product.

Usually the reboiler is considered as one theoretical stage so that the
vapor to the bottom of the column is in equilibrium with the liquid bottoms product. The operating line for the stripping section must pass
through the bottoms composition. In a binary distillation, the feed
should be introduced into the column at the equilibrium stage represented by the intersection of the two operating lines. The theoretical
stages are determined using a stepwise procedure between the operating
lines and the equilibrium curve. Figure 6-3 demonstrates this graphical
procedure for a separation requiring three theoretical stages rectifying
and four theoretical stages stripping.

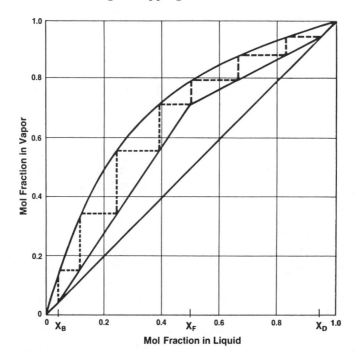

Figure 6-3. McCabe-Thiele procedure.

One of the more widely used methods for calculating the number of
theoretical stages in multicomponent systems was developed by Lewis
and Matheson [6]. Again, the molar flow rates of vapor and liquid in
each section are assumed to be constant. On each equilibrium stage, the

summation of the concentrations of all vapor components must equal unity. The same is true for the summation of the concentrations of all liquid components. Further, the vapor and liquid compositions of each component are related by the K value for that component.

The starting points for the calculations are the distillate and bottoms compositions if the concentrations of all components are known. When only a single high-boiling impurity concentration (heavy key) is specified in the distillate and only a single low-boiling impurity concentration (light key) is specified in the bottoms, a different starting point is needed. In this latter case, the calculations may be started from the feed point since the feed composition is known for all components.

Generally, this method requires considerable trial-and-error as a temperature first must be assumed, then the K values for each component are calculated. This procedure is repeated until a matched compositional profile is obtained for each stage.

When there are a number of low-boiling components similar to the light key and/or a number of high-boiling components similar to the heavy key, a method developed by Thiele and Geddes can be used to calculate the distribution of such components [7]. This method assumes the number of theoretical stages in each section and the temperature of each stage. The split of each component between overhead and bottoms then can be calculated.

Again a trial-and-error calculation is required by adjusting the temperature profile of the column until the assumed number of theoretical stages equals that required to obtain the specified separation. This method especially is useful in evaluating the performance of an existing column.

Computers have greatly reduced the effort and increased the calculation speed. They easily produce the necessary repetitive approximations required to satisfy simultaneously the material and heat balances and equilibrium relationships. In computerized calculations, the selection of the equation of state influences the number of calculated theoretical stages required. Each equation of state was developed primarily from a specific data bank that usually was confined to a certain type of compound. As an example, the Benedict-Webb-Rubin equation of state was developed from experimental data on methane, ethane, propane, and n-butane [8]. This equation is preferred to generate K values for these light hydrocarbons. The equation of state specified for the calculations should be the one based on data for compounds most closely resembling those being separated.

The Braun K-10 Correlation was developed to generate K values for light hydrocarbons at pressures below 100 psia and at temperatures above 100°F [9]. This correlation has proved useful in the calculation of refinery columns, including those processing heavy fractions. Also, it can be used for aromatic distillations so long as nonideal compounds are not present.

The Soave-Redlich-Kwong equation is a modification of the original Redlich-Kwong equation for predicting K values [10]. The Soave modification produces a significant improvement in the prediction of VLE data for mixtures as well as pure substances. This method probably is the most widely used prediction for a large variety of hydrocarbon systems from cryogenic conditions to high-pressure operations.

The Peng-Robinson equation was developed to overcome some of the shortcomings of the SRK equation [11]. This equation has been used to regress experimental data on C-2 splitters and C-3 splitters. Generally, the Peng-Robinson equation gives a better simulation of actual column performance than the SRK equation, which predicts more conservative results.

Computer programs usually calculate the properties of compounds present in the column feed from a set of equations rather than from a library of experimental data. Calculated physical properties should be checked against experimentally determined values to verify these properties during final design.

The minimum reflux ratio needed for a specific separation requires an infinite number of theoretical stages. For easy separations (i.e., an α greater than 1.6), an operating reflux ratio 25% greater than minimum usually is specified. For separations where an air-cooled condenser can be used and exhaust steam is the energy source, an operating reflux ratio as high as 1.35 times the minimum may be specified. For difficult separations (i.e., an α less than 1.4), the operating reflux ratio should be at least 12% greater than the minimum required, unless the vapor/liquid equilibrium is known with a high degree of precision.

In determining the number of theoretical stages required, the calculations usually should start at both the reboiler and the condenser and proceed toward the feed point. The bottoms product and distillate compositions are known or specified, and the bottoms and distillate product rates are known or can be calculated by material balance from the feed rate and composition. Such a procedure minimizes calculational errors while meeting the specified product compositions.

MAXIMUM OPERATIONAL CAPACITY

After the operating reflux ratio has been selected, the hydraulic vapor and liquid loadings are calculated for each column section. Unless flow rates change significantly within the column, the hydraulic loadings need be determined only at the top and bottom of the tower, as well as above and below the feed point.

A packed column diameter historically was selected to produce a pressure drop of 0.40 in. to 0.60 in. H_2O/ft of packed depth at the point of maximum hydraulic loading [12]. This rule was applied as long as the liquid specific gravity was at least 0.80. This design basis was selected from experience with $1^1/_2$-in. and 2-in. ceramic Intalox® saddle packings in columns that operated at the packing loading point [13]. Such a sizing procedure neglected any effect of flow rates on separation efficiency.

In the experimental work that led to the development of a modern, very high void fraction packing (Intalox® Metal Tower Packing) it was found that vapor velocities could be increased to such a high rate that significant liquid entrainment was produced without incurring correspondingly high pressure drops. Further, because the entrained liquid was carried up the column, separation efficiency eventually dropped at vapor velocities that still were below the packing's maximum hydraulic capacity (flooding point).

Figure 6-4 is a plot of the separation efficiency (HETP) of a random dumped tower packing as a function of vapor velocity for an atmospheric distillation. Vapor velocity is expressed as a capacity factor to account for the effect of vapor and liquid densities:

$$C_s = \frac{G^*}{[\rho_G(\rho_L - \rho_G)]^{0.5}} \tag{6-13}$$

In Figure 6-4, the liquid rate at constant reflux ratio increases in direct proportion to the vapor rate. On this curve, the region from point B to point C exhibits a constant separation efficiency typical for the packing. As C_s increases further, the vapor rate becomes great enough to begin to interact with the liquid phase. This generates increased interfacial area beyond point C. In previous publications this point has been referred to as the "loading point" of the packing [14]. At rates just greater than this point, the separation efficiency increases (height equivalent to a theoretical stage becomes lower). With further vapor rate increase, liquid entrainment finally is initiated. Because this liquid recycle reduces the concentration gradient, the effective HETP increases. This results in a maximum efficiency (minimum HETP value) at the rate represented by point D.

The column actually can be operated at a vapor rate as high as that represented by point F without exceeding the HETP value typical for the packing. Therefore, the C_s at point F has been designated as the maximum operational capacity of the packing. This rate provides perfectly stable operation because it has been determined from separation

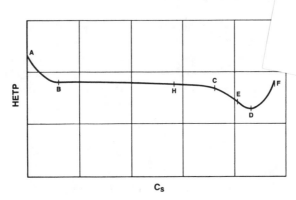

Figure 6-4. Typical packing performance. (From Strigle [13]. Reproduced by permission of the American Institute of Chemical Engineers.)

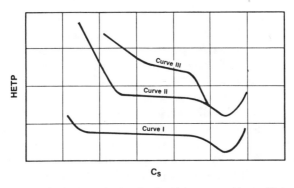

Figure 6-5. Effect of liquid distribution on packing efficiency.

efficiency. This approach to packed column capacity has been verified by the work of Kunesh et al. [15]. The maximum hydraulic capacity of the packing is about 20% higher than the rate at point F for atmospheric distillations.

MINIMUM OPERATING RATE

Similarly, the rate represented by point B in Figure 6-4 is the minimum flow at which the typical HETP value can be realized. Usually this rate represents a limitation of liquid distribution techniques rather than the minimum wetting rate of the tower packing [16]. In atmospheric distillations, liquid rates normally are not less than 1.5 gpm/ft^2.

Figure 6-5 illustrates the effect of liquid distribution on separation efficiency. Curve III shows the operation of a poorly designed liquid distributor where the natural internal distribution characteristics of the packing and the vapor flow actually are responsible for the majority of the liquid distribution. This poor liquid distribution severely curtails the operational flexibility of the packing because the separation obtained varies with the vapor rate. Curves I and II show significant improvements in column performance in that constant efficiency is maintained over a wider range of vapor flow rates. Curve II represents the performance of standard liquid distributors typical of those commercially available in the 1970s. The minimum operating capacity for Curve II is much greater than that for Curve I because of poorer liquid distribution at lower rates. Curve I illustrates the operation of high-performance liquid distributors. Curve I shows a lower HETP value as well as a wider flow range at constant HETP than Curve II since uniform liquid distribution is maintained.

Vapor maldistribution theoretically could lead to the same lack of performance as illustrated in Figure 6-5. There is, however, a much better radial mixing of the vapor phase in the packed bed because it almost always is in the turbulent flow regime. Vapor distribution normally is not a problem as long as the pressure drop through the packed bed is at least 0.10 in. H_2O/ft of packed depth and the inlet vapor nozzles are operating at F_s vapor rates not greater than 22 $lb^{0.5}/ft^{0.5}s$.

Pressure drop usually is not critical in atmospheric distillations, therefore, the design C_s normally is selected above the loading point (point C in Figure 6-4) and below the maximum efficiency rate (point D). Typically, the flow rate at point C is 70% to 75% of that at maximum operational capacity (Point F). The design C_s (Point E) should be chosen to permit at least a 15% increase in flow rates before reaching the maximum operational capacity of the packing. This will allow for normal feed and heat input variations. The design C_s should not be less than 80% of the maximum operational C_s if the greatest possible turndown ratio is desired. Although the separation efficiency from point C to point F is greater than that typical of the packing, this advantage normally is not used for design purposes.

COLUMN DIAMETER SELECTION

It may be desirable to change column diameter if the hydraulic loading varies greatly from top to bottom of the column or from one packed bed to another. The cost of a column diameter change may be excessive for small diameter columns or where the diameter change is less than 12 in. Another option is to change packing size at constant column diameter to accommodate variations in hydraulic loading. However, there may be a problem of mechanical stability, if the bottom of the column is of a smaller diameter than the top.

By experimentation with systems, such as those listed in Table 6-1, the maximum operational capacity for Intalox® Metal Tower Packing was determined. This capacity is expressed as a function of the flow parameter. The flow parameter is a ratio of the square roots of the liquid kinetic energy to the vapor kinetic energy:

$$X = \frac{L}{G} \left[\frac{\rho_G}{\rho_L} \right]^{0.5} \tag{6-14}$$

Flow parameter values from 0.04 to 0.17 are normal for atmospheric distillations.

Table 6 – 1
Experimental Systems

System	Pressure (absolute)
Acetone and water	740 mm Hg
Cyclohexane and n-heptane	260 mm Hg
Cyclohexane and n-heptane	740 mm Hg
Cyclohexane and n-heptane	24 psi
Cyclohexanone and cyclohexanol	70 mm Hg
Ethyl benzene and styrene	50 mm Hg
Ethylene and ethane	300 psi
Ethylene glycol and diethylene glycol	45 mm Hg
Ethylene glycol and water	230 mm Hg
Iso-octane and toluene	100 mm Hg
Iso-octane and toluene	740 mm Hg
Propylene and propane	280 psi
Propylene and propane	330 psi
Propylene and propane	430 psi

Figure 6-6 is a plot of the maximum operational capacity as a function of the flow parameter for three sizes of IMTP® packing. The C_s factor is based on the overall column cross-sectional area. Data used to generate this plot indicate that the C_s value at a constant flow parameter varies as the surface tension of the liquid phase to the 0.20 to 0.25 power. This variation is similar to that reported by Fair for the capacity of sieve trays with respect to jet flooding [17]. Thus, in a toluene/aromatics fractionator where the liquid phase has a surface tension of 15 dyne/cm the maxi-

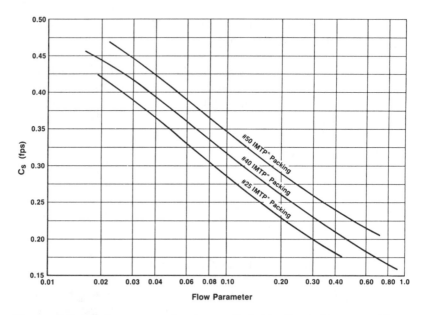

Figure 6-6. Maximum operational capacity Intalox® metal tower packing.

mum operational C_s will be 4% lower than in a benzene/aromatics fractionator with an 18 dyne/cm liquid surface tension (see Figure 6-7). Figure 6-6 is based on a liquid surface tension of 20 dyne/cm. The data do not justify an increase of more than 8% for the maximum operational C_s as surface tension is increased above 20 dyne/cm.

In addition, the experimental data indicate that the C_s value at constant flow parameter varies as the liquid viscosity to the – 0.10 power to – 0.13 power. Therefore, an ethanol/water distillation column would have a 3% lower maximum operational C_s in the ethanol-rich rectifying section where the liquid viscosity is 0.39 cps than in the water-rich stripping section with a liquid viscosity of only 0.30 cps. Figure 6-6 is based on a liquid viscosity of 0.20 cps. Likewise, the data do not support an increase of more than 9% for the maximum operational C_s as liquid viscosity is decreased below 0.20 cps. This correlation, shown as Figure 6-6, was developed from data on liquids with surface tensions as low as 7 dyne/cm and viscosities as high as 1.0 cps.

EFFICIENCY CONSIDERATIONS

Distillation efficiency commonly is expressed as height equivalent to a theoretical stage (HETP). In a trayed column, the HETP value is the

Figure 6-7. Atmospheric fractionators: These packed columns are used for aromatics processing.

tray spacing divided by the fractional overall tray efficiency. A theoretical stage (as described in Chapter 3) is a mass transfer stage from which the liquid and vapor streams leave in equilibrium. In a packed column, the liquid in the packed bed would be in equilibrium with the gas stream located one HETP value above it in the packed bed. Thus, the stepwise procedure McCabe and Thiele developed to simulate the performance of a trayed column is somewhat difficult to envision for operation of a packed column.

Because a packed bed is a continuous contacting device, an equilibrium stage concept based on a transfer unit has been proposed. The height of a transfer unit is defined as that depth of packing required to produce a change in the composition equal to the mass transfer driving force causing that change (which is discussed in Chapter 3). It can be shown that when the equilibrium curve is a straight line:

$$H_{OG} = H_G + \frac{mGm}{Lm} H_L \tag{6-15}$$

This equation is based on the two-film theory which assumes that the vapor film is in equilibrium with the liquid film at the interface. The operating line slope for a distillation column is Lm/Gm. The ratio of the equilibrium curve slope to the operating line slope is called the lambda factor. At total reflux, the lambda factor equals m because Lm equals Gm. The operating pressure has little effect on the values of H_G or H_L in itself. However, the resultant higher temperatures encountered in high pressure distillations decrease the value of H_L; probably because of reduced liquid viscosity and the increased value of liquid diffusivity.

In practical cases, the equilibrium relationship seldom is linear. If the operating line and equilibrium curve were straight and parallel, then HETP would equal H_{OG}. If the operating line and equilibrium curve are linear, but not parallel, then:

$$HETP = \frac{\ln \lambda}{\lambda - 1} H_{OG} \tag{6-16}$$

At total reflux, the λ value in the stripping section must be greater than one and the λ value in the rectifying section must be less than one. From Equation 6-16, a higher HETP value might be expected in the rectifying section than in the stripping section of a fractionator if the value of H_{OG} is constant. However, in commercial applications, the HETP value varies less than the H_{OG} value. This was demonstrated by Eckert and Walter for 1-in. and 2-in. metal Pall ring packings [18]. Therefore, the efficiency of tower packings in distillation usually will be considered in terms of HETP values.

HETP PREDICTION

Despite the great amount of data available, no method yet exists for HETP prediction with a high degree of confidence. The prudent designer, therefore, resorts to commercial experience for the separation of similar compounds as a first choice for selection of the design HETP value. Vital, et al. present an extensive list of HETP values for various tower packings in more than 40 different services [19]. Although not stated, these HETP values probably were obtained using commercial-quality liquid distributors. If industrial experience is not available, as may be the case with a new process, the designer uses pilot plant data to estimate the HETP value for design purposes.

However, there are a number of occasions where the designer is faced with developing a design HETP value without any actual experience. He then must rely on a calculated value obtained from some correlation. A model has been proposed by Onda and co-workers to calculate H_{OG} by means of Equation 6-15 [20]. This model evaluates H_G and H_L values from mass transfer coefficients:

$$H_G = \frac{Gm}{k_G a\ AP} \tag{6-17}$$

$$H_L = \frac{Lm}{k_L a\ A} \tag{6-18}$$

This model requires a calculation of the interfacial area. The equation used for this calculation is based on the geometric surface area of the packing and a critical surface tension that is, in turn, dependent on the packing material.

Because the Onda model showed an average deviation of about 40% for the calculated value compared to the experimental HETP value, Bolles and Fair proposed an improved model for predicting separation efficiency [21]. This model also calculates H_{OG} by means of Equation 6-15. The H_{OG} value then is converted to an HETP value by use of Equation 6-16. Unfortunately, this model makes a correction for the effect of the packed bed depth on both H_G and H_L; thus, the calculation becomes an iterative procedure. In addition, there is a proposed correction for tower diameter that is greater for ceramic Raschig ring packing than for ceramic Berl saddle packing. Therefore, this model has incorporated within it corrections for lack of proper packing performance which really were specific to the actual testing device.

The improved Bolles and Fair model still had a standard deviation of almost 25% for the calculated values compared to the experimental data; therefore, Porter and Jenkins conducted an extensive review of the data bank from which that model was developed [22]. They eliminated the runs made at very high and very low vapor rates and confined the data base only to distillation runs. Porter and Jenkins then found that this improved model needed only about a 20% safety factor to give the calculated design HETP value a 95% confidence limit for prediction of the residual data base.

Based on this work, Porter has proposed that HETP at total reflux is a function of the flow parameter and the liquid viscosity:

$$\text{HETP} = \lambda \ H_S \ (v \ X^{0.5} + w \ \mu) \tag{6-19}$$

In this correlation v and w are constants and H_S is the HETP value for the packing as determined experimentally for a standard distillation system.

Norton Chemical Process Products has developed a proprietary correlation for prediction of HETP values based upon a regression of their own data, plus that of Billet and Fractionation Research, Inc. [23]. This model indicates that the HETP value primarily is a function of surface tension and liquid viscosity. The flow parameter and vapor density also show minor influences. This correlation is applicable to systems with a liquid-phase surface tension above 4 dyne/cm and less than 36 dyne/cm and a liquid viscosity of at least 0.08 cps but not greater than 0.83 cps.

The Norton correlation for atmospheric pressure distillations is:

$$\ln \text{HETP} = n - 0.187 \ln \sigma + 0.213 \ln \mu \tag{6-20}$$

The data of Strigle and Porter give the relative HETP values for IMTP® packings, metal Pall ring packings, and ceramic Intalox® saddle packings of three different sizes [24]. Using these data, Table 6-2 has been prepared to give the values for n in Equation 6-20 for each of these packings. These predicted HETP values are based upon the use of high-performance column internals (as discussed in Chapter 9). However, a correction for the lambda effect must be applied to this calculated value if λ has a value > 1.8.

The HETP value used for final specification of packed depth should be based on the same vapor/liquid equilibrium, equation of state, and physical properties as used in the calculation of the required number of

Table 6 – 2
Constant for HETP Correlation
(Equation 6-20)

Tower Packing	Value of n
#25 IMTP® Packing	1.13080
#40 IMTP® Packing	1.31850
#50 IMTP® Packing	1.56860
1 in. Pall Ring	1.13080
1½ in. Pall Ring	1.35820
2 in. Pall Ring	1.65840
1 in. Intalox® Saddle	1.13080
1½ in. Intalox® Saddle	1.39020
2 in. Intalox® Saddle	1.72330

theoretical stages. For easy separations, less than 15 theoretical stages, a 20% design safety factor can be applied to a typical HETP value without severe economic penalty. For separations requiring 15 to 25 theoretical stages, a 15% design safety factor commonly is applied to the HETP value. For more difficult separations, the design HETP value used must be as precise as possible.

TYPICAL DESIGN EFFICIENCY

Packed columns maintain a high separation efficiency in both liquid-film-controlled and gas-film-controlled systems. For many years packed columns have been used for absorption systems that characteristically are liquid-film controlled. As an example, the HETP value for a trayed column might be twice as great in an absorption operation as compared to a distillation operation. For the same systems, the HETP value for IMTP® packing in the absorption operation typically would be only one-third greater than for the distillation operation.

In atmospheric distillations, the gas film many times offers a resistance to mass transfer similar to that of the liquid film. The vapor density is low providing a high molecular diffusion rate in that phase. The diffusion coefficient in the vapor phase at atmospheric pressure may be several orders of magnitude times that in the liquid phase. The liquid-phase resistance becomes increasingly important as the liquid viscosity increases, which reduces the diffusion rate in that phase. Also, there is a tendency for the liquid-film resistance to increase as the liquid molecular weight increases.

Table 6 – 3
Typical Separation Efficiency

IMTP® Packing Size	HETP (ft)
#25	1.2 to 1.6
#40	1.5 to 2.0
#50	1.8 to 2.5

Source: Strigle [25].

Table 6-3 gives the range of HETP values obtained with three sizes of IMTP® packing in typical distillation systems [25]. These values apply to systems with liquid surface tensions of 13 dyne/cm or greater and liquid viscosities of 0.70 cps or less. For liquids with lower surface tension or higher viscosity, the HETP value increases. However, the efficiency loss at higher liquid viscosities is much less for tower packings than for trays.

The values in Table 6-3 apply to paraffins, naphthenes, aromatics, alcohols, and ketones with molecular weights not greater than 100. These HETP values do not apply to systems with chemical reactions, chemical association, or high level ionization in the liquid phase. Values for such systems should be determined by commercial experience or from pilot plant data.

Tray efficiencies for 54 columns refining petroleum were reported by Drickamer and Bradford, which they correlated against feed viscosity [26]. This correlation contains data on systems having liquid viscosities from 0.07 cps to 0.50 cps. O'Connell produced a similar correlation which also included the effect of relative volatility [27]. From their correlations, the HETP for trays on 18-in. spacing increases by 50% to 75% for a change from a liquid viscosity of 0.15 cps to a viscosity of 0.44 cps. For the same viscosity change, the HETP value for random dumped tower packing would be only 25% higher at the greater viscosity than at the lower viscosity.

In many cases, for a trayed column which is being revamped with tower packing, the overall tray efficiency is known. In such cases, a correlation published by Dolan and Strigle has been used for a preliminary estimate of the design HETP value of the packing [28]. This correlation is shown in Figure 6-8.

If the sum of the mol fraction of light key plus the mol fraction of heavy key in the feed does not exceed the sum of the mol fractions of the two largest lighter-than-light key components plus the sum of the mol fractions of the two largest heavier-than-heavy key components, the designer should use caution in determining the design HETP value. In this case, the physical properties of the phases may not be representative of a binary separation of the light key and heavy key that provided the basis

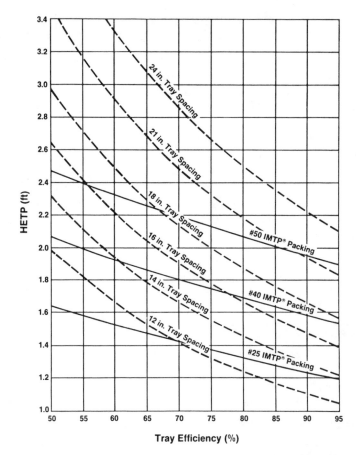

Figure 6-8. Relative efficiency of packing and trays. (From Dolan [28]. Reproduced by permission of the American Institute of Chemical Engineers.)

for determining the number of theoretical stages required or the design HETP value. It is possible to specify a minor light component to control bottoms product purity, or a minor heavy component to control distillate purity. The number of theoretical stages of separation required then must be calculated by a rigorous method, rather than by a pseudobinary procedure.

The concentration of components lighter than the light key in the distillate will be greater than the ratio of x_D/x_B for the light key. Likewise, the concentration of components heavier than the heavy key in the bottoms will be greater than the ratio of x_B/x_D for the heavy key. If the light key and the heavy key are not adjacent boiling compounds, the method developed by Geddes can be used to predict the distribution of intermediate boiling components at total reflux [29].

EFFECT OF LAMBDA ON EFFICIENCY

The values for HETP shown in Table 6-3 apply to systems with relative volatilities not greater than 2. From Equation 6-12, the value of the equilibrium curve slope (m) at constant relative volatility varies from α at very low light-key concentrations (x approaches zero) to $1/\alpha$ at very high light-key concentrations (x approaches unity).

In a feed consisting of an equal molar binary mixture, the lambda factor value for components of differing relative volatilities can be examined. In each case the distillate is assumed to be 90 mol % light component and the bottoms to contain 10 mol % light component. Table 6-4 gives the lambda factor values at total reflux for three different difficulties of separation. Note that the λ value deviates further from unity as α is increased.

Table 6 – 4
Lambda Factors at Total Reflux

	$\alpha = 1.20$	$\alpha = 1.60$	$\alpha = 2.00$
Top of Rectifying Section	0.862	0.675	0.554
Bottom of Rectifying Section	0.992	0.947	0.889
Average for Rectifying Section	0.928	0.811	0.721
Top of Stripping Section	0.992	0.947	0.889
Bottom of Stripping Section	1.153	1.424	1.653
Average for Stripping Section	1.073	1.185	1.271

Because commercial columns do not operate at total reflux, the same column as illustrated in Table 6-4 now will be operated at an external reflux ratio of 9 to 1. This reflux ratio is high enough to permit operation of a system with a relative volatility as low as 1.20. Table 6-5 gives the lambda factor values for this column at the same relative volatilities as listed in Table 6-4.

At a finite reflux ratio, the λ value in the rectifying section increases compared to total reflux because Lm/Gm for this section is less than unity. The value of λ in the stripping section is reduced because Lm/Gm is greater than unity in this section.

At λ values between 0.6 and 1.8, the HETP achieved is relatively insensitive to the lambda factor value [30]. At greater deviations of λ from unity, the HETP value increases. At very high values of λ, the HETP values can be almost twice those given in Table 6-3. Thus, the HETP for a methanol/water system at atmospheric pressure can increase from 1.33 ft at a λ value of about 1.5 to an HETP of 2.58 ft at a λ value of 4.6.

Table 6 – 5
Lambda Factors at 9:1 Reflux Ratio

	$\alpha = 1.20$	$\alpha = 1.60$	$\alpha = 2.00$
Top of Rectifying Section	0.958	0.750	0.616
Bottom of Rectifying Section	1.102	1.052	0.988
Average for Rectifying Section	1.030	0.901	0.802
Top of Stripping Section	0.902	0.861	0.808
Bottom of Stripping Section	1.048	1.294	1.503
Average for Stripping Section	0.975	1.078	1.155

For more difficult separations (α less than 1.4) the reflux ratio usually is high; therefore, the equilibrium curve slope (m) and the operating line slope Lm/Gm are of similar values. Because λ is close to unity, the normal HETP values may be used; and no correction is needed for the effect of λ to specify the required packed depth. However, for easy separations (α greater than 2.0), the designer normally should use low reflux ratios to keep λ close to unity. If high reflux ratios are used for such systems to obtain high purity products, the λ value drops in the rectifying section and increases in the stripping section. Under these conditions, the lambda factor can be important in determining the design HETP value for the specification of packed depth. For large values of λ, the equilibrium curve slope (m) is high. This indicates that the liquid film resistance is large, resulting in greater HETP values.

HIGH PURITY PRODUCTS

In high purity distillate production, any vapor bypassing results in increased heavy-key concentration in the distillate. To avoid excessive vapor wall flow, the packing size should be selected in accordance with Table 6-6. In such operations, it is important that the reflux distributor wet the top of the packed bed all the way to the column wall. Special measures must be used to ensure that the support ring for the liquid distribu-

Table 6 – 6
Maximum Packing Size

Column Diameter (in.)	Nominal Packing Size (in.)
12	1
18	1½
30	2
48	3½

tor or bed limiter does not interfere with the liquid irrigation pattern imposed on the packed bed top surface.

Likewise, in the production of a high-purity bottoms product, any liquid flowing down the wall that is not stripped by the rising vapor causes an increase of light-key concentration in the bottoms. In such cases it may be advisable to install wall wipers in the column's stripping section. These devices must be very carefully designed to avoid limiting column capacity. Where liquid wall flow is significant, individual packed bed depth should not exceed 10 column diameters. This rule only applies to small diameter columns (less than 42-in. ID).

Where high purity distillate ($x_{LK} > 0.995$) or high purity bottoms product ($x_{LK} < 0.005$) are specified, the temperatures within the column cannot be used to control the column operation. Composition changes do not cause any significant boiling temperature variation at this low impurity level. The product composition should be measured by an on-line analyzer for control of reflux ratio or reboiler duty. This same control problem occurs in the separation of mixtures involving three or more close-boiling components.

FEED POINT LOCATION

Improper feed point location may require more theoretical stages than calculated. For a binary system, the feed point is located where the feed liquid composition matches the downflowing liquid composition in the column. With a multicomponent feed, the theoretical stage that matches the light-key concentration in the feed probably will not match the heavy-key concentration. In such a case, the feed stage should be selected so that the ratio of light key to heavy key in the liquid feed is the same as the ratio in the downflowing liquid within the column.

If the column feed is vapor, then the foregoing guidelines apply to the location of the feed point with respect to matching the upflowing vapor within the column. If the feed is a vapor-and-liquid mixture, or a liquid that flashes on entering the column, special adaptors are added to the feed distributor to separate the vapor and liquid feed portions. In this case, the feed location should be selected based on the major molar flow (vapor or liquid) of the feed in the fully flashed condition.

In the revamp of existing trayed columns, the designer faces additional challenges because both column dimensions and locations of nozzles and manholes are fixed. In cases requiring a large number of theoretical stages, it often is possible to use one of the existing trayed column feed points because a mislocation of feed by only 5% or less of the total number of stages is not likely to have a significantly adverse effect on separation performance.

The suitability of the feed location should be evaluated by the effect it produces on the separation curve. This curve is a plot of separation factor against theoretical stages. The separation factor is defined as:

$$S_F = \log \frac{x_{LK}}{x_{HK}} \tag{6-21}$$

If the selected feed point location produces a region of little or no change in S_F, fewer theoretical stages may be required. If the S_F shows a reversal in the value near the feed stage, a new feed point location should be selected.

Table 6 - 7
Tray Support Rings

Column Diameter (in.)	Acceptable Ring Width (in.)	Excessive Ring Width (in.)
48	1¼	1⅝
72	1⅞	2⅜
96	2½	3¼
120	3⅛	4
144	3¾	4¾

Usually it is desirable to locate the packed beds so that the liquid distributors are accessible through the existing manholes. On new columns, an additional manhole may be located above the support plate to facilitate removal of the packed bed if necessary. Tower internals normally are supported on existing tray rings. These rings must be completed to provide full circumferential support of the tower internals if a liquid-tight seal is required. Tray support rings with an inside diameter that provides an open area of at least 90% of the column cross-sectional area usually need not be removed. Tray support rings with an inside diameter that provides an open area of 87% or less of the column cross-sectional area should be removed if the column is to operate near maximum capacity (see Table 6-7). Tray rings are removed by cutting or grinding so that no more than a 0.5-in. projection from the tower wall remains. Downcomer bolting bars should be removed if they interfere with the column internals or are of a size or shape that causes liquid flow diversion within the packed bed.

AZEOTROPIC DISTILLATION

Ordinary distillation cannot be used to separate azeotropes (constant boiling mixtures) and may not be practical for the separation of very close boiling components. Minimum boiling azeotropes have activity coefficients > than unity, while maximum boiling azeotropes have activity coefficients < unity. In azeotropic distillation, another component (entrainer) is added to the system. The entrainer must form a lower-boiling azeotrope with at least one of the feed components than the azeotrope formed by the components in the feed to be separated. The entrainer cannot be separated from the condensed overhead vapor by distillation; therefore, if possible, this azeotrope with the entrainer should form two liquid phases when the overhead vapor is condensed. In this way the entrainer is separated easily from the distillate so that it can be returned to the column as reflux. Alternately, if the distillate is a single liquid phase, the entrainer may be recovered by liquid extraction from the condensed overhead to permit its return to the azeotropic distillation column. The entrainer selected must be sufficiently volatile so that it can be stripped from the bottoms product to avoid its loss from the column and contamination of the bottoms liquid. The entrainer should not be too volatile because it must be present in large concentrations in the liquid phase.

Although the reflux usually is a single liquid phase, redistributors in the rectifying section may handle two liquid phases; therefore, special designs may be required for this service. Even in the distillation of some feed mixtures that do not form azeotropes, a low-boiling component can be vaporized in such quantity that it causes the remaining components to form two immiscible liquid phases. The presence of two liquid phases in the packed bed does not adversely affect packing capacity or efficiency. However, such an occurrence may cause the liquid phase to foam, producing a higher-than-calculated pressure drop. To maintain uniform liquid-phase composition when operating with two liquid phases in the column, liquid redistributors as well as the feed distributor require special designs.

EXTRACTIVE DISTILLATION

Another method for separating very close boiling components takes advantage of the chemical dissimilarity of the feed compounds. In extractive distillation, the other component (solvent) that is added to the column is a high-boiling liquid which alters the relative volatilities between feed components. The solvent normally is added to the distillation column above the feed point, while above the solvent feed point is a wash bed to which some of the liquid distillate is returned as reflux. This arrangement prevents any solvent vapor being carried overhead from the column which would represent a solvent loss from the system as well as contamination of the distillate product. The solvent feed distributor may require special design if the mixture of reflux and solvent feed either foams or flashes.

The solvent selected is distilled easily from the bottoms liquid because it normally has a boiling point 50°F to 100°F higher than the feed components to be separated. This solvent should be miscible in all proportions with the feed components at distillation temperatures. It should have great selectivity for altering the relative volatility between feed components. Because the bottom column temperature increases due to the higher solvent boiling point, the reboiler duty should be evaluated in solvent selection.

The presence of the solvent in the liquid phase flowing down the column materially changes the liquid properties. The designer must take account of these altered properties as well as the flow rates in hydraulic sizing calculations. Further, these altered properties may cause a reduction in separation efficiency (an increase in HETP) because of a liquid-phase resistance increase.

Extractive distillation usually is preferred over azeotropic distillation if both methods can be used to separate the feed components. The bulk of the solvent in extractive distillation is not vaporized in each cycle, as compared to azeotropic distillation where the entrainer is recovered from the overhead vapor stream. The energy input necessary to effect separation usually is lower for extractive distillation than for azeotropic distillation. Also, an extractive distillation column can operate over a wider range of pressures than an azeotropic distillation column since the azeotropic composition is a function of pressure. Finally, there usually is a wider choice of solvents than entrainers, thus enabling the designer to minimize added component cost.

EXAMPLE PROBLEM

A 6-ft 6-in. ID aromatics distillation column operates at a top pressure of 21.4 psia. The column feed consists of benzene through C-10 aromatics from a heavy naphtha reformer. It is desired to separate the toluene and lighter components from the xylenes and heavier aromatics.

The present column contains 60 actual valve trays on 20-in. spacing that develop 42 theoretical stages of separation. The feed to the column is 61,750 lb/h which produces 18,580 lb/h of distillate containing 0.40 wt % total xylenes and 43,170 lb/h of bottoms containing 0.25 wt % toluene. The feed is a superheated liquid that undergoes a 12 wt % flash on entering the column.

The reflux flow required with trays is 70,600 lb/h. Can this column be revamped with tower packing to increase its capacity? Will this tower packing provide a greater number of theoretical stages in order to reduce the reflux ratio and energy costs?

The analysis of the feed to the column is:

Component	Wt %
benzene	0.3
heptane	0.6
toluene	25.5
octane	4.2
p-xylene	9.9
m-xylene	26.7
o-xylene	19.2
nonane	1.3
indene	12.0
naphthalene	0.3

The mass transfer height available in the column is 102 ft from tray #1 to tray #60. A simulation of the present column operation indicates that the bottom of the rectifying section has a higher loading than the top of that section. Likewise, the bottom of the stripping section has a higher loading than the top of that section.

The use of #40 IMTP® packing will be considered to revamp this column. At the present feed rate to the trayed column, the flow parameter at the bottom of the rectifying section is:

$$X = \frac{2,180}{2,740} \left[\frac{0.235}{46.6} \right]^{0.5} = 0.0565$$

From Figure 6-6, the maximum standard C_s value for #40 IMTP® packing is 0.365 fps. After adjustment of the maximum capacity for system properties, the trayed column operating at a C_s of 0.231 fps is at only 66% of the maximum capacity of the #40 IMTP® packing.

Likewise, at the present rate, the flow parameter at the bottom of the stripping section is:

$$X = \frac{4,019}{2,718} \left[\frac{0.245}{46.2} \right]^{0.5} = 0.108$$

From Figure 6-6, the maximum standard C_s value for #40 IMTP® packing is 0.310 fps. Here the trayed column operating at a C_s of 0.225 fps is at 76% of the maximum capacity of #40 IMTP® packing after adjustment for system properties. Thus, a revamp with this packing can increase the trayed column capacity by 15% even if the efficiency is no greater.

This system gives an average HETP value of 1.68 ft for #40 IMTP® packing so that a design HETP of 1.90 ft provides an appropriate safety factor. The rectifying section can be packed to provide 25 theoretical stages of separation. The stripping section can provide 22 theoretical stages with #40 IMTP® packing. With the increase to 47 theoretical stages possible with the #40 IMTP® packing, the external reflux ratio can be lowered from 3.8 to 3.2 to produce the same separation.

Due to the lower reflux ratio, the vapor flows within the column are reduced substantially. The feed rate, after revamp with the #40 IMTP® packing, can be increased by 30%. The design will be checked at these higher rates.

If the reflux flow now is increased to 77,290 lb/h from 70,600 lb/h, the flow parameter at the bottom of the rectifying section is:

$$X = \frac{2,388}{3,116} \left[\frac{0.235}{46.6} \right]^{0.5} = 0.0544$$

From Figure 6-6, the maximum standard C_s value for #40 IMTP® packing is 0.368 fps. After adjustment of the maximum capacity for system physical properties, the #40 IMTP® packing will operate at 74% of its maximum capacity at the bottom of the rectifying section.

In the stripping section at the bottom the flow parameter is:

$$X = \frac{4,751}{3,060} \left[\frac{0.245}{46.2} \right]^{0.5} = 0.113$$

From Figure 6-6, the maximum standard C_s value for #40 IMTP® packing is 0.306 fps. The packed column will operate at 87% of the maximum capacity of #40 IMTP® packing at the bottom of the stripping section after adjustment for system properties.

Thus, a revamp of this column with #40 IMTP® packing can increase the feed capacity by 30% while still maintaining a 15% excess capacity allowance for operating variations. Further, the packed column will have a lower condenser duty and a lower reboiler duty per ton of feed than the presently trayed column.

NOTATION

A	Column cross-sectional area (ft^2)
a	Interfacial area (ft^2/ft^3)
C_s	Capacity factor (fps)
F_s	Vapor capacity factor ($lb^{0.5}/ft^{0.5} \cdot s$)
G	Gas mass velocity ($lb/ft^2 \cdot h$)
G^*	Gas mass velocity ($lb/ft^2 \cdot s$)
Gm	Gas-phase flow (lb-mol/h)
HETP	Height equivalent to a theoretical stage (ft)
H_G	Height of a gas-film transfer unit (ft)
H_L	Height of a liquid-film transfer unit (ft)
H_{OG}	Overall height of gas transfer unit (ft)
H_S	Standard HETP for a packing (ft)
K	Equilibrium ratio
K'	Equilibrium ratio for ideal liquid
k_G	Gas-film mass transfer coefficient ($lb\text{-}mol/h \cdot ft^2 \cdot atm$)
k_L	Liquid-film mass transfer coefficient ($lb\text{-}mol/h \cdot ft^2 \cdot mol/mol$)
L	Liquid mass velocity ($lb/ft^2 \cdot h$)
Lm	Liquid-phase flow (lb-mol/h)
m	Slope of equilibrium curve
P	Total system pressure (atm)
p	Partial pressure in gas phase (atm)
p^*	Vapor pressure of solute (atm)
S_F	Separation factor
T	Absolute temperature ($^\circ K$)
VLE	Vapor/liquid equilibrium
X	Flow parameter
x	Mol fraction in liquid phase
x_B	Mol fraction in bottoms liquid
x_D	Mol fraction in distillate liquid
x_{HK}	Mol fraction heavy key in liquid
x_{LK}	Mol fraction light key in liquid
y	Mol fraction in gas phase
α	Relative volatility
γ	Activity coefficient for liquid phase
λ	Lambda factor
μ	Liquid viscosity (cps)
ρ_G	Gas density (lb/ft^3)
ρ_L	Liquid density (lb/ft^3)

REFERENCES

1. Reid, R. C., Prausnitz, J. M., and Sherwood, T. K., "The Properties of Gases and Liquids," Appendix A, McGraw-Hill, 1977.
2. Van Laar, J. J., *Z. Phys Chemie,* Vol. 83, 1913, p. 599.
3. Wilson, G. M., *Journal of the American Chemical Society,* Vol. 86, 1964, p. 127.
4. Frendenslund, A., Jones, R. L., and Prausnitz, J. M., *American Institute of Chemical Engineers Journal,* Vol. 21, No. 6, 1975, p. 1086.
5. McCabe, W. L., and Thiele, E. W., *Industrial and Engineering Chemistry,* Vol. 17, 1925, p. 605.
6. Lewis, W. K., and Matheson, G. L., *Industrial and Engineering Chemistry,* Vol. 24, 1932, p. 494.
7. Thiele, E. W., and Geddes, R. L., *Industrial and Engineering Chemistry,* Vol. 25, 1933, p. 289.
8. Benedict, M., Webb, G. B., and Rubin, L. C., *Chemical Engineering Progress,* Vol. 47, No. 9, 1951, p. 449.
9. Cajander, B. C., Hipkin, H. G., and Lenoir, J. M., *Journal of Chemical Engineering Data,* Vol. 5, 1960, p. 251.
10. Soave, G., *Chemical Engineering Science,* Vol. 27, No. 6, 1972, p. 1197.
11. Peng, D. Y., and Robinson, D. B., *Industrial and Engineering Chemistry Fundamentals,* Vol. 15, 1976, p. 59.
12. Strigle, R. F., and Rukovena, F., *Chemical Engineering Progress,* Vol. 75, No. 3, 1979, p. 86.
13. Strigle, R. F., *Chemical Engineering Progress,* Vol. 81, No. 4, 1985, p. 67.
14. Leva, M., *Tower Packing and Packed Tower Design,* 2nd ed., United States Stoneware, Chap. 2, 1953, p. 35.
15. Kunesh, J. G., Lahm, L. L., and Yanagi, T., "Liquid Distribution Studies in Packed Beds," American Institute of Chemical Engineers Meeting, Nov. 1985.
16. Schmidt, R., *Institution of Chemical Engineers Symposium Series No. 56,* Vol. 2, 1979, p. 3.1/1.
17. Fair, J. R., *Petroleum/Chemical Engineering,* Vol. 33, No. 10, 1961, p. 45.
18. Eckert, J. S., and Walter, L. F., *Hydrocarbon Processing,* Vol. 43, No. 2, 1964, p. 107.
19. Vital, T. J., Grossel, S. S., and Olsen, P. I., *Hydrocarbon Processing,* Vol. 63, No. 12, 1984, p. 75.

20. Onda, K., Takeuchi, H., and Okumoto, Y., *Journal of Chemical Engineering, Japan,* Vol. 1, No. 1, 1968, p. 56.
21. Bolles, W. L., and Fair, J. R., *Institution of Chemical Engineers Symposium Series No. 56,* Vol. 2, 1979, p. 3.3/35.
22. Porter, K. E., and Jenkins, J. D., *Institution of Chemical Engineers Symposium Series No. 56,* Vol. 3, 1979, p. 75.
23. Billet, R., *Chemical Engineering Progress,* Vol. 63, No. 9, 1967, p. 53.
24. Strigle, R. F., and Porter, K. E., *Institution of Chemical Engineers Symposium Series No. 56,* Vol. 2, 1979, p. 3.3/19.
25. Strigle, R. F., and Dolan, M. J., *Canadian Process Equipment and Control News,* Oct. 1983, p. 82.
26. Drickamer, H. G., and Bradford, J. B., *Transactions of American Institute of Chemical Engineers,* Vol. 39, 1943, p. 319.
27. O'Connell, H. E., *Transactions of American Institute of Chemical Engineers,* Vol. 42, 1946, p. 741.
28. Dolan, M. J., and Strigle, R. F., *Chemical Engineering Progress,* Vol. 76, No. 11, 1980, p. 78.
29. Geddes, R. L., *American Institute of Chemical Engineers Journal,* Vol. 4, No. 4, 1958, p. 389.
30. Koshy, T. D., and Rukovena, F., *Hydrocarbon Processing,* Vol. 65, No. 5, 1986, p. 64.

7

VACUUM DISTILLATION

Distillations carried out at pressures less than 0.4 atm (300 mm Hg absolute) normally are considered as vacuum distillations from an equipment design viewpoint. Distillation commonly is carried out under vacuum to reduce the boiling temperature for one of these reasons:

1. The relative volatility between components generally increases as the boiling temperature drops. This higher relative volatility improves the ease of separation, which lowers the number of theoretical stages needed for a given separation. If the number of theoretical stages is held constant, the reflux ratio required for the same separation can be reduced. In addition, if the number of theoretical stages and the reflux ratio are maintained constant, product purity will be increased.
2. Lower distillation temperatures are desirable when processing thermally sensitive products. Lower bottoms temperatures retard undesirable reactions such as product decomposition, polymerization, or discoloration.
3. Separations can be achieved for components with very low vapor pressures or compounds that degrade at temperatures near their atmospheric boiling point.
4. Lower reboiler temperatures permit the use of less costly energy sources such as low pressure steam or hot water.

In the past, steam distillation has been used to reduce the partial pressure required of the feed components. They then can be vaporized at temperatures below their atmospheric boiling points. This type of distillation no longer is widely used because of these associated detrimental features:

1. Steam required is costly because several mols of steam usually are needed for each mol of feed component vaporized.

167

2. Presence of steam in the column usually increases the corrosion rate on commonly used metals.
3. Steam condensate, after separation of the distillate product, usually requires waste treatment before it can be discharged to the environment.

MAXIMUM CAPACITY OF PACKING

As distillation pressure drops, for the same vapor rate (C_s value), the mass flow of vapor is less than at atmospheric pressure. Therefore, at the same reflux ratio, the mass flow of liquid also is lower than for an atmospheric pressure distillation. Thus, liquid flow rates per unit of column cross-sectional area drop as the operating pressure is lowered.

The capacity of the fractionating device is determined both by its ability to handle high vapor velocities and by the pressure drop developed. Columns equipped with fractionating trays inherently produce a higher pressure drop than tower packings. This is so because the vapor not only must flow through an orifice restriction in the tray deck, but also it must bubble through some depth of liquid on that tray. In a packed column, the vapor only must overcome the aerodynamic flow resistance generated by the packing elements. Because liquid irrigation rates are low, the liquid holdup is small and the geometric void fraction of the dry packed bed only slightly reduced.

By revamping a trayed vacuum column with IMTP® packing, the pressure drop can be reduced by as much as 80%. This lower pressure drop can be used to reduce bottom column pressure and therefore the bottoms liquid temperature. In this case, the temperature difference driving force for heat transfer in the reboiler increases compared to a trayed column. For a new installation using a fixed heat source, the reboiler size is reduced. Alternately, the lower pressure drop can be used to increase the top column pressure. This option may permit the use of an air-cooled condenser rather than a water-cooled unit, with resultant operating cost savings. In any event, a higher top column pressure reduces the installed and operating costs of the vacuum producing system.

In vacuum distillations, massive entrainment of liquid upward in the vapor phase limits the maximum operational capacity (maximum C_s) since it reduces the separation efficiency. As long as the entrained liquid carried from the top of the packed bed into the condenser is of the same composition as the reflux liquid, the separation is not impaired. Thus, some entrainment in the operation of the column is acceptable and simply constitutes a recycle of liquid in addition to the usual reflux. The maximum operational C_s is the greatest vapor flow rate attained before loss of normal separation efficiency of the packing.

The maximum operational capacity of IMTP® packing can be obtained from Figure 6-6. In vacuum distillations the flow parameter (abscissa value) normally will be less than 0.04. In high-vacuum operations, the flow parameter can have a value less than 0.01. To produce a conservative design in this case, the maximum C_s, applicable to an abscissa value of 0.02, should be used for column sizing. Maximum operational capacity increases as the surface tension of the liquid phase to the 0.20 to 0.25 power. Such capacity increase is limited to a value of 8% greater than those from this chart, as surface tension reaches 29 dyne/cm or higher. Maximum operational capacity is a function of the liquid viscosity to the -0.10 to -0.13 power. This capacity reduction is limited to 13% less than the C_s values taken from this chart as the liquid viscosity at distillation temperature increases to 0.7 cps.

COLUMN DIAMETER SELECTION

Usually the top column pressure is set by the selection of the vacuum-producing equipment. In special cases involving thermally sensitive products, the bottom column pressure may be fixed by the maximum allowable product temperature. A pressure drop from top to bottom of the column is assumed for design purposes and this pressure drop is presumed constant for each theoretical stage. When the column pressure drop is greater than the absolute top column pressure, the usual design procedures may require some modification.

Feed composition and flow rate normally are known. Feed condition—temperature and pressure—must be determined carefully because a liquid feed may flash on entering a vacuum column. Feed enthalpy changes significantly with feed condition and this, in turn, affects the reboiler duty and the internal column vapor and liquid flow rates.

The distillate and bottoms specifications allow calculation of the required number of theoretical separation stages and the corresponding reflux ratios. (The procedures used are discussed in Chapter 6.) The assumed column pressure drop gives the design pressure drop per theoretical stage allowable for any reflux ratio. The minimum pressure drop per theoretical stage for random dumped tower packings is about 0.4 mm Hg, which is provided by IMTP® packing. This value gives the maximum number of theoretical stages that can be obtained with the specified pressure drop which fixes the lowest available operating reflux ratio. Normally, a vacuum column is operated at a C_s vapor rate no greater than 60% of the maximum operational C_s for the tower packing selected. The pressure drop at this vapor rate sets the minimum number of theoretical stages produced and fixes the highest usable operating reflux ratio.

After the operating reflux ratio is selected, the internal column flows can be calculated. Based on these flows, the column diameter is determined. The packed depth then is calculated from the number of theoretical stages required and the design HETP value for the packing to be used. Finally, the pressure drop for the entire column is calculated.

The generalized pressure drop correlation (Figure 1-15 or 1-16) gives the pressure drop for any flow parameter to a value as low as 0.005. Commercial experience has shown that at an absolute pressure of 75 mm Hg and lower, the pressure drop can be up to 20% less than the value given by these figures for the same C_s at a flow parameter value of 0.01. If the column pressure is 10 mm Hg absolute or less, the pressure drop can be up to 30% less than that taken from Figure 1-15 or 1-16 at an abscissa value of 0.01 and the same C_s value. Therefore, the generalized correlation always provides a conservative design pressure drop at column pressures less than 0.10 atm absolute. Additional design safety factors need not be applied to calculated values.

Because vapor density varies with absolute pressure, the pressure drop through the tower packing should be calculated at several column locations. Since ΔP is proportional to C_s^2 at low liquid rates, the C_s at any location is a function of $\Delta P^{0.5}$ at that point. Average C_s can be determined from the pressure drops calculated for the packing at the top and at the bottom of the bed. The overall pressure drop is the product of packed depth and pressure drop for the average C_s value. The average pressure drop through a packed bed is represented by:

$$\Delta P = [0.5\Delta P_T^{0.5} + 0.5\Delta P_B^{0.5}]^2 \tag{7-1}$$

The arithmetical average of the pressure drop at the tower top and the pressure drop at the tower bottom rather than Equation 7-1 may be used to calculate the overall pressure drop. This method only slightly overstates the pressure drop as long as the pressure drop at the top is less than 2.5 times the pressure drop at the bottom.

Due to the change in vapor density with absolute pressure, the pressure drop should be calculated separately for each packed bed. Total column pressure drop is the summation of the pressure drops through the packed beds plus the pressure drops through the tower internals. Overall column pressure drop determined this way must be compared with the pressure drop originally assumed. This procedure should be repeated by varying column diameter or packing size until the assumed and calculated pressure drops agree.

To reduce the number of iterations, it is suggested that the C_s value be calculated for the required pressure drop per theoretical stage at the average column pressure. The estimate of column diameter necessary for this C_s value usually is close to that generated by the final design solution.

In those cases where the column pressure drop exceeds the absolute top column pressure, special consideration must be given to the design. The pressure drop per theoretical stage no longer will be constant as the vapor density will be greatly different from top to bottom of the column. In such cases, it may be desirable to change column diameter to minimize the variation in pressure drop. The top of the column, which has the greatest vapor velocity due to the lowest vapor density, can be of larger diameter than the bottom of the column. However, it is not necessary to change the column diameter for each packed bed. Optimum column design may involve the use of a smaller packing size in the lower bed than is used in the upper bed of the same section. The smaller packing is more efficient and requires a lower height to produce the specified number of theoretical stages. Due to increased vapor density, the reduced C_s value in the lower bed permits use of the smaller packing size in the same column diameter. The pressure drop per theoretical stage may be nearly the same for this bed as for the bed above using larger size packing. Table 7-1 shows the performance of various packings at a pressure drop of 0.93 mm Hg per theoretical stage [1].

Table 7 - 1
Comparison of Packings
(0.93 mm Hg Pressure Drop per Theoretical Stage)

Packing	Relative Tower Diameter	Relative Packed Depth	Relative Packing Volume
2 in. Pall Rings	1.00	1.00	1.00
1½ in. Pall Rings	1.02	0.77	0.80
#50 IMTP® Packing	0.85	0.91	0.66
#40 IMTP® Packing	0.89	0.75	0.59
#25 IMTP® Packing	0.99	0.60	0.58
2 in. Intalox® Saddles	1.10	1.08	1.31
1½ in. Intalox® Saddles	1.15	0.81	1.07

Source: Strigle [1]. Reproduced by permission of the American Institute of Chemical Engineers.

At very low top column pressures, the vapor mass flow is lower for a given C_s value because of the low vapor density. Therefore, the mass flow of reflux liquid also is quite low. Although tower packing can be operated at very low liquid rates, especially in organic systems, the minimum liquid rate necessary to provide uniform irrigation of the packed bed top surface may be dictated by the liquid distribution system. The maximum column diameter thus is established for such a vacuum still. It especially is important in difficult separations, where the relative volatility is less than 1.4, that the liquid distributor provide a geometrically consistent distribution pattern. In addition, uniform liquid flow must be provided from each distribution point to produce a constant irrigation rate per square foot of column cross-sectional area. The typical standard liquid distributor can operate uniformly down to a liquid flow rate of about 90 gal/ft$^2 \cdot$ h. Specially designed distributors have been developed that produce uniform distribution at flow rates as low as 12 gal/ft$^2 \cdot$ h with liquids having a surface tension of 25 dyne/cm or less. Using large size packings should be considered as a way to reduce the column diameter. This increases the irrigation rate and permits operation within the capabilities of the liquid distribution system.

EFFICIENCY CONSIDERATIONS

As discussed in the preceding chapter, the relative volatility between components usually varies with the distillation temperature. Normally, the relative volatility increases as distillation pressure drops due to the accompanying reduction in boiling temperatures. In atmospheric distillations, the pressure drop through the column is such a small percentage of the pressure at the top of the column that it produces a negligible effect on the vapor/liquid equilibrium. In vacuum distillations requiring a large number of theoretical stages, the pressure at the column bottom can be significantly greater than at the top. For example, in a separation of cyclohexanone and cyclohexanol, the relative volatility between components can vary from 2.1 at the column top at 45 mm Hg absolute pressure down to a value of 1.5 at the bottom of a trayed column at 250 mm Hg absolute pressure. The resultant change in vapor/liquid equilibrium due to the increase in liquid temperature at the high pressure at the bottom of the column must be accounted for when calculating the required number of theoretical stages. If this is not done and the VLE applicable to the pressure at the top of the column is used for a calculation of the entire column, the number of theoretical stages required for the specific separation can be seriously underestimated. While such a modification of the VLE is a very arduous undertaking for manual calculations, it can be accomplished by computer, especially for ideal systems where the vapor pressure of the components can be expressed by simple equations. This separation is discussed in detail later in this chapter.

The tower packing efficiency in vacuum distillation need not be less than in distillation at atmospheric pressure. Typical values of HETP for IMTP® packing are given in Table 6-3. Diffusion in the vapor phase is quite rapid as long as this phase consists of the same components as the

liquid phase. Due to the reduced column pressure, the boiling temperature of the liquid phase is lower than at atmospheric pressure. This may
change the liquid physical properties significantly. In vacuum distillation, therefore, the liquid phase usually offers a substantial resistance to
mass transfer.

In particular, the liquid viscosity of many high-boiling organic materials tends to increase sharply at lower temperatures. This especially is
likely to occur if the liquid phase is approaching the solid transition temperature of one or more of the components. If the viscosity of the liquid
phase increases from 0.22 cps (common of many organic liquids at their
atmospheric boiling point) to 0.75 cps, the HETP value can increase by
30%. If the viscosity of the liquid increases to 1.5 cps (as occurs in some
vacuum distillations), the HETP will increase by 50% above the value
typical for atmospheric distillation. Table 7-2 shows the effect of liquid
viscosity on typical HETP values in distillations.

Table 7 - 2
Effect of Liquid Viscosity on Packing Efficiency

Liquid Viscosity (cps)	Relative HETP (%)
0.22	100
0.35	110
0.75	130
1.5	150
3.0	175

In the past, steam sometimes was added to the vapor phase for the
purpose of reducing the partial pressure of the organic material necessary to cause its vaporization. However, because the steam represents a
noncondensable inert vapor, it tends to increase the vapor phase resistance to mass transfer. Thus, the HETP may be higher for steam distillations than for distillations at lower absolute pressures. Further, adding
steam requires a capacity increase from the system producing the vacuum. The distillate also must be separated from the condensed water
and dried. With modern high capacity, low pressure drop packings, the
design trend is toward elimination of steam distillation and the use of a
lower absolute column pressure.

Condensers for vacuum towers often are operated at temperatures
substantially below the dew point of the overhead vapor from the column. This is done to reduce the vapor pressure above the liquid distillate and minimize its loss in the noncondensable inerts that must be
vented. The condenser must be operated above the solidification tem-

perature of any components present in the entering vapor which may require the use of tempered cooling water. If highly subcooled reflux is returned to the column, one additional theoretical stage should be added to the rectifying section to allow for reheating of the reflux liquid to its boiling temperature.

At very low column pressures, the pressure drop through a typical tube-and-shell condenser may be great enough to require unreasonably expensive vacuum-producing equipment. In these cases, an internal pumparound condensing bed, installed in the top of the column, should be considered instead of the more conventional external tubular condenser. This packed bed can be designed to operate at a pressure drop as low as 0.7 mm Hg. (The design of such a packed bed is described in detail in Chapter 5.)

PASTEURIZATION

In the distillation of products from naturally occurring raw materials the feed may contain a small percentage of very low-boiling compounds that are not desired in the distillate product. A separate column could be used to stabilize the feed by removal of these very low boilers before distillation in the main column. This stabilizer would require additional energy to operate the reboiler and condenser. However, it may be possible to install a pasteurization section at the top of the main column to remove these very low boilers.

As an example, consider a mixture of components ranging from C-12 to C-22 alcohols. (An analysis of the feed is given in Table 7-3.) The distillation is to recover at least 95% of the C-16 alcohol in the feed mixture; however, the product is to contain a minimum of 65 wt % C-16 alcohol and a maximum of 1.0 wt % C-12 alcohol.

Table 7 - 3
High Molecular Weight Alcohol Distillation

Alcohol	Feed (wt %)	Product (wt %)	Bottoms (wt %)
C-12	2.3	0.8	—
C-14	21.0	28.6	—
C-16	46.7	65.4	5.3
C-18	17.2	5.2	48.8
C-20	7.8	—	28.0
C-22	5.0	—	17.9

The feed enters such a column between the rectifying and stripping sections as a liquid. If 10,000 lb/h of feed were subjected to simple vacuum fractionation, the distillate product would contain all 230 lb of C-12 alcohol present in the feed. In a simple fractionation, therefore, the distillate contains 3.2 wt % C-12 alcohol, which does not meet the product specifications. The bottoms containing 5.3 wt % C-16 alcohol represents only a 3.2% loss of the C-16 alcohol in the feed.

However, another packed bed can be installed above the rectifying section as a pasteurization section to separate C-12 alcohol from C-16 alcohol. Because less than 4% of the feed is removed as distillate at the column top, the reflux liquid returned to the column is about 48 times this distillate flow. At this high reflux ratio in the pasteurizing bed, only a few theoretical stages are needed to make the desired separation.

Below the pasteurization section, the product is removed as a liquid sidedraw. This product contains only 0.8 wt % C-12 alcohol and represents 95.5% recovery of the C-16 alcohol present in the feed. The total energy input for the operation of this column is less than that required for a more conventional arrangement of two columns operated in series.

STYRENE PURIFICATION

Perhaps the largest scale application of vacuum distillation is the separation of ethyl benzene from styrene monomer. Such a column typically operates at a top pressure of 50 mm Hg absolute or higher so that the distillate may be condensed in an air cooler. The distillate primarily consists of ethyl benzene but also contains any water, benzene, and toluene present in the feed. This distillate also contains up to 5% styrene. The bottoms product is styrene monomer, purified to a specification of about 400 ppm ethyl benzene content. The bottoms product also contains some tars formed in the reactors and polymer which is present in the feed or formed in the distillation column. The bottoms product specification is fixed by market requirements; however, the styrene present in the distillate merely recycles through the dehydrogenation reactor.

The feed styrene is a reactive monomer that tends to polymerize in the stripping section of this column. Any styrene polymer formed in this recycle column is removed in the subsequent finishing column, thereby representing a loss of product that otherwise would be available for sale. This loss can be as high as 24 lb of styrene monomer per ton of styrene in the feed. The rate of polymerization is a function of time, temperature, and styrene concentration [2]. The concentration of styrene in the liquid phase of the column stripping section is fixed by the feed composition and the bottoms product specification. The liquid temperature in the column stripping section is a function of the pressure in that column section. Trayed columns usually are designed to restrict the styrene monomer bottoms product temperature to a maximum of 223°F to minimize polymer formation. By the use of IMTP® packing, the pressure drop can be reduced by 65% to 70%, compared to customary trays. At this lower bottom column pressure of only 104 mm Hg absolute, the temperature is about 182°F.

One of the properties of IMTP® packing is its very low liquid holdup characteristic. This feature provides about a 70% reduction in liquid retention time in the column stripping section with IMTP® packing as compared to a column equipped with trays. The lower stripping section temperatures and reduced liquid retention time prevent around 85% of the styrene polymerization that normally occurs in a trayed column. In addition, the free draining ability of IMTP® packing avoids any polymer buildup in the packed bed.

A typical trayed column design has a rectifying section that provides about 45% greater cross-sectional area than the stripping section. Because this column is designed to a pressure drop limitation, and IMTP® packing provides a very low pressure drop, a small packing size can be used to revamp a trayed column if no additional capacity is desired. Such a revamp increases the number of theoretical stages developed by almost 20% as compared to the trays. This permits a reduction in the operating reflux ratio that reduces the heat input required per ton of styrene product by 15% [3].

Obviously, a larger size of tower packing would provide a greater feed capacity when operated at the same reflux ratio as the trayed column. Such a revamped column still would provide the advantages of lower bottoms product temperature and reduced polymer formation. In addition, the bottoms liquid temperature of only 182°F does not require the use of high pressure steam as an energy source for the reboiler. The reduced product temperature allows the use of low pressure steam, generated by cooling the reactor effluent vapor, as a source of energy for the distillation column.

CAPROLACTAM MANUFACTURE

The manufacture of Nylon® 6 (trademark of E.I. DuPont DeNemours and Company) involves another large vacuum distillation application: the separation of cyclohexanone from cyclohexanol in the production of caprolactam. Such a column normally operates at a top pressure of 45 mm to 70 mm Hg absolute and usually is equipped with 70 to 80 actual trays. The distillate is cyclohexanone containing about 1,000 ppm cyclohexanol impurity, while the bottoms contains up to 4% cyclohexanone. Such a trayed column typically uses an external reflux ratio of 7.2 [3]. The distillate specification is fixed; however the cyclohexanone present in the bottoms is recycled back through the reaction system. The feed contains some high molecular weight reaction products, which are separated from the bottoms liquid in a subsequent vacuum still before recycling the cyclohexanol.

A typical trayed column develops a pressure drop of 190 mm to 250 mm Hg. This system changes relative volatility significantly with temperature. At the column top with a pressure of 45 mm Hg absolute, the relative volatility between cyclohexanone and cyclohexanol is 2.1. At the bottom of the trayed column, with a pressure of 250 mm Hg absolute, the relative volatility is reduced to 1.5. It is apparent that the difficulty of separation increases rapidly at higher temperatures. Therefore, the higher the operating pressure, the larger the number of theoretical stages required at any fixed reflux ratio. Additional trays in the column become less and less effective due to the reduction in relative volatility because the resultant increased column pressure raises the boiling temperature.

Strigle et al. have published the results of a pilot plant test on this system which indicates #25 IMTP® packing provides an HETP value of 21 in. throughout its operating range [4]. The pressure drop varies with the vapor rate, which is influenced by the reflux ratio. In turn, the required reflux ratio for a fixed number of theoretical stages is controlled by a relative volatility. To study the effect of revamping such a sieve tray column with #25 IMTP® packing, a computer model was used. This study showed that when the column is revamped with IMTP® packing, the pressure drop at the same feed rate is only 20% of that produced by 76 sieve trays. The absolute pressure at the bottom of the packed column is 115 mm Hg, compared to 298 mm Hg at the bottom of the trayed column. The relative volatility at the bottom of the packed column has increased to almost 1.7 from a value of only 1.4 with the trays. The increase in average relative volatility permits a 40% reduction in reflux flow. This means a 35% reduction in condenser load through the use of IMTP® packing, as compared to the trayed column.

Fringe benefits from the use of a packed column include a lower temperature at the bottom of the column. This reduces the formation of polymeric material that must be separated from the cyclohexanol. The loss of raw material and subsequent tar disposal problems, therefore, are minimized.

DIMETHYL TEREPHTHALATE PURIFICATION

DMT is produced by oxidation of p-xylene followed by esterification with excess methanol. In some processes, the oxidation and esterification are carried out stepwise with p-toluic acid and methyl p-toluate as intermediate products. The DMT must be purified to polymer grade by a combination of distillation and crystallization. The most difficult separation involves a vacuum distillation of dimethyl terephthalate from monomethyl terephthalate. Under consideration is a typical DMT distillation column operating at a top column pressure of 40 mm Hg absolute and containing 30 actual trays that each develop a pressure drop of 4 mm Hg. This column operates at a bottom pressure of 160 mm Hg absolute and a temperature of 457°F. The reboiler is heated by 600 psig saturated steam that has a temperature of 489°F. Overhead vapor, at a temperature of 352°F, goes through an air-cooled condenser. The reflux liquid returns to the column subcooled by almost 50°F.

This column could be revamped using #40 IMTP® packing, which would reduce the pressure drop at the same capacity by 70%, as compared to the 30 trays. However, the very low pressure drop of this packing can be used to reduce the plant energy consumption because the system relative volatility is constant throughout a pressure range of 40 mm to 160 mm Hg. Rather than lower the pressure at the bottom of the column, the pressure at the top of the column could be increased to 120 mm Hg absolute. The result would be an increase in the temperature at the top of the column to 414°F. Such an arrangement permits installation of a low-pressure steam generator to act as a condenser for the overhead vapor. Thus, 100 psig saturated steam at 338°F can be generated by the column. Such steam can be used for general purpose, low grade process applications, or it can be reduced in pressure for space heating purposes.

GLYCOL SEPARATION

In the manufacture of ethylene glycol, product separation is accomplished by vacuum distillations. The glycol mixture first is dehydrated, then the MEG is recovered from the higher glycols. In commercial practice, the monoethylene glycol separation from higher glycols is carried out in two columns operated in series. The pressure at the bottom of the column is limited to 165 mm Hg absolute by the boiling temperature necessary to avoid product degradation. Each column typically operates at a top pressure of 50 mm Hg absolute and contains 33 actual trays. Each of these trayed columns has a reboiler and a condenser that consume significant amounts of energy.

The low pressure drop available with #50 IMTP® packing reduces the pressure drop to only 34 mm Hg per column at the same flow rates. Such a tower revamp permits the use of two columns in series with only one reboiler and one condenser. This reduces the overall energy consumption by 50%. Further, the vertical height available in these towers, if revamped with #40 IMTP® packing, provides an almost 30% increase in the number of theoretical stages available as compared to the trays. Even with this smaller size packing, total pressure drop through both columns in series is only 90 mm Hg. However, this increase in theoretical stages also can reduce the required reflux flow by almost 15%. A significant reduction in the energy requirement thus is possible for this distillation.

The low pressure drop of IMTP® packing, as compared to trays, provides a capital cost savings as well as an operating cost savings. A capital cost saving can be realized by using only one column shell for the complete separation. Such a design permits the column to operate at a top pressure of 85 mm Hg absolute and still have a bottom pressure of only 153 mm Hg absolute. Not only is the one column and one foundation less costly than two towers, but the additional pumps, piping, and controls are eliminated. In addition, the overhead vapor temperature is more than 20°F hotter, due to the higher pressure at the top of the column while the bottom column temperature is reduced slightly because the pressure has been lowered from 165 mm Hg. Therefore, both the condenser heat exchange surface and the vacuum-producing equipment can be smaller and less costly, as compared to that required for the trayed columns previously used.

HIGH VACUUM DISTILLATION

Vacuum stills for naturally occurring products, such as fatty acids, vegetable oils, and ester fragrances, typically handle a feed that consists of a homologous series of compounds. These distillations are carried out at pressures below 25 mm. Hg absolute at the top of the column for the high molecular weight materials. Pressure drop is severely restricted because the thermal stability of the bottoms products limits column pressure at the bottom. In most cases, a repeated number of distillations is required to obtain product of the purity desired. The first distillation normally removes undesirable low-boiling impurities. Then, a second distillation separates the desired product from a high-boiling residue.

Such a column previously employed trays and was designed from a low-pressure drop restriction; thus, the required column diameter was large. Because the tray efficiency is rather low in these high molecular weight systems, tower packings can be used to revamp such systems with significant advantages. The pressure drop of IMTP® packing is so low that a small size packing can be used to meet the hydraulic capacity required, as well as the pressure drop limitation. This size packing provides at least 50% more theoretical stages of separation than the typical trays in the same mass transfer height. These additional theoretical stages permit recovery of the desired product and separation of low-boiling impurities in one distillation operation. Not only does such a revamp reduce energy costs, but product purity is better than that previously obtained with trays. There is less decomposition of the products as a result of lower liquid residence time as well as reduced temperature at the bottom of the column. In addition, the distillation system capacity increases because double distillation no longer is required.

In the past, some columns have been equipped with grids to obtain a low pressure drop. Although the grid has a very low pressure drop, it is quite inefficient as a fractionating device. Therefore, the actual pressure drop per theoretical stage of separation is 60% greater for the grid than for #50 IMTP® packing. Further, the grid requires over twice the mass transfer height as this packing which means a higher column shell.

HEAT SENSITIVE MATERIALS

Packed columns are favored in the distillation of thermally unstable materials such as cumene hydroperoxide, acrylic monomers, diisocyanates, tall oil, and terpenes. Top column pressures below 5 mm Hg absolute frequently are not used because of the high operating and capital costs of the vacuum-producing equipment. Thus, it may be necessary to develop a pressure drop in the range of only 0.5 to 0.8 mm Hg per theoretical stage of separation. This minimizes the pressure and temperature at the bottom of the column to avoid product degradation. Fortunately, in many cases, only a few theoretical stages are required so the total pressure drop through the column is only 5 to 10 mm Hg.

The vapor velocity at the column top may be 50% greater than that at the bottom due to the difference in absolute pressure affecting the vapor density. Usually the column size is determined by the loadings at the top of the packing. However, diameter selection must be done carefully. The liquid flow rates may be so low that excessive hydraulic safety factors will lead to problems in liquid distributor design.

Most chemical changes in products are responses to temperature, time, and reactant concentration. In addition to lowering the temperature, packed columns also greatly reduce the liquid residence time in the fractionator. Average liquid residence time in a column is determined by dividing the total liquid holdup by the volumetric liquid flow rate. In a vacuum fractionator, revamped with #40 IMTP® packing, the liquid residence time may be only 30% of that experienced with the trays [5]. Even though the concentration profile in the column remains unchanged, because of product specifications, the amount of product degradation can be reduced by 85% as compared to a trayed column in typical applications.

When handling highly flammable or toxic liquids, local laws may regulate the amount of material that can be contained in a single vessel. In these cases, packed columns of much larger dimensions than trayed columns can be installed. They still can comply with such regulations because of greatly reduced liquid holdup of the packing per unit volume. Further, metal packings have been used as flame arresters because of their high surface area and low vapor flow resistance.

In summary, it has been demonstrated that packed columns should be the first choice for vacuum distillation operations. Such a service normally involves a column design restricted by the allowable pressure drop for the number of theoretical stages necessary to produce the specified product. Inherently, modern packed columns always provide a lower pressure drop than a trayed column designed to perform the same function.

EXAMPLE PROBLEM

There is a 54-in. ID column separating a mixture of C-12 through C-26 linear alpha olefins. The column contains 26 valve trays on 24-in. spacing and operates at a top pressure of 72 mm Hg. The feed is a liquid of the following composition that enters the column at a rate of 7,250 lb/h and is subcooled by 8°F.

Component	Feed	Distillate	Bottoms
(alpha olefin)	(mol %)	(mol %)	(mol %)
C-12	24.4	33.2	—
C-14	16.9	23.0	—
C-16	11.5	15.5	—
C-18	8.6	11.6	—
C-20	5.0	6.8	—
C-22	11.1	6.6	23.7
C-24	12.4	3.3	37.7
C-26	10.1	—	38.6

Because recovery of all the C-20 and lighter alpha olefins in the feed is desired, the distillate product rate is fixed at 4,640 lb/h. To assist stripping the lighter components, steam is added to the reboiler so that the overhead vapor contains 3.55 mol of steam per mol of hydrocarbon. The distillate and bottoms analyses are shown in the preceding table. All analyses in this table are on a water-free basis.

The overall tray efficiency is 60% so that the present trays are providing 15 to 16 theoretical stages of separation. The vertical height from tray #1 to tray #26 is 51 ft 6 in. Can tower packing be installed to increase the column capacity by at least 40% without losing separating efficiency?

A possible revamp with #50 IMTP® packing will be examined. The design HETP for this packing equivalent to 60% tray efficiency is 2.7 ft. To replace 17 actual trays in the rectifying section requires a 27.5-ft-deep bed of #50 IMTP® packing. To replace 9 actual trays in the stripping section requires a 14.5-ft-deep packed bed. Because sufficient height is available to accommodate this size packing, the column can continue to operate at the present external reflux ratio of 0.55 on a water-free condensate basis. Therefore, the capacity of the #50 IMTP® packed column will be determined.

The flow parameter at the top of the column at the present rates is:

$$X = \frac{2,552}{9,324} \left[\frac{0.00947}{47.6} \right]^{0.5} = 0.00386$$

The maximum standard C_s value from Figure 6-6 is 0.475 fps at a flow parameter as high as 0.020 for #50 IMTP® packing. After adjustment for physical properties, the design C_s for this packing at the top of the column could be as great as 0.349 fps.

The present C_s for the trayed column at the top is only 0.243 fps. Thus, the column capacity could be increased by 44% over the present rates after a revamp with #50 IMTP® packing.

The flow parameter at the top of the column still has a value of 0.00386 at these higher rates. The ordinate value for Figure 1-16 is now:

$$Y = 0.349 \, (18)^{0.5}(0.66)^{0.05} = 1.45$$

The pressure drop for #50 IMTP® packing at the top of the column is 0.42 in. H_2O/ft at these higher flow rates and a flow parameter of 0.005.

The flow parameter at the bottom of the column at the higher rates is:

$$X = \frac{14,440}{13,750} \left[\frac{0.0135}{42.5} \right]^{0.5} = 0.0187$$

At 44% higher flow rates, the C_s at the bottom of the column is 0.317 fps. The ordinate value for Figure 1-16 is:

$$Y = 0.317 \ (18)^{0.5}(0.68)^{0.05} = 1.32$$

The pressure drop for #50 IMTP® packing at the bottom of the column is 0.40 in. H_2O/ft of packed depth.

Thus, the #50 IMTP® packing can revamp the trayed column to obtain a 44% increase in capacity at the same separation efficiency. The total pressure drop through the packed column is only 37 mm Hg, even at a 44% higher feed rate. This is only about one-half the pressure drop through the 26 valve trays at the present lower flow rates. Further, the reduced pressure at the bottom of the column enhances the stripping action and lowers the bottom column temperature.

NOTATION

C_s	Capacity factor (fps)
HETP	Height equivalent to a theoretical stage (ft)
VLE	Vapor/liquid equilibrium
X	Flow parameter
ΔP	Pressure drop (in. H_2O/ft)
ΔP_T	Pressure drop at top (in. H_2O/ft)
ΔP_B	Pressure drop at bottom (in. H_2O/ft)

REFERENCES

1. Strigle, R. F., and Rukovena, F., *Chemical Engineering Progress,* Vol. 75, No. 3, 1979, p. 86.
2. Boundy, R. H., and Boyer, R. F., "Styrene, Its Polymers, Copolymers, and Derivatives," Reinhold Publishing, 1952.
3. Murthy, A., and Zudkevitch, D., *Institution of Chemical Engineers Symposium Series,* Vol. 1, No. 56, 1979, p. 1.1/51.
4. Strigle, R. F., Rukovena, F., and Koshy, T. D., *Informations Chimie,* Vol. 243, No. 11, 1983, p. 231.
5. Strigle, R. F., and Perry, D. A., *Hydrocarbon Processing,* Vol. 60, No. 2, 1981, p. 103.

8

PRESSURE DISTILLATION

Distillation usually is carried out under pressure to permit condensation of low-boiling materials at ambient temperatures. Propylene and ethylene of polymer grade have been distilled at pressures as low as 4 atm and 6 atm absolute respectively; however, the condenser must be operated at temperatures of $+10°F$ for propylene and $-90°F$ for ethylene. This latter very low temperature level will be produced by a costly refrigeration system. Propylene usually is distilled at a pressure of at least 16 atm so that the condenser can be cooled with water. Ethylene normally is distilled at a pressure of about 20 atm which permits operation of the condenser at a temperature of $-20°F$ and allows the use of less expensive propane or ammonia refrigeration.

Very low-boiling hydrocarbons, such as methane, normally are distilled at pressures of about 70% of their critical pressure. Of course, all distillations must be carried out below critical temperature in order to provide liquid reflux. Ethylene and ethane usually are distilled at 40% to 55% of critical pressure while propylene and propane are distilled at 35% to 50% of critical pressure. Hydrocarbons in the C-4 and C-5 range normally are distilled at pressures up to 20% of critical. Higher hydrocarbons are distilled at pressures up to 25 psig simply to ensure complete condensation of the overhead vapor. These latter operations usually are considered atmospheric distillations. High molecular weight organic chemical compounds (which have atmospheric boiling points in excess of 320°F) normally are distilled under vacuum. However, refining of petroleum will involve atmospheric pressure distillations for hydrocarbons with boiling points above 600°F.

As discussed in Chapter 6, the relative volatility in general will decrease as the pressure, and therefore boiling temperature, is increased. Since separation becomes more difficult with reduced relative volatility, the number of theoretical stages required is greater for the same separation at higher pressures. Even though the capacity of a column increases

184

at higher pressure due to the greater vapor density, the number of theoretical stages or the reflux ratio required also will be greater. Usually a distillation column should be designed at the lowest operating pressure which is economically feasible.

CHARACTERISTICS OF PACKINGS AND TRAYS

Modern tower packings provide a much lower pressure drop per theoretical stage than trays, thus packed columns have been accepted readily for vacuum separations. As the operating pressure is increased, pressure drop becomes less important as a basis for selection of the fractionation device. Therefore, we will examine the other characteristics of both packings and trays to ascertain the potential applications for tower packings in high-pressure distillations.

As the distillation pressure is increased, the vapor density increases. When critical pressure is approached, the compressibility factor of a saturated vapor usually has a value less than 0.75. Thus the density of the gas phase is quite high at pressures greater than 40% of critical. As the operating pressure is increased for the same C_s value, the mass flow of vapor will be much greater than at atmospheric pressure because of the high vapor density; while at the same reflux ratio, the mass flow of liquid also will be greater than for an atmospheric distillation. Therefore, liquid flow rates per unit of column cross-sectional area will be higher as operating pressure increases. The capacity of the fractionating device at high pressure may be dependent on its ability to handle these high liquid flow rates.

In a trayed column, the tower cross-sectional area is the sum of the active area plus the areas of the downcomer transferring liquid to the tray below and the downcomer receiving liquid from the tray above. The active area required for trays (in which the vapor bubbles through the liquid phase) usually is determined by the vapor flow rate. The downcomer handles a mixture of froth, aerated liquid, and clear liquid. The downcomer area required for trays not only increases with liquid flow rate, but also with the difficulty in achieving separation between the vapor and the liquid phases. The volume required for the downcomer (downcomer residence time) increases at a lower surface tension and a smaller density difference between vapor and liquid. Because of the large downcomer area required to handle the high liquid flow rates typical of high-pressure distillations, a trayed column cross-sectional area may be 40% to 80% greater than the active tray area calculated from the vapor flow rates for such distillations. Thus, the downcomer area becomes a significant factor in the determination of the diameter of a trayed column.

A packed column does not have a fixed geometry like a trayed column in which a percentage of column cross-sectional area is assigned to the active area handling only vapor flow and another portion to the downcomer area handling only liquid flow. The packed column can use any part of the cross-sectional area for the flow of either phase provided the sum of the vapor and liquid flow areas required does not exceed the total column cross-sectional area. Thus, the revamp of a trayed high-pressure fractionator with IMTP® packing often can increase column capacity by 25% while achieving the same separation into distillate and bottoms products [1].

MAXIMUM COLUMN CAPACITY

For atmospheric pressure or vacuum distillations, the vapor flow rate is limited by the entrainment of liquid upward in the vapor phase. The amount of entrainment increases rapidly above a threshold C_s value for the particular system. As the vapor flow rate is increased further, the mass of entrained liquid becomes sufficient to reduce the concentration profile established in the column. The maximum operational C_s has been defined as the greatest vapor flow rate attained before loss of normal separation efficiency. Figure 6-6 gives a correlation which predicts the maximum operational C_s for three sizes of IMTP® packing as limited by liquid entrainment.

Table 8-1 gives the pressure drop in inches of operating fluid per foot of packed depth at the maximum operational C_s as determined at atmospheric pressure [2]. The system tested was iso-octane and toluene at total reflux. The maximum usable hydraulic capacity seems to occur at a pressure drop of about 2.4 in. of fluid per foot for high-capacity, saddle, and ring types of packings. Below the loading region of the packing (as

Table 8 – 1
Pressure Drop at Maximum Operational Capacity

Packing	Maximum Operational C_s (fps)	Pressure Drop (in. fluid/ft)
#50 IMTP® Packing	0.345	1.29
#40 IMTP® Packing	0.310	1.45
#25 IMTP® Packing	0.278	2.37
2 in. Metal Pall Rings	0.315	1.89
1½ in. Metal Pall Rings	0.287	2.17
2 in. Ceramic Intalox® Saddles	0.279	2.55
1½ in. Ceramic Intalox® Saddles	0.237	2.75

Source: Strigle [2]. Reproduced by permission of the American Institute of Chemical Engineers.

described in Chapter 6), the pressure drop will increase as at least the square of the vapor flow rate [3]. At higher rates, as the column loading approaches the hydraulic limit, pressure drop increases much faster than the second power of the vapor rate. In high-pressure operations, the usable hydraulic capacity of the tower packing may be reached because of excessive liquid holdup before the maximum operational C_s is attained [4].

The operating holdup of liquid in a packed bed has been shown to increase as the liquid flow rate to the 0.57 power [5]. Below the loading region, the liquid holdup is not greatly influenced by the vapor rate (see Chapter 1). As the vapor rate is increased above a pressure drop of about 0.6 in. fluid/ft, the downward flow of liquid is retarded by the upward flow of vapor thereby increasing liquid holdup in the packed bed.

The amount of operating liquid holdup in a packed bed is influenced by the density of the continuous vapor phase. The apparent density of the liquid in the tower is the true liquid density less the actual vapor density even when there is no aeration of the liquid phase. This buoyancy effect normally is imperceptible at atmospheric pressure since the density of the vapor is only about 0.5% of the liquid density; but at higher pressures this effect becomes significant.

In light hydrocarbon systems, the surface tension of the liquid phase can be less than 6 dyne/cm at the temperatures encountered in high-pressure fractionators. Some high density vapor is dispersed into a liquid phase of low surface tension. This aeration of the liquid tends to increase as the surface tension of the liquid becomes lower and as the vapor density increases. Thus, the higher the pressure of operation of a specific system, the greater will be the quantity of vapor dispersed in the liquid phase. Also, the higher the operating pressure the smaller will be the size of the dispersed vapor bubbles in the liquid phase. This aeration of liquid reduces the effective liquid density, thus the volume occupied by a given mass of liquid is increased even further. The aeration factor is the ratio of aerated liquid density to clear liquid density. For atmospheric pressure distillations of nonfoaming liquids, the aeration factor normally is not less than 0.9. In light hydrocarbon fractionators operating at 35% of critical pressure, the aeration factor may be as low as 0.7.

From kinetic theory, the viscosity of a gas should be independent of pressure from 60 mm Hg to about 6 atm pressure, but it should increase as the 0.5 power of the absolute temperature. Experimental data confirm this increase in viscosity occurs to about the 0.7 power of the absolute temperature for fixed gases; however, gas mixtures containing more than 25% hydrogen exhibit unusual viscosity characteristics. In systems of light hydrocarbons (methane through pentane), the vapor viscosity increases more rapidly with temperature than for fixed gases.

Since liquid viscosity decreases with increasing temperature produced by higher pressures of distillation and the vapor viscosity increases with temperature, the viscosities of the two phases tend to approach each other in high pressure fractionators. For C-4 or C-5 hydrocarbon fractionators, the vapor viscosity will be only 6% of the liquid viscosity. In C-2 or C-3 hydrocarbon fractionators, the vapor viscosity is about 11% of the liquid viscosity. In distillations involving methane, the vapor viscosity can be 35% of the liquid viscosity.

The high ratio of vapor density to liquid density, the low values of the aeration factor for the liquid phase, and the high ratio of phase viscosities all tend to increase the volume of liquid holdup in a packed bed. As the liquid holdup increases, the void fraction in the packed bed becomes lower with a resultant increase in pressure drop.

PRESSURE-DROP CONSIDERATIONS

The pressure drop for high-pressure distillations of light hydrocarbons in commercial columns has been found to be over twice that predicted from the generalized correlation (Figure 1-15 or Figure 1-16). For distillations in which the vapor density is at least 6% of the liquid density, the observed pressure drop is given by the following empirical equation:

$$\Delta P = \frac{33\ F^{0.5}}{\sigma}\ C_s^{2.4} \tag{8-1}$$

In Equation 8-1 the C_s is in fps and the surface tension in dyne/cm so that the pressure drop will be given in in. H_2O/ft of packed depth. The packing factor for various packings is given in Table 1-3.

As shown in Table 8-1, the pressure drop is greater for small-size packings than for larger packings of the same type at the maximum operational C_s. This leads to the conclusion that in actual operation the total void fraction in a bed of small-size packing must be less than in a bed of larger-size packing. These values of C_s from Table 8-1 were used in the preparation of Figure 6-6 with corrections to the C_s values to adjust them to a liquid surface tension of 20 dyne/cm and a liquid viscosity of 0.20 cps. Table 8-2 gives the void fractions of the packings themselves. This table shows that the void fraction does not vary significantly by size for the same type of packing. Therefore, increased liquid holdup must be responsible for the apparent reduction of void space in a bed of small-size packing. The use of a larger-size packing will minimize the possibility of reaching maximum usable hydraulic capacity as determined by excessive liquid holdup before reaching maximum operational capacity as determined by liquid entrainment.

Table 8 – 2
Void Fractions of Tower Packings

Packing	Void Fraction
#50 IMTP® Packing	0.977
#40 IMTP® Packing	0.971
#25 IMTP® Packing	0.962
2 in. Metal Pall Rings	0.965
1½ in. Metal Pall Rings	0.956
1 in. Metal Pall Rings	0.942
2 in. Ceramic Intalox® Saddles	0.748
1½ in. Ceramic Intalox® Saddles	0.734
1 in. Ceramic Intalox® Saddles	0.721

Table 8 - 3
Pressure Drop as a Function of Column Loading

Packing	Pressure Drop at Maximum Efficiency (in. fluid/ft)	Pressure Drop at Onset of Loading Region (in. fluid/ft)
#50 IMTP® Packing	0.76	0.32
#40 IMTP® Packing	0.88	0.38
#25 IMTP® Packing	1.41	0.60
2 in. Metal Pall Rings	1.19	0.53
1½ in. Metal Pall Rings	1.39	0.60
2 in. Ceramic Intalox® Saddles	1.41	0.59
1½ in. Ceramic Intalox® Saddles	1.60	0.80

Table 8-3 shows the pressure drop for the same system as Table 8-1 at the maximum efficiency C_s (minimum HETP value) and at the onset of the loading region of the packing [6]. Note that the pressure-drops are the same for 2-in. ceramic Intalox® saddles, 1½-in. metal Pall rings, and #25 IMTP® packing at equivalent rates. A generalized pressure-drop equation would indicate that all three packings have nearly the same total void fraction in the operating packed bed.

SELECTION OF COLUMN DIAMETER

Because of the high cost of the vessel shell needed for high-pressure operation, the design of such a column should be approached in a conservative manner. The recommended correlation has been developed from data on organic systems in distillation operations. Because of the limited amount of high-pressure data available, the correlation in this area may not be as accurate as at lower operating pressures. The following procedure has been used for the design of several hundred high-pressure distillation columns. It is possible that operation of high-pressure columns in aqueous systems or with nonboiling liquids could be carried out at higher rates than suggested by this method.

The recommended design procedure utilizes a design vapor rate (C_s) which is a percentage of the maximum operational capacity of the packing, as determined from Figure 6-6. This maximum C_s value must be adjusted for the effect of liquid viscosity and surface tension. The maximum operational capacity of the tower packing, as shown in Figure 6-6, varies as the 0.20 to 0.25 power of the surface tension of the liquid phase. This effect does not increase the capacity beyond that which applies to liquids of 29 dyne/cm surface tension. The holdup in the packed bed will be a function of liquid viscosity, although high liquid viscosity normally is not a limiting factor in high pressure distillations. Capacity of a packing is increased as the reciprocal of liquid viscosity to the 0.10 to 0.13 power. This capacity increase is limited liquid viscosities not less than 0.09 cps.

If a trayed column in high pressure service does not have sufficient downcomer residence time to clarify the liquid phase, the vapor/liquid mixture will be carried down to the next lower tray. This recycling of vapor lowers the capacity as well as the separation efficiency of the trays. Conditions which prevent rapid disengagement of vapor and liquid in a tray downcomer are high liquid viscosity, low surface tension, and a small density difference between liquid and vapor. Also, any tendency for the liquid to foam will increase the downcomer residence time required.

In a packed column, the hydraulic capacity will be restricted as the liquid holdup volume increases. Eventually local gas velocity will become sufficient for the vapor to entrain liquid upward because of the reduction of total void fraction in the packed bed. This entrainment will result in a lower degree of separation produced by the column. A packed column does not suffer reduction in capacity in a foaming system to nearly the extent exhibited by a trayed column. The presence of a foaming liquid, however, will raise the pressure drop compared to a nonfoaming system.

A design C_s should be selected that provides the added capacity necessary for fluctuations in normal column operation as well as temporary surges in feed rate and reboiler heat input. Usually this requires 15% to 25% additional capacity above the design rate; thus the design C_s should be between 80% and 87% of the maximum operational C_s for the packing selected. This design criterion is based on loss of separation efficiency due to excessive liquid entrainment; however, in high-pressure fractionators using small-size packings, liquid holdup may limit the hydraulic capacity. If the gas density exceeds 6% of the liquid density, the pressure drop should be checked by Equation 8-1. It is suggested that pressure drop not exceed $0.19 \ F^{0.7}$ in. of fluid/ft (where F is the packing factor) at the design rate for such columns.

As critical conditions are approached, the liquid holdup will increase dramatically since the vapor density will approach the difference between the aerated liquid density and the vapor density. If the pressure of distillation is so high as to give a vapor density which is greater than 20% of the liquid density, the maximum capacity of the column probably will be determined by system properties as well as by the vapor/liquid contacting device. From experience in such applications, it is suggested that column size be limited by a maximum pressure drop of 0.090 $F^{0.7}$ in. of fluid/ft when calculated by means of Figures 1-15 or 1-16 with ΔP corrected for liquid specific gravity.

TYPICAL DESIGN EFFICIENCY

As might be expected, the vapor phase may offer the controlling resistance to mass transfer in high-pressure distillations. The liquid-phase temperature has increased, which reduces liquid density and viscosity; thus liquid diffusivity should be increased. The vapor phase, on the other hand, increases in density and viscosity at higher pressures and temperatures; so that the diffusivity in the vapor phase will be reduced. High-pressure distillations of light hydrocarbons may involve separations of low relative volatility. Thus ethylene/ethane splitters may have an average α of 1.45 while propylene/propane splitters have an average α of only 1.11. In such separations we should not expect any increase of HETP typical of a high lambda system as discussed in Chapter 6.

Increasing the operating pressure changes the physical properties in a manner that should increase the efficiency of separation. However, the efficiency of trayed columns has been shown to increase only from atmospheric pressure up to a pressure of 165 psia. At higher operating pressures, the efficiency of the trays decreases with increasing pressure. Hoek and Zuiderweg report that there is an entrainment of vapor in the liquid phase which is carried back down the column [7]. They have calculated that the entrained vapor increases from 0.05 mol/mol liquid at 165 psia to 0.43 mol vapor/mol liquid at a pressure of 400 psia for a C-4 hydrocarbon separation. This recycle of vapor reduces the separation efficiency as well as reducing column capacity. These investigators predict that tray efficiency will be reduced by 16% as the pressure is raised from 165 psia to 400 psia.

The HETP values in high pressure separations of similar light hydrocarbons are very low. Separation efficiency appears to be greatest in C-3 splitters. The same packing in a C-2 splitter will have almost a 20% higher HETP value. In C-4 fractionations, the packing will have an efficiency intermediate between these other two separations. Table 8-4 gives typical design HETP values for fractionations of C-3 and C-4 hydrocarbons at pressures of 22 atm to 6 atm absolute respectively. In fractionators separating similar light hydrocarbons, the efficiency in the stripping section may be lower (as much as a 10% higher HETP value) than in the rectifying section with the same packing. The HETP for 2-in.-size packing will be 40% to 45% greater than the HETP for 1-in.-size packing of the same type.

Table 8 - 4
Separation Efficiency in C-3 and C-4 Fractionations

IMTP® Packing Size	HETP (in.)
#25	16 to 18
#40	19 to 21
#50	23 to 26

In the stripping of light hydrocarbons from heavier ones the HETP value normally will be greater than for fractionators separating hydrocarbons of similar molecular weights. For #40 IMTP® packing, the design value of HETP in such a stripping operation is given by the following empirical equation:

$$HETP = 4.5 - 0.6 \ln L_{MW} \tag{8-2}$$

In Equation 8-2, the HETP value is expressed in feet. Equation 8-2 applies to a liquid phase with a molecular weight between 22 and 72. The #25 size IMTP® packing will give an HETP lower than #40 IMTP® packing by 0.41 feet while the #50 size will give an HETP value 0.53 feet higher. In those applications with high methane or hydrogen concentrations in the rectifying section, the HETP can be up to 30% greater than that predicted by Equation 8-2 for the stripping section. In separations of aliphatic hydrocarbons of 84 to 114 molecular weights, the HETP will decrease by up to 10% compared to the values given by Equation 8-2 for $L_{MW} = 72$. Higher molecular weight compounds normally are not fractionated at pressures above 4 atm absolute.

Aromatic hydrocarbons normally are fractionated at a pressure not greater than 75 psia which is less than 15% of the critical pressure. HETP values for such distillations are 5% greater than those obtained in C-4 fractionations for the same type and size of packing.

THEORETICAL STAGES AND REFLUX RATIO

The number of theoretical stages required for separation of light hydrocarbons can be calculated by the usual methods as described in Chapter 6. C-4 and heavier paraffin and mono-olefin hydrocarbons generally act like ideal compounds in the liquid phase. In C-3 splitters, the relative volatility between propylene and propane tends to decrease as the concentration of propylene increases; thus α may go from 1.14 in the bottom of the stripping section to 1.08 at the top of the rectifying section in the production of polymer grade propylene. In C-2 splitters, the relative volatility (therefore the number of theoretical stages) varies with the methane content of the feed. The K value for ethylene may be less than unity at the top of the column, thus ethylene enrichment of the vapor is not occurring. The actual separation taking place in this portion of the column is between the methane impurity and ethylene. The top of the column functions as a pasteurization section so that the methane in the feed can be removed from the product which is recovered as a side-draw liquid stream. Because of the large number of theoretical stages required for C-2 and C-3 fractionations, the same VLE as was used to evaluate the HETP value of the packing must be used to design the column. Small changes in VLE can change significantly the number of theoretical stages calculated that would result in a considerable difference in HETP values for the same packing.

Usually it is desirable to operate near the minimum reflux ratio if energy costs are more important than capital costs of equipment. However, unless there is actual operating experience, columns should be designed to operate at a reflux ratio at least 112% of the calculated minimum reflux ratio. Designs at a closer approach to minimum reflux ratio may result in a column operating below the actual minimum reflux ratio due to inaccuracy of the VLE data. In such a case the product specifications never will be achieved.

DEMETHANIZERS

One of the most difficult high-pressure separations for a trayed column is the removal of methane from a light hydrocarbon feed. In an olefins plant, the demethanizer typically is operated at a top pressure of 430 to 520 psia. This column has a partial condenser that is cooled by an ethylene refrigeration system and operates at a temperature of $-130°$ to $-145°F$. Usually, an olefin plant demethanizer has a smaller diameter upper section than the lower section because the majority of the feed leaves the bottom of the column. At the bottom of the column, the liquid rate will be at least 25 gpm/ft^2, which produces a flow parameter of about 1.0 on the generalized pressure drop correlation (Figure 1-15). At the top of the column the flow parameter will be at least 0.20, however the liquid irrigation rate will be only 50% to 60% of that in the bottom section. Achieving separation of the vapor from the liquid in downcomers is difficult because of the approach of vapor density to liquid density. At the bottom of this column, the vapor density is about 15% of the liquid density; while at the top of the column, the vapor density still is more than 10% of the liquid density. Further, the surface tension is low (below 4 dyne/cm) which also increases the difficulty of obtaining phase separation in the downcomers. As the vapor density approaches the liquid density and the surface tension of the liquid phase becomes low, the residence time required for vapor and liquid separation increases. Therefore, the downcomer area required may be as much as 40% of the total cross-sectional area in a trayed column.

In most cases, where additional capacity is not required, a demethanizer can be revamped with #25 size IMTP® packing thereby gaining an increase in the number of theoretical stages available. Such a revamp of the 8-ft diameter bottom section of an olefin plant demethanizer operating at 30 atm top pressure is described by Buffenoir [8]. The 29 trays on 18-in. spacing were replaced with two beds of #25 IMTP® packing. The bottom (highest molecular weight) feed was piped down the column and introduced between these two packed beds. The revamped column thus had additional rectifying stages that produced an 87% reduction in the ethylene loss overhead. At the same time the reflux ratio required was lowered by 18%, thereby reducing the $-140°F$ refrigeration load on the condenser. All of this was accomplished while actually reducing the methane concentration in the bottoms liquid. The pay-out time for this revamp was reported to be less than one year (see Figure 8-1).

In those cases where a capacity increase is desired, the #40 size IMTP® packing has been employed in the revamp of a trayed olefin plant demethanizer. This size packing has permitted the column feed rate to be increased by 20% over that for the original tower which was equipped with single-pass valve trays on 600 mm spacing in the upper section and two-pass valve trays on the same spacing in the lower section. Even when handling 120% of the trayed column rates, the #40 IMTP® packing was utilizing only 84% of its maximum operational capacity.

Figure 8-1. Olefin plant demethanizer: When this tower was revamped to IMTP® packing, overhead ethylene losses were reduced.

The trays in such a column have a relatively low efficiency compared to more common fractionation operations. This could be the result of vapor entrainment through the downcomer as previously discussed. The physical properties of the system which lower the tray efficiency do not have as drastic an effect on the efficiency of packed columns. Thus, the #40 IMTP® packing used to revamp this demethanizer also increased the number of theoretical stages developed by 13%. By design, this revamp was carried out so that two-thirds of these additional theoretical stages were located in the upper section of the column in order to permit a reduction in the reflux ratio with the accompanying energy savings.

DEPROPANIZERS

The function of these columns is the removal of propylene and propane plus any lower boiling components from the feed mixture. The column operating pressure typically will be 240 to 340 psia, which is sufficient to condense the overhead vapor with cooling water or ambient air.

In these systems the surface tension of the liquid phase is below 6 dyne/cm, the liquid density is near 30 lb/ft³, and the vapor density is about 7% of the liquid density. Under such conditions the downcomer residence time required can be a significant factor in the specification of the tower diameter for a trayed column. The downcomer normally is designed so that the froth height is no more than 70% of the tray spacing; therefore, downcomer area must be large to avoid the need for excessively tall columns.

In high-pressure distillations where column size is critical, the advantages of packed columns can be substantial. One such installation, located on a remote offshore platform, is processing natural gas liquids. The depropanizer in this unit produces HD-5 propane as distillate. The addition of new wells to the gathering system would increase the quantity of natural gas liquids to be processed by 50%. The depropanizer was among the columns that must handle this higher feed rate. At 235 psig operating pressure, the shell thickness and column weight would increase substantially if a larger-diameter column were installed. Overall tower height was restricted by wind load, foundation requirements, and platform space.

The existing column contained 43 actual trays on 24-in. spacing and developed 72% overall tray efficiency. This column was revamped utilizing IMTP® packing to provide the required fractionation and accommodate a 50% greater feed rate than the original trayed tower. Since the packed column developed 18% more theoretical stages than the trayed column, operation at a lower reflux ratio enhanced the feed capacity.

There was no significant difference in the operating weight for the trayed tower and for an IMTP® packed column because of the low liquid holdup of this packing.

CHEMICAL SEPARATIONS

Nonhydrocarbon distillations of chemicals usually do not operate at pressures greater than about 15% of the critical pressure. Table 8-5 gives typical operating pressures for purification of some of these commercially important chemicals. Only a few chemical separations qualify as high-pressure distillations (greater than 80 psia operating pressure). One of the principal reasons for operating chemical fractionators under pressure is to raise the condensing temperature for low-boiling compounds. In addition, a high-pressure column can be of a smaller diameter than an atmospheric column because the higher vapor density produces a lower C_s capacity factor for the same mass vapor rate.

Table 8 – 5
NonHydrocarbon Distillations at High Pressure

Chemical Product	Distillation Pressure (psia)
Carbon disulfide	40
Ethylene oxide	60
Fluorinated refrigerants	65
Methanol	90
Methyl amines	120
Methylene chloride	100
Vinyl chloride	50

In summary, tower packings are used instead of trays or to revamp trayed columns in high pressure distillations to accomplish the following objectives:

1. To increase the capacity of downcomer limited trayed columns.
2. To improve product purity or yield by providing a greater number of theoretical stages than developed by the trays.
3. To conserve energy by providing a greater number of theoretical stages in order to reduce the reflux ratio.
4. To permit the use of vapor recompression due to the reduced pressure drop produced by tower packings as compared to that developed by trays in the separation of close-boiling materials [9].

5. To reduce energy use by operation of columns in parallel, which because of the low pressure drop of tower packings permits the overhead vapor from the first column to supply reboiler heat to the second column.
6. To lower the residence time for materials that degrade or polymerize.
7. To reduce the inventory in the column of flammable or hazardous materials.
8. To increase product recovery in batch distillations due to the lower liquid holdup in a packed column.

EXAMPLE PROBLEM

It is desired to recover the C-3 components from a feed of the composition listed below. The distillate is to contain 1.0 mol % maximum C-4 hydrocarbons while the bottoms is to have a maximum of 2.0 mol % C-3 hydrocarbons. There is available a 5-ft 0-in. ID column containing 22 actual trays on 24-in. spacing. The vertical height from tray #1 to tray #22 is 43 ft. Can this column be revamped with IMTP® packing to perform the separation? If so, what will be the column capacity?

Feed Analysis

Component	mol %
propylene	62.4
propane	24.6
iso-butane	4.0
1-butene	6.0
iso-pentane	0.5
n-hexane	2.0
n-heptane	0.5

The column will be operated at a top pressure of 220 psia and a 98°F condenser temperature. The feed to the column is a liquid at a temperature of 115°F. This feed will undergo a 2.4 mol % flash to vapor on entering the column.

A computer simulation indicates that 7 theoretical stages rectifying and 7 theoretical stages stripping plus the reboiler will satisfy the separation requirements at an external reflux ratio of 1.70. If #50 IMTP® packing is selected for the revamp, from Equation 8-2 we obtain a design HETP of 2.76 ft rectifying and 2.63 ft stripping. These design HETP values include an ample safety factor when compared to the values in

Table 8-4. Thus a 19.5-ft-deep rectifying bed and an 18.5-ft-deep stripping bed will be specified.

The maximum loading in the rectifying section is at the top of the column. Here the flow parameter is:

$$X = \frac{1.70}{2.70} \left[\frac{2.02}{30.0} \right]^{0.5} = 0.163$$

The maximum standard C_s value from Figure 6-6 for #50 IMTP® packing at this flow parameter is 0.305 fps. After adjustment for system physical properties a design C_s of 0.227 fps normally would be used at this point in the rectifying section. Because this is a high-pressure light hydrocarbon system, the pressure drop will be checked for hydraulic capacity as determined by liquid holdup. The pressure drop from Equation 8-1 at a C_s of 0.227 fps is 0.75 in. H_2O/ft which is equivalent to 1.55 in. fluid/ft of packed depth. Because this pressure drop is higher than the maximum design value of 1.44 in. fluid/ft calculated as $0.19\ F^{0.7}$, the design C_s will be reduced to 0.199 fps at the top of the column. Now from Equation 8-1, we obtain a pressure drop of 0.54 in. H_2O/ft or 1.13 in. fluid/ft of packed depth, which is an acceptable value.

The overhead vapor mass flow rate is:

$$G = 0.199\ (3600)\ [2.02(30.0 - 2.02)]^{0.5} = 5386\ lb/ft^2 \cdot h$$

For a 5-ft 0-in. ID column, the allowable overhead vapor flow is 105,780 lb/h. This gives a reflux flow rate of 66,600 lb/h and a distillate product rate of 39,180 lb/h.

By material balance, the feed to the column is 47,620 lb/h and the bottoms product rate is 8,440 lb/h. Next we will calculate the flow rates just below the feed, which is the point of highest loading in the stripping section. The flow parameter here is:

$$X = \frac{5680}{5250} \left[\frac{1.99}{30.5} \right]^{0.5} = 0.276$$

The maximum standard C_s value from Figure 6-6 for #50 IMTP® packing is 0.266 fps. Thus, at a C_s of 0.194 fps produced by the rates fixed for the rectifying section, the top of the stripping section would be operating at 86% of the maximum operational capacity of the #50 IMTP® packing after adjustment for system properties. The pressure drop from Equation 8-1 at this point is 1.06 in. fluid/ft of packed depth.

Since the vapor rate at the top of the rectifying section is only 77% of the maximum operational capacity of the packing, the feed rate to the column can be specified as 47,620 lb/h. The available column shell can be revamped with #50 IMTP® packing to produce the desired separation at this feed rate.

NOTATION

C_s	Capacity factor (fps)
F	Packing factor
HETP	Height equivalent to a theoretical stage (ft)
K	Equilibrium ratio
L_{MW}	Molecular weight of liquid
VLE	Vapor/liquid equilibrium
X	Flow parameter
α	Relative volatility
ΔP	Pressure drop (in. H_2O/ft)
σ	Surface tension (dyne/cm)

REFERENCES

1. Robinson, K., "High Pressure Distillation Using Random Packings," European Federation of Chemical Engineers Meeting, June 1985.
2. Strigle, R. F., and Rukovena, F., *Chemical Engineering Progress,* Vol. 75, No. 3, 1979, p. 86.
3. Leva, M., *Tower Packings and Packed Tower Design,* 2nd ed., Chap. 2, United States Stoneware, 1953, p. 37.
4. Billet, R., *Chemical Engineering Progress,* Vol. 43, No. 9, 1967, p. 53.
5. Shulman, H. L., et al., *American Institute of Chemical Engineers Journal,* Vol. 1, No. 2, 1955, p. 259.
6. Strigle, R. F., *Chemical Engineering Progress,* Vol. 81, No. 4, 1985, p. 67.
7. Hoek, P. J., and Zuiderweg, F. J., *American Institute of Chemical Engineers Journal,* Vol. 28, No. 4, 1982, p. 535.
8. Buffenoir, M. H., *Oil and Gas Journal,* Vol. 80, No. 36, 1982, p. 78.
9. Strigle, R. F., and Perry, D. A., *Hydrocarbon Processing,* Vol. 60, No. 2, 1981, p. 103.

9

COLUMN INTERNALS

Modern tower packings as well as the refined design concepts now available have brought about an increasing need to update the technology concerning column internals. No longer are packed columns designed at only one-half their maximum capacity nor is a 50% safety factor added to the calculated packed depth. In today's competitive environment, the column internals must function as an integral part of the total packed column design, rather than limit the performance of the packing.

The most commonly employed column internals are:

1. Packing support plates.
2. Vapor distributors.
3. Bed limiters and hold-down plates.
4. Feed and reflux distributors.
5. Liquid redistributors.
6. Wall wipers.
7. Liquid collectors.

Not all of these internals are used in every column. In addition, some plates may serve more than one function.

PACKING SUPPORT PLATES

The primary function of the packing support plate is to serve as a physical support for the tower packing plus the weight of the liquid holdup. In the design of the packing support plate no allowance is made for the buoyancy due to the pressure drop through the packed bed nor for the support offered by the column walls. In addition, the packing support plate must pass both the downwardly flowing liquid phase as well as the upwardly flowing gas phase to the limit of the capacity of the tower packing itself.

The first packing support plates for random dumped packings were slotted or perforated, flat ceramic plates. The use of 1-in. to 2-in.-size ceramic Raschig ring packings, common in those days, required small holes or narrow slots that gave the plate a low open area of only 15% to 25%. Even though these plates were very heavy (up to 2½ in. thick), they did not have sufficient strength to support deep beds of ceramic tower packings.

This same type of design also was used in large cast iron grids for supporting stacked packings in the ammonia soda industry. Similar grids of cast iron also were used in the manufacture of sulfuric acid. In addition, sections of subway grating were used as packing support plates where the corrosion resistance of the metal was adequate. The then commonly used Raschig ring packing tended to align along these slots or orifices in such support plates, thus leaving very little effective free area for gas and liquid passage. Flooding of the packed bed frequently was initiated from the bottom of the bed, and progressed upward until eventually the column became inoperable.

Until about 1952 tower internals were designed specifically for each individual column. Many times these designs emphasized the mechanical requirements for the internal, with the process function of the internal receiving only secondary consideration. The first standardized line of column internals was marketed about 1960. For the most part these internals were made from ceramics, then later the designs were adapted for fabrication from metals.

With the increasing use of ceramic saddle packings, the older support plates proved inadequate. Leva proposed a *gas injection weir-type* support plate design to circumvent previous limitations [1]. This design injected the gas phase into the packed bed above the level where the liquid phase left the packing. Such a design avoids the difficulty of trying to pass the two phases in opposite directions through the same openings.

This type of support plate proved adequate for ceramic packings up to a 2-in.size, which then were in wide use. However, when 2-in. metal Pall ring packing was tested by an independent research organization in the early 1960s, it was found that the pressure drop through the packing support plate and first two feet of packing was much higher than the average pressure drop for the balance of the packed bed. Thus, the packing capacity was limited by the packing support plate.

Further development work resulted in the improved *multi-beam gas injection* packing support plate design. Repeated tests in the later 1960s

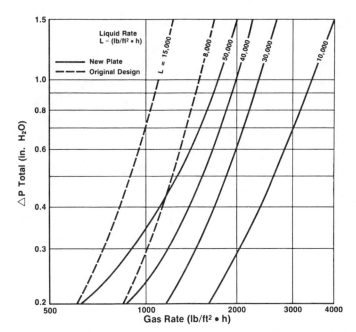

Figure 9-1. Performance of packing support plates. (Courtesy of Norton Company.)

verified the capacity of this design again using 2-in. metal Pall ring packing. Figure 9-1 shows the pressure drop developed by this improved support plate as compared to the original design.

As the output of the chemical industry grew, column sizes became larger. With columns of 42-in. or larger diameter, a man could enter the column easily; thus, the packing support plate also had to hold a man's weight. Further, it was impractical to use removable heads on these larger-size columns; therefore, the tower internals had to enter the column through a manhole. The multi-beam design support plate, shown in Figure 9-2, met the desired criteria for most applications. This plate utilizes the gas injection principle to put the gas phase into the packed bed through openings in the almost vertical sidewalls of each beam. The liquid phase flows down along the sides of the beams to the horizontal bottom legs where it leaves the bed through perforations. Thus the gas phase flows through one set of openings while the liquid phase passes through a different set of openings.

The beam-style design provides a high mechanical strength permitting single spans 12 ft long or greater. The modular design allows instal-

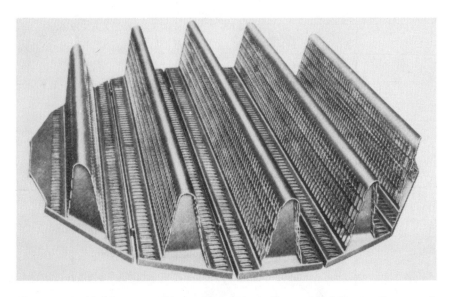

Figure 9-2. Multibeam packing support plate. (Courtesy of Norton Company.)

lation through standard 18-in. manholes and permits its use in any column 48-in. ID and larger. Pressure drop through this packing support
plate will not exceed 0.3 in. H_2O for almost all applications.

VAPOR DISTRIBUTORS

Because a packing support plate usually is located immediately above
the gas inlet in an absorber or the reboiler return in a distillation column, this plate could be used to control vapor distribution. Obviously,
vapor maldistribution can reduce column efficiency in the same way as
liquid maldistribution; although the vapor phase radial cross-mixing
rate is at least three times that of the liquid phase. The potential for vapor maldistribution increases as column diameters increase. Fortunately,
the vapor phase tends to maintain a uniform distribution once it has
been established. Thus, only the packing support plate immediately
above the vapor inlet needs to act as a vapor distributor.

Vapor flow control usually is accomplished by establishing a pressure
drop across the support plate that is at least equal to the velocity head of
the vapor phase through the column inlet nozzle. The pressure drop
through a multi-beam packing support plate is too low for this type of
plate to control vapor distribution.

A vapor sparger could be used to produce uniform flow of vapor up
the column. This approach to vapor distribution control frequently is

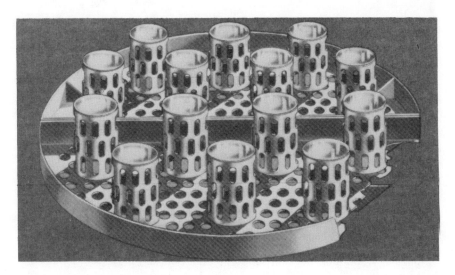

Figure 9-3. Vapor distributing packing support plate. (Courtesy of Norton Company.)

used for high-pressure stripping steam. However, in many cases (such as with a thermosiphon reboiler vapor return) it is not desirable to take a sufficiently high pressure drop on the inlet gas stream to permit use of a sparger. Where the inlet vapor nozzle operates at an F_s vapor capacity factor greater than 22 $lb^{0.5}/ft^{0.5} \cdot s$, a vapor-distributing support plate should be installed. Such a plate, as shown in Figure 9-3, can provide the required pressure drop by controlling the size of the openings through the plate holding the cylindrical gas risers. The liquid phase then will pool on the horizontal deck to a depth equal to the sum of the gas-phase pressure drop and the resistance to liquid flow through the deck orifices. The bottom part of the gas risers is left unperforated to allow for this liquid head. In this design, the risers inject the gas phase into the bed above the surface of the liquid pool on the support plate.

In extremely corrosive services, ceramic support plates may be required. For smaller process columns, as shown in Figure 9-4, a modified multi-beam support plate commonly is used. In larger diameter columns (such as sulfuric acid plant towers), a series of ceramic grids is installed resting on brick arches or piers. Then a layer of cross-partition rings or grid blocks is stacked on these grid bars to support the dumped ceramic packing as shown in Figure 9-5.

Plastic packing support plates also are available. Thermoplastic support plates are similar in design to metal plates. Fiberglass reinforced plastic internals use metal internal designs adapted for hand lay-up. These plates are designed for use with plastic tower packings because

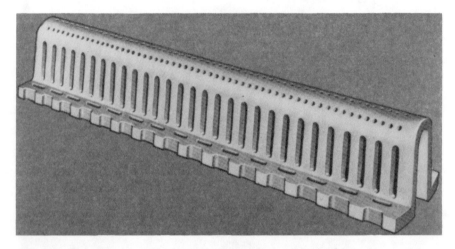

Figure 9-4. Ceramic packing support plate. (Courtesy of Norton Company.)

their load-bearing capabilities are limited. Generally free-span length does not exceed 4 ft due to possible high temperature creep.

Packing support plates usually are designed to rest on a continuous ledge. This ledge should be level and perpendicular to the tower's vertical axis. Also, the ledge must be flat to provide a uniform load bearing surface if a ceramic support plate is used. The width of this ledge should not exceed the values shown in Table 9-1 if the column is to be operated near maximum capacity. For columns smaller than 48-in. ID, continuous ledges may restrict the ultimate capacity of the tower packing. Support plates for columns over 12 ft diameter usually require at least one mid-span supporting beam or truss. The sidewall of the column must be sufficiently rigid to support the point loading imposed at the beam seats.

Table 9 – 1
Ledges for Tower Internals

Tower ID (in.)	Support Ledge Width (in.)
48	1½
60	1¾
72	2
84	2¼
96	2½
120	3
144	3½

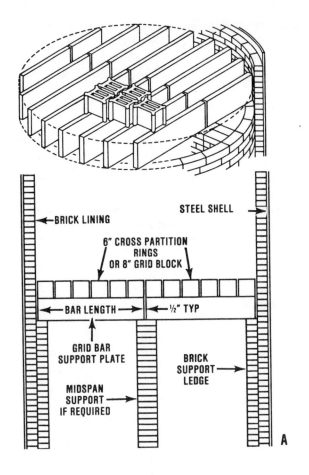

STEEL SHELL

BRICK LINING

6" CROSS PARTITION
RINGS
OR 8" GRID BLOCK

BAR LENGTH   ½" TYP

GRID BAR
SUPPORT PLATE

BRICK
SUPPORT
LEDGE

MIDSPAN
SUPPORT
IF REQUIRED

A

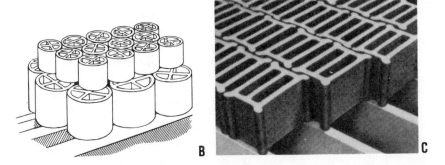

B

C

Figure 9-5. (A) Ceramic grid support system. (B) Typical arrangement of cross-partition rings. (C) Typical arrangement of Norton grid blocks.

In columns 72 in. or larger diameter, the packing support plates usually are clamped to the supporting ledge at both ends. This prevents movement of the individual beams during operating upsets that could allow some packing pieces to fall out of the packed bed.

BED LIMITERS AND HOLD-DOWN PLATES

Bed limiters commonly are used with metal or plastic tower packings. The primary function of these devices is to prevent expansion of the packed bed, as well as to maintain the bed top surface level. In large-diameter columns, the packed bed will not fluidize over the entire surface. Vapor surges fluidize random spots on the top of the bed; so that after return to normal operation the bed top surface is quite irregular. Thus the liquid distribution can be affected adversely by such an occurrence.

Bed limiters are fabricated from a light-weight metal or plastic structure. Usually a mesh backing is used to prevent passage of individual pieces of tower packing. Because the bed limiter rests directly on the top of the packed bed, structurally it must be only sufficiently rigid to resist any upward forces acting on this packed bed.

Usually the bed limiter is fastened to clips on the column wall or it is restrained by the column internal located immediately above it. It is not recommended that a continuous ledge be used to support the bed limiter. This ledge can interfere with the liquid distribution to the top of the packed bed. Likewise, the bed limiter should not contain horizontal structural members that can intercept and divert the downflowing liquid.

Hold-down plates are used with ceramic or carbon tower packings. With these packings, it is especially important to prevent fluidization of the packed bed top surface. These brittle materials can be fractured during an operating upset so that the resulting fragments migrate down into the packed bed where they can severely reduce column capacity.

The hold-down plate must rest freely on the top of the packed bed because beds of ceramic and carbon packings tend to settle during operation. These plates usually act by their own weight to prevent bed expansion; therefore, the plates weigh 20 lb to 30 lb per ft^2.

Both bed limiters and hold-down plates should be of sectional construction to permit entry into the column through a manhole. These plates must fit closely to the column wall to prevent passage of individual packing pieces. The free space for these plates must be high enough not to restrict the capacity of the tower packing.

FEED AND REFLUX DISTRIBUTORS

From a process standpoint, the most important column internals are the liquid distributors. A liquid distributor is required at all locations in the tower where an external liquid stream is introduced. In addition to providing a uniform liquid distribution pattern to the top of the packed bed, the distributor also must provide sufficient gas passage area to avoid a high pressure drop or liquid entrainment. The liquid distributor should have a high turn-down ratio and be resistant to fouling.

Figure 6-5 demonstrates the effect of liquid distributor performance on the separation efficiency of a packed bed. Curve II shows the performance typical of commercial liquid distributors available in the 1970s. Curve I represents the operation of high-performance liquid distributors now available. In evaluating distributor performance, the following points should be considered:

1. Uniformity of liquid flow from each point of irrigation.
2. Geometric uniformity of the location of each point of irrigation.
3. Uniformity of liquid flow to each square foot of cross-sectional area at the packed bed top.
4. Number of liquid irrigation points per square foot of column cross-sectional area.
5. Wetted area compared to dry area at the column wall.

To maintain uniform flow from each irrigation point, the orifice or weir controlling the liquid flow rate must be manufactured to a high tolerance. The minimum pressure loss through this flow control device should be established to allow for variations in support ledge levelness, distributor deflection due to mechanical loading, and head gradients required to flow liquid throughout the entire distributor. In addition, the minimum head must take into account the gas-phase pressure loss through the distributor. High performance distributors provide a flow rate variation per irrigation point that is a maximum of $\pm$ 5% to 6% of average flow.

Every liquid irrigation point must be located in a uniform geometric pattern. This pattern must not be sacrificed to insert the necessary gas risers into the distributor. Thus, the designer of such a device is faced with an intriguing challenge that becomes more complex as the gas rate, and thus the gas riser area required, increases.

If the flow per irrigation point is uniform, there must be the same number of irrigation points for every square foot of bed cross-sectional area. This causes the liquid flow to every square foot of the packed bed surface to be the same. To ensure conformance with these criteria, the design can be checked by any of several methods. One method involves dividing the column into quadrants plus concentric circles of equal areas. Thus, a 7-ft 6-in.-ID column uses 8 equal areas to be evaluated, while an 11-ft 0-in.-ID column uses 12 areas, and a 15-ft 0-in.-ID column 16 areas. Usually, the area adjacent to the column wall requires special consideration to accomplish such uniform liquid irrigation. Also, it is necessary to ensure that this uniform distribution pattern extends under the ledge supporting the liquid distributor. If a high-purity distillate product is specified, all of the vapor phase must be rectified by the liquid phase to prevent high-boiling components from being carried overhead.

The number of distribution points per square foot of column cross-sectional area need not exceed ten. A larger number than this does not improve packed bed efficiency. The geometric uniformity of liquid distribution has more effect on packing efficiency than the number of distribution points per square foot. However, it is easier to produce a high degree of uniformity with a larger number of distribution points.

The size of the orifice or weir required depends on the total liquid flow and the number of irrigation points per square foot. If the liquid to be distributed is perfectly clean, the minimum orifice diameter or weir width should be 0.14 in. For fouling services, this minimum dimension should be increased to 0.20 in. Such large-size orifices or weirs may require a reduction in the number of irrigation points per square foot when handling low liquid rates. Packed bed efficiency normally can be maintained with five distribution points per square foot, if the other four criteria are maintained.

In the past, it had been thought that the necessity for uniform liquid distribution was reduced as the liquid irrigation rate per square foot increased. However, it has been found that regardless of the liquid rate, the necessity for uniform irrigation increases as the number of theoretical stages per packed bed is increased. For less than five theoretical stages per bed, the column is not so sensitive to the uniformity of liquid distribution [2]. For over five theoretical stages per bed, the liquid distribution has a significant effect on packing efficiency, as shown in Figure 9-6. In this figure the increase in the value of HETP is shown as a function of liquid distribution quality. With 15 or more theoretical stages per bed liquid distribution uniformity is extremely critical to the attainment of the desired packing efficiency.

As a consequence of the foregoing, for packed beds of equal depth, the larger packing sizes are less sensitive to the uniformity of liquid distribution than smaller-size packings. This occurs because the large packings have higher HETP values and develop fewer theoretical stages than

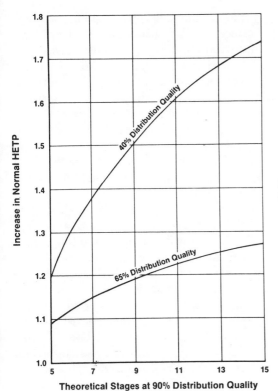

Figure 9-6. Effect of liquid distribution quality.

Table 9 – 2
Comparison of Commercial vs. High Performance Distributors

Pall Ring Size (in.)	Possible Number of Theoretical Stages	Percent Efficiency Loss for Commercial Unit
1	14.3	47
1½	10.5	36
2	8.6	29
3½	5.8	17

Packed bed depth of 19 ft – 0 in.

smaller packings in the same bed depth. Table 9-2 illustrates the performance loss of various sizes of metal Pall ring packings with a typical commercial distributor compared to a high-performance distribution system in a distillation operation with a 19-ft bed depth.

Ideally, each individual piece of packing on the top surface of the bed should be irrigated by a liquid stream. This could be accomplished for a bed of 3½-in.-size Pall ring packing, but would be impractical for the 1-

in.-size of this packing. Albright found that every packing has a natural liquid flow distribution [3]. Perfect initial distribution will degrade to the natural pattern. Initial maldistribution of liquid will improve slowly to the natural distribution given sufficient bed depth. He concluded that there exists an initial liquid distribution pattern which will minimize the depth of packing required to attain the natural distribution pattern.

Bemer and Zuiderweg showed that a significant maldistribution of liquid occurred in a bed of Raschig ring packing [4]. Local flow rates differed from a normal pattern when measured at various liquid flows and with different size packings. They concluded that the bulk of the liquid flows in stable channels. Further, a high percentage of the radial liquid mixing is due to this irregular flow distribution.

Later experiments in small diameter columns have shown that a bed of random dumped packing develops a definite number of preferred paths of internal liquid flow [5]. If liquid is distributed onto the packed bed with a greater number of streams per square foot than number of preferred liquid paths, the liquid streams within the bed coalesce until the number of preferred liquid paths is reached. If liquid is distributed onto the packed bed with a smaller number of streams per square foot than the number of preferred liquid paths, the packing redistributes the liquid until the number of preferred liquid paths is established. In this latter case, the upper portion of the packed bed has a lower-than-normal separating efficiency. Figure 9-7 shows the performance of such a packed bed in a binary distillation. Curve I represents the separation obtained with a high-performance liquid distribution system. Curve II shows the effect of inadequate liquid distribution to the top surface of the 10-ft-deep packed bed.

In spite of the irregularity of the internal liquid streams, the overall liquid residence time in a packed bed exhibits a normal curve. This has been verified in a commercial column using radioactive tracers which demonstrate that the average liquid residence time is the same as for plug flow of liquid.

Liquid distributors are of two general types: the gravity-fed distributor and the pressure-fed distributor. Gravity-fed distributors are more common and are illustrated in Figures 9-8 through 9-10. These distributors may use a deck that is sealed to the supporting ledge with orifices for metering the liquid flow (Figure 9-8). Also, these distributors can use pans or boxes that are liquid-tight (Figures 9-9 and 9-10). In these two designs, either orifices or weirs can be used to meter the liquid flow.

Pressure-fed distributors typically are of the ladder-type that may use pipe arms containing liquid-metering orifices as shown in Figure 9-11.

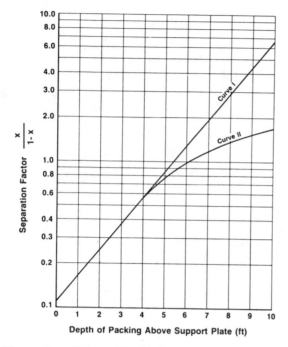

Figure 9-7. Effect of liquid distribution on separation.

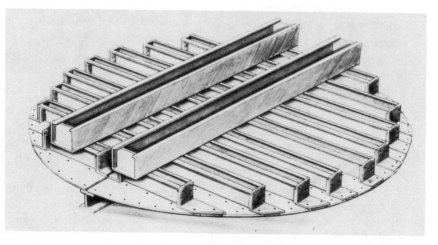

Figure 9-8. Orifice deck liquid distributor. (Courtesy of Norton Company.)

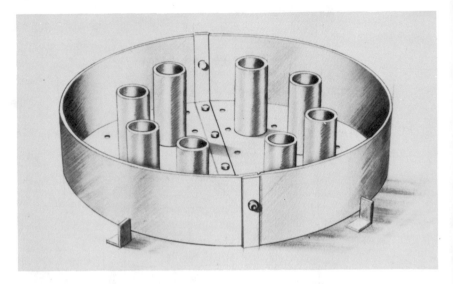

Figure 9-9. Orifice pan liquid distributor. (Courtesy of Norton Company.)

Figure 9-10. Weir trough liquid distributor. (Courtesy of Norton Company.)

Because of the greater pressure drop available, the orifice sizes in these distributors usually are smaller than in gravity-fed distributors. The feed liquid first should be passed through a fine strainer to remove any materials that would foul these smaller orifices. While gravity-fed distributors usually are limited to a 2-to-1 turn-down ratio, because of the limitations of gas riser height due to the manhole size, pressure-fed distributors can operate at a 3-to-1 or greater turn-down ratio.

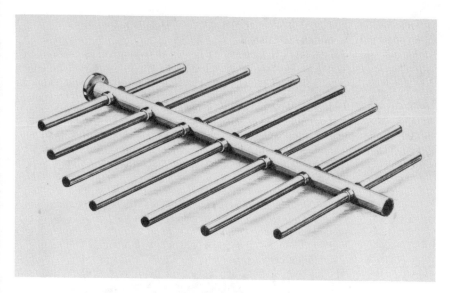

Figure 9-11. Orifice ladder liquid distributor. (Courtesy of Norton Company.)

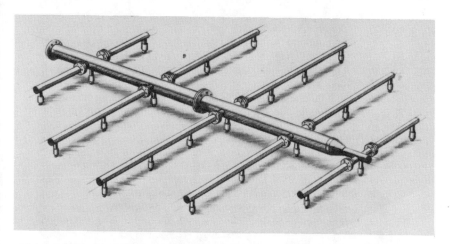

Figure 9-12. Spray nozzle liquid distributor. (Courtesy of Norton Company.)

In addition, spray-nozzle distributors have been used to irrigate packed beds (Figure 9-12). Spray nozzles for distributing liquid usually are not used in fractionating columns or absorbers. Their use is limited to heat transfer operations where liquid entrainment from the bed top is not likely to occur or will not constitute an operational problem. Spray nozzles do not generate a uniformly distributed liquid-flow pattern. A reasonably uniform liquid irrigation of the top of the packed bed requires 100% overlap (double coverage) for a spray distributor which normally is impractical to install.

As we have discussed, uniformity of liquid distribution is essential to the attainment of the maximum packed bed efficiency. In those cases where a mixed vapor/liquid feed is used or where the liquid feed would flash on entering the column, special designs are necessary. To avoid excessive turbulence in the liquid distributor, it is customary to install a device that separates the vapor and liquid phases ahead of the final distributor. Such a device used for small columns is shown in Figure 9-13 and is located immediately above the orifice-type distributor. For large-

Figure 9-13. Vapor/liquid separator. (Courtesy of Norton Company.)

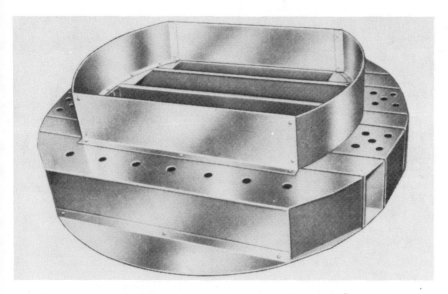

Figure 9-14. Distributor with gallery. (Courtesy of Norton Company.)

diameter towers where feed rates are much greater, the usual parting boxes above the distributor can be replaced with a gallery as illustrated in Figure 9-14. For these mixed vapor/liquid feeds, a gravity-fed liquid distributor should be used.

LIQUID REDISTRIBUTORS

⊘ A liquid redistributor is required at the top of each packed bed. The liquid flow from a typical support plate is not sufficiently uniform to properly irrigate the next lower packed bed. The multi-beam type of packing support plate, which is widely used, tends to segregate the liquid downflow from a packed bed into a pair of parallel rows of liquid streams about 2 in. apart with a 10-in. space between adjacent pairs. Gas-distributing support plates likewise do not give a sufficiently uniform liquid irrigation pattern because gas riser locations take precedence in the design of such a plate.

Liquid redistributors must operate in the same manner as gravity-fed distributors. To intercept all of the liquid downflow, these distributors usually have a deck that is sealed to a supporting ledge as shown in Figure 9-15. If light-tight pans or boxes are used for a redistributor, a collector plate generally must be installed above it to intercept all the liquid downflow. Whenever the liquid falls directly onto the redistributor, the

Figure 9-15. Orifice deck liquid redistributor. (Courtesy of Norton Company.)

gas risers must be provided with covers to prevent liquid from raining into this area of high vapor velocity [6].

In any mass transfer operation, the compositions of the liquid and vapor phases are assumed to follow the relationship illustrated by the column operating line. This line represents the overall calculated profile down the column; however, the composition on each individual square foot of a particular column cross section may vary from that represented by the operating line. These variations are the result of deviations in the hydraulic flow rates of the vapor and liquid phases, as well as incomplete mixing of the phases across the entire column.

One of the functions of a liquid redistributor is to remix the liquid phase so as to bring the entire liquid flow onto the next lower bed at a more uniform composition. To perform this function, the liquid redistributor must intercept all the liquid that is flowing down the column, which includes any liquid on the column walls. Likewise, the redistributor must maintain the uniform vapor distribution that should have been established at the column bottom. To perform these functions, the redistributor must have a large flow area available that is transverse to the gas risers since only very low gradient heads are available for cross-mixing of the liquid. In addition, the vapor flow area must be sufficient to avoid a high pressure drop in the gas phase, and this area must be distributed uniformly across the column cross section.

There has been considerable speculation regarding the depth of packing which could be installed before liquid redistribution is required. Silvey and Keller found no loss of efficiency in distillation with 18-ft-deep beds of 1½-in. ceramic Raschig rings and 35-ft-deep beds of 3-in. ceramic Raschig rings [7]. On the basis of their reported average HETP values, these beds were developing only 7 and 10 theoretical stages, respectively. Strigle and Fukuyo showed that with high performance redistributors over 20 theoretical stages per packed bed could be obtained repeatedly with 1-in. size packing [8].

WALL WIPERS

In small-diameter columns, the tower wall surface area is substantial when compared to the total packing surface area. As the column diameter becomes larger, the wall area diminishes in significance compared to the packing area. Thus, in a 6-in.-ID column perhaps as much as 30% of the liquid feed could flow down the column wall. However, in a 60-in.-ID column as little as 3% of the liquid feed may flow down the column wall.

There have been many questions raised about the effect of wall flow in a packed column. If the liquid reaching the column wall continues to flow down the wall, it represents a bypassed stream which reduces the overall separation efficiency. Furzer showed that 1-in. Lessing rings (and presumably 1-in. Raschig rings) were poor at transferring liquid to and from the column wall with a distributor having three distribution points per square foot [9]. Later work using a distributor having 6.5 distribution points per square foot with the same packing indicated that the wall flow frequently interchanged with the liquid in the packed bed.

Liquid flowing on the wall must be in dynamic equilibrium with the liquid in the packed bed, or the overall separation will be reduced. In small columns with a high percentage of wall flow, wall wipers frequently are installed. Wall wipers fit tightly against the column wall to intercept all of the liquid flowing down the wall. If the bottom product is to be of high purity, all of the low-boiling component must be removed in the column stripping section. Any liquid feed that flows down the column wall may not be completely stripped. The wall wiper is used to remove this liquid from the wall and place it into the packed bed where it will be adequately contracted with the rising vapor phase. Generally, wall wipers are required only in the lower portion of the stripping section. These devices usually are spaced apart by about two theoretical stages of packed height.

Because wall wipers are installed within the packed bed itself, they must be designed carefully to avoid severely reducing the column capacity. As illustrated by Table 9-1, any ledge installed must be rather nar-

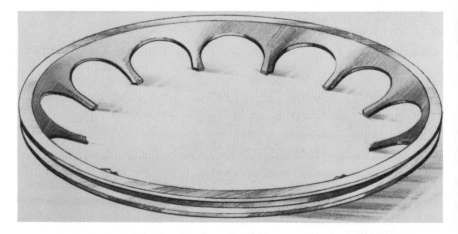

Figure 9-16. "Rosette" wall wiper. (Courtesy of Norton Company.)

row; thus the ledge itself is incapable of returning the intercepted liquid a sufficient distance back into the packed bed to ensure its mixing with the main liquid phase. Figure 9-16 illustrates a patented design for such a plate that overcomes this problem. This design maintains a constant, very high percentage of the column cross-sectional area open to vapor and liquid flows. The finger extensions convey the intercepted liquid back into the packed bed and the main downflowing liquid phase.

LIQUID COLLECTORS

Quite often it is necessary to intercept all of the liquid flowing down the column. This may occur due to an enlargement or contraction of the column diameter. If the lower portion of the column is of a larger diameter than the upper portion, the liquid must be collected at the bottom of the smaller diameter section. It then is fed to a redistributor located at the top of the larger-diameter section to irrigate uniformly the lower section. If the lower portion of the column is of a smaller diameter than the upper portion, the liquid must be collected at the bottom of the larger diameter section. It then is fed to a redistributor at the top of the smaller diameter section to prevent excessive wall flow in the lower section.

In a number of applications, liquid pumparound sections are installed. Such sections are used in caustic scrubbers where only a small addition of sodium hydroxide is required to neutralize the absorbed acid gas. However, the liquid irrigation rate of each section must be adequate to ensure good gas scrubbing in the packed bed. In absorbers where the solute has a high heat of vaporization or heat of solution, the downflowing liquid progressively increases in temperature. This heated liquid must be removed from the column and cooled before it is returned to irrigate the next lower packed bed. The absorption otherwise is limited by the high vapor pressure of the solute above the hot rich solution. In some operations, liquid is removed and recirculated back to the top of the same packed bed after cooling. Such a situation is common when the packed bed is used as a total or partial condenser.

Figure 9-17 shows a typical liquid collector plate for a column that uses one side downcomer to withdraw the liquid. The maximum diameter for such a design is about 12 ft, which is limited by the hydraulic gradient necessary for such a liquid flow-path length. For larger diameter columns, two opposite side downcomers or a center downcomer normally are used unless the total amount of liquid collected is relatively small.

A liquid collector plate must be of gasketed construction so that it can be sealed to the supporting ledge and will be liquid-tight. The sections could be seal-welded together, however future removal would be difficult. There must be sufficient liquid head available to cause the liquid to flow out the side nozzle in the column shell. The use of sumps provides such a liquid head without pooling liquid across the entire plate where leakage could be greater.

The gas risers must have a sufficient flow area to avoid a high gas-phase pressure drop. In addition, these gas risers must be uniformly positioned to maintain proper gas distribution. The gas risers should be equipped with covers to deflect the liquid raining onto this collector plate. These gas riser covers must be kept a sufficient distance below the

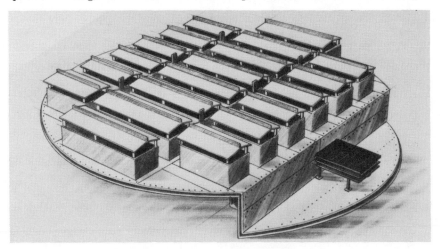

Figure 9-17. Liquid collector plate. (Courtesy of Norton Company.)

next packed bed to allow the gas phase to come to a uniform flow rate per square foot of column cross-sectional area before entering the next bed [10].

Where only 6% or less of the liquid downflow is to be withdrawn from the column, a special collector box can be installed within the packed bed. This box can remove small quantities of intermediate boiling components that otherwise would accumulate in a sufficient quantity to interfere with the fractionation operation. Such a collector box must be designed very carefully to avoid interference with the vapor distribution above it or reduction in the quality of liquid distribution below it.

REFERENCES

1. Leva, M., *Tower Packings and Packed Tower Design,* 2nd ed., United States Stoneware, Chap. 2, 1953, p. 25.
2. Spiegel, L., and Yuan, H. C., "The Influence of Maldistribution at Partial Reflux," World Congress II of Chemical Engineering, October, 1981.
3. Albright, M. A., *Hydrocarbon Processing,* Vol. 63, No. 9, 1984, p. 173.
4. Bemer, G. G., and Zuiderweg, F. J., *Chemical Engineering Science,* Vol. 33, No. 12. 1978, p. 1637.
5. Hoek, P. J., "Large and Small Scale Liquid Maldistribution in a Packed Column," Ph.D. Thesis, Delft University, June 1983.
6. Fadel, T. M., *Chemical Engineering,* Vol. 91, No. 2, 1984, p. 71.
7. Silvey, F. C., and Keller, G. J., *Institution Chemical Engineers Symposium Series,* No. 32, 1969, p. 4:18.
8. Strigle, R. F., and Fukuyo, K., *Hydrocarbon Processing,* Vol. 65, No. 6, 1986, p. 47.
9. Furzer, I. A., *Chemical Engineering Science,* Vol. 39, No. 7/8, 1984, pp. 1283 and 1301.
10. Chen, G. K., *Chemical Engineering,* Vol. 91, No. 5, 1984, p. 40.

10

OLEFINS PRODUCTION

Olefins manufacture provides many good examples of how tower packing improves the performance of columns that initially were constructed with trays. No new olefins production capacity is likely to be built in industrialized nations in the late 1980s. The emphasis in the following discussion, therefore, is directed toward improving the performance of existing trayed columns.

Olefins are the most widely consumed *building blocks* of petrochemical production. Production plants for olefins represent the largest capital investment in the chemical processing field. Typically olefins are produced by the steam cracking of ethane, propane, butane, LPG, natural gas liquids, naphtha, or atmospheric gas oil. Plants designed and constructed prior to 1973 normally handled just one or two types of feedstocks. Further, because feedstocks and energy were relatively abundant and inexpensive then, designers usually attempted to minimize the capital cost rather than the operating cost for such plants.

With the oil crisis of 1973, the economic picture changed significantly. To keep costs low, as the feedstock prices and availability fluctuated, producers had to be able to operate with different feedstocks. Greater selectivity for the desired products and increased product recovery became much more important in plant design.

Energy costs also increased along with the hydrocarbon prices. Improved operational practices might lower the design energy consumption by up to 20%; however, the really large reductions in energy requirements could be realized only through process modifications and integration of the total operating plant. Plants designed after 1973 incorporate some of these energy saving features. Because the capital investment in older plants cannot be written off, revamp of these units is necessary to maintain them in a competitive position.

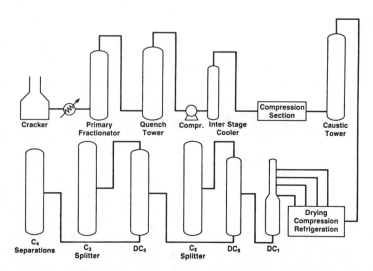

Figure 10-1. Typical ethylene plant flow diagram.

Figure 10-1 shows the flowsheet of a typical olefins plant using a heavy liquid feedstock. When an olefins plant is operated with a light hydrocarbon feedstock, the primary fractionator is not required. This flowsheet shows only the major columns; not shown are the many smaller columns such as condensate strippers, naphtha stabilizers, and sour water strippers. In addition, the aromatics recovery system for processing the debutanizer bottoms and the aromatic naphtha condensate from the water quench column is not shown.

Product yield changes with the feedstock to the cracking furnace. Table 10-1 gives the yields of products for a typical high-severity cracking operation [1]. Ethane/propane feed is an equal molar mixture. LPG feed is an equal weight mixture of propane and n-butane. Cracking of naphtha typically produces 14% methane and 4% fuel oil, based on the feed weight. A gas oil feed decreases methane production to 8%, but

Table 10 – 1
Product Distribution From Steam Cracking Various Feedstocks
(lb product per 1,000 lb feed)

Feed	Ethylene	Propylene	Butadiene	BTX
Ethane/Propane	600-630	100-120	20-30	15-30
LPG	440-460	160-180	30-40	30-45
Full Range Naphtha	320-350	130-160	40-50	110-150
Atmospheric Gas Oil	255-300	115-135	45-55	95-135

Source: Petrochemical Handbook [1].

significantly increases fuel oil production to about 20 wt %. The ethylene/propylene yield for light hydrocarbon feedstocks is 65% to 70% of the feed weight. However, cracking heavier liquid feedstocks gives only about a 45% yield of ethylene and propylene.

OLEFINS PLANT HOT SECTION

The *hot section* of an ethylene plant consists of the cracking furnace through the compression train and adsorbant driers. A reduction in pressure drop in the section would offer the following operational advantages:

1. Suction pressure on the first-stage compressor increases, which reduces the compression ratio and power requirements.
2. Furnace pressure can be reduced, which usually increases the ethylene yield at constant steam/hydrocarbon ratio.
3. Furnace pressure can be reduced to lower steam consumption at the same hydrocarbon partial pressure.

In the cracking of ethane and propane feedstocks, the primary products are ethylene and propylene plus small quantities of C-4 olefins and dienes and some aromatics. With naphtha and gas oil feedstocks, the coproduction of unsaturated C-4 hydrocarbons and aromatics is substantial, compared with the quantities of ethylene and propylene primarily manufactured. Thus plants using heavier feedstocks are of more complex design than are ethane/propane cracking units.

PRIMARY FRACTIONATOR OPERATION

In a typical heavy liquids cracking plant, the gas stream leaving the cracking furnaces at a temperature of 1,470° to 1,610°F, is cooled in transfer line exchangers, before going to a primary fractionator (oil quench column). This gas stream, at a temperature of about 730°F, usually is contacted with a large excess of quench oil in a quench fitting before entering the primary fractionator column itself. Thus the cracked gas, plus unevaporated oil mixture, enters this column at a temperature of 360° to 420°F. The function of the primary fractionator is to cool the gas stream. In addition, the primary fractionator must remove the C-10 and heavier hydrocarbons from the vapor stream without loss of C-8 and lighter hydrocarbons.

The typical design of a primary fractionator column consists of at least four open-type trays in the lower section with a minimum of seven fractionating trays in the upper section. The lower section can be equipped with angle trays, baffle trays, or splash decks. Quench oil is removed from the bottom of the column at a temperature of 350° to 400°F and cooled by 20° to 40°F to recover heat. The majority of the cooled quench oil is pumped to the quench fitting. The balance of the quench oil is cooled by a further 40° to 70°F and returned to the primary fractionator to irrigate the lower section trays. Trays in the column's upper section can be valve trays, sieve trays, or counterflow trays. The liquid reflux to the upper section is aromatic naphtha condensate returned directly from the decanter following the water quench tower.

The primary fractionator lowers the cracked gas temperature, first by sensible heat exchange with the cooled recirculated quench oil in the lower section, and then by evaporation of the naphtha reflux in the upper section. The column's upper section also serves to remove C-10 and heavier hydrocarbons from the gas stream which otherwise would raise the end point temperature of the recovered naphtha. A small slipstream of quench oil from the column bottom is sent through a fuel-oil stripper where C-8 and lighter compounds are removed before the heavy hydrocarbons are purged from the system. The stripped fuel oil has only heating energy value, so any C-8 hydrocarbons present represent a loss of valuable byproducts.

The cooled vapor leaves the top of the primary fractionator at a temperature of 210° to 250°F at its hydrocarbon dew point. All of the water vapor in the entering cracked gas passes through this column. The quantity of reflux liquid fed to the upper section should be controlled so that the exit gas stream is not cooled too near the water dew point temperature. However, there must be sufficient reflux to keep the recirculated quench oil viscosity low enough for effective heat-exchanger cooling.

As an example, nine valve trays in the upper section of a 17.4-ft diameter primary fractionator were removed and replaced with #50 IMTP® packing. Because pressure-drop reduction was the primary object, only enough packed depth was installed to equal the efficiency of these nine valve trays. Table 10-2 illustrates the temperature profile of this column before and after the revamp with packing [2]. The pressure drop was lowered from 47.4 in. H_2O with the trays to 10.0 in. H_2O after the revamp at the same capacity. The change to an IMTP® system reduced the pressure drop through the upper section of the column by 86% compared to the nine valve trays, or an overall reduction of 79% of the pressure drop through the entire column.

As plants became larger, the volume of cracked gas flow increased proportionally. To increase column throughput, without having the column diameters become excessively large, tray spacing was increased from 24 in. to 30 in. In such a column there are opportunities for further operational efficiency improvements. The lower open-type trays can re-

Table 10 – 2
Primary Fractionator Temperature Profile

Function	Trayed Column	Packed Column
Vapor to oil quench system	727°F	714°F
Vapor to primary fractionator	367°F	365°F
Quench oil from primary fractionator	361°F	360°F
Quench oil to quench fitting	340°F	342°F
Quench oil to primary fractionator	282°F	275°F
Naphtha reflux to primary fractionator	183°F	180°F
Vapor from primary fractionator	239°F	232°F

Source: Strigle [2].

main in the column and continue to be irrigated with cooled quench oil. With 30-in. tray spacing in the column's upper section, a bed of IMTP® packing can be installed in the top of the column to a depth that equals the efficiency of the seven or more trays replaced. Below this packed bed, another shorter bed of IMTP® packing can be installed which is irrigated with a pumparound of gas oil. This pumparound oil typically is withdrawn from the column at a temperature of 290° to 310°F and returned to the top of this bed at a temperature of 240° to 250°F. Up to 15% of the total cracked gas cooling load for this column can be recovered from the gas oil pumparound bed at a temperature high enough to preheat boiler feedwater. In addition, the column pressure drop still will be almost 70% less than the original trayed column. The high heat transfer efficiency and low pressure drop of IMTP® packing make such a second generation modification possible.

WATER QUENCH COLUMN OPERATION

The overhead vapor from the primary fractionator flows to the water quench column. In this tower the vapor is cooled by direct contact with water. A large percentage of the hydrocarbons of 90 and greater molecular weight condense, as well as most of the water vapor in the cracked gas. The primary function of this column is to condense the dilution stream which was added in the cracking furnaces. In addition, the gas stream temperature is lowered to reduce compression energy requirements.

A typical design for this column involves a lower section equipped with up to 12 open-type trays and an upper section with five to nine fractionating trays. The liquid effluent leaves such a column at a temperature of 170° to 190°F. This effluent is sent to a decanter where the smaller hydrocarbon phase is separated from the larger water phase.

Most of the hydrocarbon from the decanter is fed back to the primary fractionator as reflux; however, a smaller stream is sent to a stabilizer where C-4 and lighter hydrocarbons are removed before further processing of the aromatic naphtha. Overhead vapor from this stripper is returned to the water quench column below the upper section. A part of the water phase, equivalent to the water vapor condensed from the gas stream, is sent to a low pressure stream stripper to remove lower boiling hydrocarbons. Overhead vapor from this stripper is returned to the water quench column below the lower section.

Most of the water phase is recirculated through heat exchange systems to recover energy for reboiling light hydrocarbon fractionators, such as the C-3 splitter. The majority of the recirculated water is returned at a temperature between 125° and 140°F to the center of the water quench tower where it irrigates the lower section. The remainder of the recirculated water typically is cooled to a temperature between 75° and 95°F, and used to irrigate the tower's upper section. Some of the recirculated water may be used to preheat the cracking furnace's liquid feed. The cracked gas leaves the top of the water quench column saturated with both hydrocarbon and water vapor. This gas has a temperature from 8° to 14°F higher than the temperature of the water feed to the upper section in the usual trayed column.

In another example, five two-pass valve trays in the upper section of a 16.7 ft diameter water quench column were replaced with an IMTP® system. Packed depth was only about one-half the column diameter. Table 10-3 shows the column temperature profiles both with the original trays and after revamp with an IMTP® system in the upper section [2]. Pressure drop through the entire water quench tower was 23.7 in. H$_2$O with the original trays, which dropped to 6.0 in. H$_2$O after revamp of the upper section. Pressure drop through the upper section of the column was 90% less than with valve trays, while the overall column pressure drop was reduced by 75% at the same capacity.

The pressure profile through the plant revamped with an IMTP® system in the upper sections of both the primary fractionator and the water

Table 10 – 3
Water Quench Tower Temperature Profile

Function	Trayed Column	Packed Column
Vapor to quench column	239°F	232°F
Liquid from quench column	183°F	181°F
Water to middle of column	129°F	127°F
Water to top of column	79°F	86°F
Vapor from quench column	93°F	91°F

Source: Strigle [2].

Table 10 - 4
Hot Section Pressure Profile

Function	Trayed Columns	Packed Columns
Steam cracker discharge	30.0 psia	30.2 psia
Primary fractionator inlet	27.0 psia	27.2 psia
Primary fractionator outlet	25.3 psia	26.8 psia
Quench column inlet	24.5 psia	26.0 psia
Quench column outlet	23.6 psia	25.7 psia
First stage compressor suction	23.2 psia	25.3 psia

Source: Strigle [2].

quench tower is shown in Table 10-4. In this plant, the discharge pressure from the first-stage compressor was 51.2 psia. Before revamp, a 2.21 compression ratio was required from the first-stage compressor. Revamping the upper sections of both columns with IMTP® systems lowered the required compression ratio to 2.02 for the same discharge pressure (see Figure 10-2).

Typically, the vapor entering the water quench column has a water dew point temperature of 180° to 195°F. If the effluent liquid temperature could be increased by only 5°F, the useful heat available for *cold section* reboilers would increase from 77% to 82% of the total heat load on the water quench column. A closer temperature approach between vapor and liquid at the bottom of the tower would require an increase in the number of transfer units obtained from the lower section of the tower. Replacing the open-type trays in this section with an IMTP® system increases the number of transfer units available by at least 70%, but does not increase the pressure drop.

When the cracking furnace feed is ethane or propane, only a small amount of C-4 hydrocarbons and aromatics are present in the cracked gas stream (see Table 10-1). The gas stream from the transfer line exchangers, at a temperature of 360° to 630°F, is fed directly to the water quench column. The previous discussion of revamp opportunities for this tower also applies to such a plant. However, pressure drop reductions are limited to those resulting from revamp of the water quench column only.

INTERSTAGE GAS COOLING

The cooled cracked gas from the water quench column is compressed to a pressure greater than the operating pressure of the demethanizer. Usually four or five stages of compression are required. This is necessary because the temperature rise per stage is controlled to prevent poly-

Figure 10-2. This primary fractionator and water quench tower were revamped with IMTP® packing.

merization of dienes in the gas stream and reduce the fouling rate of the gas coolers. The gas is cooled after each compression stage and liquid condensates separated from the gas stream. Gas coolers typically are tube-and-shell heat exchangers. The discharge pressure from the first compression stage is about 50 psia, and the suction pressure on the second compression stage is 5 psi to 6 psi lower, primarily due to the pressure drop through these heat exchangers. If the discharge pressure from the second compression stage is to be 90 psia, then the second-stage compressor in the conventional plant requires a compression ratio of 2.02.

The usual heat exchangers can be replaced with a packed column that will cool the gas by direct contact with water which is available at 75° to 95°F. This is the same temperature as the pumparound feed to the top of the water quench column. The pressure of this water can be raised by a single-stage pump so that it can be fed to the top of a packed interstage cooler. Gas leaving the first compression stage will be at a temperature of about 180° to 200°F. The packed interstage cooler can be designed to cool this gas stream to a temperature within 5° to 9°F of the inlet water temperature. Liquid effluent from the packed cooler typically will be at a temperature of 130° to 135°F. This effluent can be returned directly to the center of the water quench column because its temperature is similar to that of the water return at that location. A vapor/liquid separator is not needed following a packed cooler since the condensed water vapor and hydrocarbon are sent to the water quench column.

Because the gas-phase density in the first interstage cooler is much greater than that in the water quench tower, the packed cooler diameter will be a maximum of 75% that of the top of a well-designed packed quench tower. The packed interstage cooler will have less than 10% of the pressure drop of the tube-and-shell heat exchangers; thus, the compression ratio for the second-stage compressor with 90 psia discharge pressure would be reduced from 2.02 to only 1.86. This compression power reduction is almost as great as that obtained by replacing trays in the upper sections of the primary fractionator and water quench columns. If the discharge pressure from the third-stage compressor is about 170 psia, a similar reduction in the pressure drop between stages could be obtained by using a packed second interstage cooler. In addition to reducing the power requirements on these compression stages, the lower compression ratios decrease outlet gas temperatures. This will reduce the formation of polymer from dienes present in the cracked gas.

ACID GAS REMOVAL

After several compression stages, the gas stream pressure has been raised to between 140 psia and 180 psia. At this pressure the gas stream is washed with a caustic soda solution to remove all the acidic components present. Typically, the inlet gas stream will contain from 300 ppm to 1,000 ppm of H_2S plus CO_2. The exit gas specifications will be 1 ppm to 5 ppm of the total acid gas by volume, which will prevent icing in the cold section fractionators. The caustic scrubber usually consists of a column with 30 to 50 total trays. The upper three to five trays serve as a water-wash section to prevent caustic carry-over in the exit gas stream. The remaining trays comprise either two or three pumparound sections. Fresh sodium hydroxide solution is fed to the upper scrubbing section along with the pumparound return liquid. Excess partially spent solution overflows the trap tray at the bottom of each section and goes into the next lower scrubbing section where it is mixed with pumparound liquid returned from the bottom of that section. The liquid effluent from the column is a salt solution in which 65% to 75% of the sodium hydroxide has been consumed. Pressure drop through the trayed column normally is 5 psi to 8 psi.

The design of trayed columns for this service is limited by caustic carry-over in the exit gas stream and solution foaming in the column. The use of #50 IMTP® packing for the column revamp permits a 40% increase in capacity compared to trays on 24 in. spacing. Even at this higher throughput, pressure drop for the packed column will be only 40% to 50% that of a trayed column at the lower capacity. A caustic scrubber using an IMTP® system requires a packed depth that is only 80% of the mass transfer height with trays for the same acid gas removal efficiency. A three-stage packed scrubber can be designed to utilize 80% to 85% of the sodium hydroxide in the feed; thus, chemical costs are reduced as well as spent caustic disposal problems. In addition, the lower pressure drop of a packed caustic scrubber reduces power requirements for the compressors that follow it.

OLEFINS PLANT COLD SECTION

The *cold section* of an ethylene plant consists of the gas chillers through the aromatic naphtha recovery system. Each operation in the cold section will be considered with respect to the following criteria:

1. Increase in capacity possible without separation efficiency loss.
2. Increase of product recovery at a fixed purity without capacity reduction.
3. Reduction of energy requirements per unit of capacity at the same product specification.

Following the last compression stage, the cracked gas is dried by a dessicant. This lowers the water dew point enough to prevent formation of solid hydrates in the cryogenic distillation columns that follow. The dried gas is passed through a series of coolers and gas/liquid separators to remove most of the hydrogen and other non-condensable gases, plus about 30% of the methane. Condensed liquids are fed to the demethanizer at several different locations from the top downward in order of increasing molecular weights.

The bottoms from the demethanizer is fed to the deethanizer as shown in Figure 10-1. Overhead from that column contains all of the C-2 hydrocarbons present in the feed. After removal of the acetylene content, this overhead product serves as feed to the C-2 splitter for separation of the ethylene product.

The bottoms from the deethanizer is fed to the depropanizer. Overhead from that column contains all of the C-3 hydrocarbons present in the feed. Both methyl acetylene and propadiene must be removed from this stream before further processing. The purified distillate then serves as feed to the C-3 splitter for separation of the propylene product.

The bottoms from the depropanizer is fed to the debutanizer. Overhead from that column is processed further to recover the valuable monomers—1,3 butadiene and 1-butene—from the other C-4 hydrocarbons. The bottoms from the debutanizer contains all the C-5 and heavier hydrocarbons present in the feed gas to the cold section. This liquid is valuable as a gasoline blending stock. Alternatively, the debutanizer bottoms can be combined with the bottoms liquid from the naphtha stabilizer following the water quench tower. This mixture then can be processed to recover its aromatic hydrocarbon content.

DEMETHANIZER OPERATION

The primary function of this column is removing methane from the heavier hydrocarbons in the condensed liquid feed streams. Any methane remaining in the bottoms otherwise will be eliminated in the pasteurization section at the top of the C-2 splitter. The ethylene can be recovered by recycling this C-2 splitter overhead vapor stream through the last two compression stages for return to the demethanizer. However, this vapor stream consists of 10 to 16 times as many mols of ethylene as methane. This large recycle gas stream consumes additional energy for compression as well as for reboiling in the demethanizer. A second function of the demethanizer is the recovery of C-2 and higher molecular weight hydrocarbons from the liquid feeds. Additional information on the design of such columns has been presented in Chapter 8.

The demethanizer normally has a smaller diameter upper section than lower section. This column usually operates at a pressure of 430 psia to 520 psia with a refrigerated partial condenser which produces a top column temperature of − 130° to − 145°F. A trayed column typically contains 50 to 70 actual trays with 50% to 60% of these trays below the bottom feed point. In this column the liquid surface tension is very low as is the density difference between liquid and vapor phases. As a result, trayed column capacity normally is limited by downcomer performance. Due to the active area required for vapor flow, plus the large size of downcomers, the cross-sectional area of a trayed demethanizer is rather generous compared to throughput. In many cases this tower can be revamped using #25 IMTP® packing to provide the same capacity, while using larger sizes of IMTP® packing would permit capacity increases of 20% to 40%.

By revamping the demethanizer with #25 IMTP® packing, the number of theoretical stages can be increased by 50% to 60% over the trayed column. These additional theoretical stages can reduce the methane content of the bottoms liquid, as well as reduce the ethylene loss in the overhead vapor. With an IMTP® system, the column configuration can be modified without welding on the shell so that the additional theoretical stages can be used to the greatest advantage. In one such revamp of a 280,000 metric ton/year naphtha-fed plant, ethylene losses overhead were reduced by 87% while the methane content of the bottoms also was lowered by over 80% [3].

The minimum ethylene content of the overhead vapor is controlled by the dew point at the operating pressure and temperature. The dew point, in turn, is a function of the vapor's hydrogen and methane contents. However, additional theoretical stages in the demethanizer permit a reduction in reflux ratio which reduces the condenser refrigeration load.

DEETHANIZER OPERATION

Bottoms liquid from the demethanizer, at a temperature of 30° to 50°F, is fed to the deethanizer. The primary function of this column is recovery of ethylene and ethane from the feed. The overhead vapor also contains all the methane and acetylene present in the feed, as well as some propylene that is stripped to ensure complete C-2 recovery.

The deethanizer in a naphtha-fed olefins plant also is a column with a smaller diameter upper section than lower section. This column operates at a pressure between 340 psia and 410 psia with a top temperature of 0° to 20°F. A trayed column typically contains 45 to 70 actual trays. Again the liquid surface tension is very low and the density difference between the liquid phase and the vapor phase is small. The capacity of a trayed column, therefore, usually is limited by the downcomers. In a trayed tower, the cross-sectional area is rather large compared to vapor flow rate. Replacing trays with an IMTP® system increases the capacity by about 35% above the design rate for the trays.

If no additional capacity is needed, revamp of a trayed column with a smaller size of IMTP® packing increases the number of theoretical stages by up to 20%. These additional theoretical stages permit operation at a lower reflux ratio. This, in turn, reduces the condenser's refrigeration duty requirement.

ETHYLENE/ETHANE FRACTIONATOR

The overhead from the deethanizer, after removal of acetylene, serves as a superheated vapor feed to the C-2 splitter. The primary function of this tower is production of a polymer-grade ethylene. The secondary function is recovery of ethylene from the feed, because the bottoms from this column usually is reprocessed by recycling to an ethane/propane cracking furnace.

The C-2 splitter normally operates at a pressure of 260 psia to 320 psia with a top temperature of − 30° to − 10°F. The C-2 splitter typically consists of two columns, operated in series, that are equipped with a total of 120 to 160 actual trays. The feed enters the first column which has a reboiler at its base. The overhead vapor from this column goes to the bottom of the second column. Liquid from the bottom of the second column is pumped to the top of the first column. The upper 8 to 11 actual trays in the second column serve as pasteurization section that removes the small amount of methane present in the feed. The ethylene product is withdrawn as a liquid sidestream below the pasteurization section. Any propylene in the feed leaves in the liquid bottoms from the first column.

In the past, the polymer-grade product specification called for 99.90% pure ethylene. However, there recently has been an increased demand for greater purities, up to 99.97% ethylene. Impurities in the product consist of methane and ethane usually in the ratio of 2.4 to 3.0 mol of ethane per mol of methane. The ethylene recovered as product should not be less than 94% of that present in the feed stream.

A revamp of a 10-ft 3-in. ID C-2 fractionator with IMTP® packing provided a 27% increase in feed rate over the design capacity of the original trayed column. In addition, the packed column developed almost 25% more theoretical stages than the trayed column. This permitted an 11% reduction in reflux ratio, while simultaneously increasing product purity from 99.92% to 99.95% ethylene. This C-2 splitter used an external heat pump system that condensed propylene in the reboiler and evaporated it in the condenser. The revamp reduced the energy consumption for this system as a result of the lower reflux ratio. Further, the lower fractionator pressure drop provided by the packing reduced the propylene condensing pressure required, thereby saving energy on the external vapor compressor. Thus, the IMTP® system provided the desired increase in column capacity as well as in product purity.

DEPROPANIZER OPERATION

The bottoms liquid from the deethanizer serves as the principal feed to the depropanizer. A second feed stream to this column consists of the bottoms liquid from the condensate stripper for the fourth and fifth compression stages. The primary function of this column is propylene and propane recovery from these two feeds. This column can be operated at a pressure from 240 psia to 340 psia with a top temperature of 100° to 140°F. The overhead from this column contains all of the C-3 hydrocarbons present in the feed, as well as some C-4 hydrocarbons that' are stripped to provide complete recovery of C-3 components. C-2 hydrocarbon content in the distillate is negligible due to the overstripping commonly carried out in the preceding deethanizer.

A depropanizer normally contains 35 to 55 actual trays and has a uniform diameter. When no additional capacity is required, a revamp of this column with an IMTP® system can develop at least a 20% increase in the number of theoretical stages over the trayed tower. These additional separation stages allow use of a lower reflux ratio, thus reducing the reboiler and condenser heat loads.

In this tower the liquid surface tension is low and the vapor density is about 7% of the liquid density. The downcomers, therefore, require a large percentage of the column cross-sectional area, so vapor rates are low compared to column diameter. A revamp with a large size of IMTP® packing permits up to a 30% increase in column throughput. This greater capacity is obtained without loss of separating efficiency.

In a depropanizer diene polymers may tend to form in the stripping section of the column. The polymer formation is a function of time, temperature, and diene concentration in the column. The temperature and concentrations in both trayed and packed columns are similar; however, the liquid holdup with the IMTP® packing is reduced by 70% to 75% compared to trays, which greatly decreases liquid residence time in the depropanizer. Although there may be a slow deposition of polymer on the packing elements, just as on the tray surfaces, because of the accessibility of all IMTP® packing surfaces, polymer build-up has been removed simply by circulating a solvent over the packed bed.

PROPYLENE/PROPANE FRACTIONATOR

Overhead from the depropanizer, after removal of highly unsaturated C-3 hydrocarbons, is fed to the C-3 splitter. The primary function of this tower is production of polymer grade propylene; or, in some cases, chemical grade propylene. A secondary function is the recovery of propylene from the feed because the bottoms from this column either is re-cycled to an ethane/propane cracking furnace or is used as propane fuel.

A C-3 splitter producing polymer grade propylene normally consists of two columns in a series containing a total of 150 to 180 actual trays. The feed usually enters the first column, which has a reboiler at its base. Overhead vapor from the first column goes to the bottom of the second column. The liquid from the bottom of the second column is pumped back to the top of the first column. The C-3 splitter normally operates at a minimum pressure of 230 psia, which is sufficient to condense the overhead vapor at a temperature of 100°F with available cooling water. Because the bottom column temperature is only about 120°F, the lower pumparound water from the water quench tower can serve as an energy source for this column. To use this source of heat, as well as to keep the relative volatility as high as possible, operating pressure for this column normally does not exceed 290 psia.

The polymer grade product is 98.4% to 99.6% propylene with propane as the major impurity. The distillate also contains the small amount of ethane present in the feed; however, a pasteurization section usually is not required to meet the product specifications. Chemical grade has a wide range of purities, but typically contains around 93% propylene. Normally, about 98% of the propylene in the feed is recovered in the product.

Because of the very high percentage of propylene recovery, plus high product purity specified for polymer grade, the reflux ratio required for a C-3 splitter usually is greater than 10 to 1. This system also is complicated by a shift in relative volatility of propylene to propane with the liquid-phase composition. The relative volatility drops from 1.14 in the propane-rich bottom section of the column to only 1.08 in the propylene-rich top section. Revamping such a column with an IMTP® system provides up to a 20% increase in the number of theoretical stages available, as compared to the trayed tower, without reduction in column capacity.

Where capacity is the primary interest, revamping the tower with an IMTP® system permits an increase of 15% in the feed rate without any operational changes. However, because IMTP® packing provides more theoretical stages of separation, the reflux ratio can be reduced. This combination of higher allowable vapor rate and lower reflux ratio provides a 25% increase in the available product rate for a column revamped with an IMTP® system.

In some situations, refinery feedstock is fractionated to polymer grade propylene. In such a case, surplus energy is not available as 170° to 190°F water from a *hot section*. Lower reflux ratios therefore are desired to reduce energy consumption. In these situations, a heat-pumped fractionator offers a viable option when a packed column is used because of the lower operating pressure drop [4]. A heat-pumped system can operate at a reduced column pressure—150 psia to 180 psia—which increases the relative volatility between propylene and propane. The lower permissible reflux ratio, as well as the pressure drop of only 2.6 psi per 100 theoretical stages for IMTP® packing, keeps energy input to a minimum and permits the use of a single-stage vapor compressor.

DEBUTANIZER OPERATION

The bottoms liquid from the depropanizer is fed to the debutanizer. The primary function of this column is recovery of all C-4 compounds from the feed. This column usually operates at a pressure from 70 to 130 psia and is equipped with 25 to 40 actual trays. The distillate product contains 98% to 99% of the C-4 hydrocarbons present in the feed. This distillate also contains all the propane present in the feed, plus a small amount of C-5 hydrocarbons.

Replacing the trays with an IMTP® system provides up to a 30% increase in the number of theoretical stages compared to a trayed column with the same capacity. These additional theoretical stages can be utilized to reduce the reflux ratio. This lower reflux flow, plus the increased vapor handling capacity of IMTP® packing, permits an increase in product rate up to 30%. In addition, the greatly reduced liquid residence time provided by IMTP® packing minimizes any formation of diene polymers in the rectifying section.

OTHER FRACTIONATING ARRANGEMENTS

The processing scheme just discussed is the most common sequence of fractionating columns in the *cold section* of an olefins plant; however, it is not the only sequence in industrial use. The process offered by Linde A. G. utilizes the deethanizer as the first column in the *cold section* [5]. The overhead from this column contains all the hydrogen, methane, and C-2 hydrocarbons present in the feed. This stream is hydrogenated to remove the acetylene, then cooled to condense the hydrocarbons leaving a gaseous hydrogen product. The condensed liquid fractions serve as feeds to the demethanizer in which the methane is stripped overhead. The demethanizer bottoms is fed to the C-2 splitter for fractionation of the ethylene product. The bottoms from the original deethanizer is the feed to the depropanizer, and the balance of the fractionation train uses the same sequence as previously described.

A different scheme is offered by C. F. Braun and Co., which takes the effluent vapor from the acid gas removal system and, after drying and cooling, feeds it to the depropanizer [6]. The overhead from this column is compressed to around 540 psia, hydrogenated to remove acetylenes and dienes, and chilled to separate a hydrogen stream from the condensed hydrocarbons. Liquid condensates contain methane plus the C-2 and C-3 hydrocarbons present in the feed to the depropanizer. These liquids are fed to the demethanizer, which strips the methane overhead. The demethanizer bottoms serve as feed to the deethanizer. The overhead from that column goes to the C-2 splitter, while the bottoms is the feed to the C-3 splitter. The bottoms liquid from the original depropanizer is sent to the debutanizer for separation of the C-4 hydrocarbons from the aromatic gasoline fraction.

This chapter has reviewed all the major columns in an olefins plant. In addition, there are many smaller columns that can justify either a revamp to tower packing or a combination with another packed column. This discussion has not considered the towers which further process the C-4 hydrocarbons or those which recover the aromatic fractions from the debutanizer and the aromatic naphtha stabilizer. IMTP® systems have been installed in such applications, as well as in the aromatics processing section. Naturally, each application must be evaluated for its own economics. The justification for each revamp will depend on capacity requirements and local energy charges, as well as construction and capital costs.

REFERENCES

1. "Petrochemical Handbook," *Hydrocarbon Processing*, Vol. 48, No. 11, 1969, p. 176.
2. Strigle, R. F., and Hiramatsu, K., *Oil and Gas Journal*, Vol. 81, No. 39, 1983, p. 63.
3. Buffenoir, M. H., *Oil and Gas Journal*, Vol. 80, No. 36, 1982, p. 78.
4. Danziger, R., *Chemical Engineering Progress*, Vol. 75, No. 1, 1979, p. 58.
5. "Petrochemical Handbook," *Hydrocarbon Processing*, Vol. 58, No. 11, 1979, p. 161.
6. Clancy, G. M., and Townsend, R. W., *Chemical Engineering Progress*, Vol. 67, No. 2, 1971, p. 41.

11

LIQUID-LIQUID EXTRACTION

Many industrially important solutions of liquids form constant boiling mixtures (azeotropes) or have components with such close boiling points that separation of these liquids by ordinary distillation is not practical. Various other methods of separation have been applied to such systems including liquid-liquid extraction. Compared to distillation as a means of separation, liquid-liquid extraction is a more recent operation. It has reached industrial significance only since 1930 [1].

Liquid-liquid extraction involves the contacting of a solution with an immiscible solvent in which one or more of the original solution components is soluble. Thus, two liquid phases are formed after addition of the new solvent. These two immiscible phases separate because of a difference in densities. Some component of the original solution will be more soluble in the new solvent than in the original solvent; thus, this component will be extracted from the original solution through contact with the new solvent.

GENERAL CONSIDERATIONS

In liquid-liquid extractions, at least one component in the original mixture to be separated must be soluble in the new solvent while the other components are not as soluble. Thus, we are concerned with two separate immiscible or partially miscible liquid phases and at least one solute component. These two phases must be mutually insoluble or exhibit a very limited mutual solubility. However, the transferred component which is to be separated is soluble in both liquid phases.

Systems using liquid-liquid extractions fall into two categories:

1. Those systems in which mass transfer takes place because of differences in solubility of the solute in the two solvents.

240

2. Those systems in which mass transfer takes place due to a subsequent chemical reaction of one or more of the solutes in the original mixture with the new solvent.

Examples of some liquid-liquid extractions are given in Table 11-1.

Table 11 - 1
Typical Liquid-Liquid Extractions

Original Solvent	Solute	New Solvent
Water	Acetic Acid	Benzene
Water	Adipic Acid	Diethyl Ether
Reformate	Aromatics	Diethylene Glycol
Water	Benzoic Acid	Carbon Tetrachloride
Water	Diethylamine	Toluene
LPG	H_2S	MEA
Naphtha	Mercaptans	NaOH Solution
Water	MEK	Toluene
Lubricating Oil	Naphthenes	Furfural
Water	Phenol	Chlorobenzene

It is necessary that we define the terms customarily used in connection with extraction. The mixture which is to be separated consists of the solute C to be recovered which is present in solvent A. This solution is the *feed* to the extractor. This solvent A feed, after removal of at least some solute C, is called the *raffinate* as it leaves the extractor. The second liquid phase, with which the original mixture is contacted, consists of solvent B containing little or no solute C, and is termed the *solvent*. This solvent B, after being enriched in solute C, is called the *extract* as it leaves the extractor. Thus in an extractor operating in the usual countercurrent manner, the feed is in contact with the extract leaving at one end and the solvent is in contact with the raffinate leaving at the other end. The solute C which is separated from the feed mixture leaves in the extract phase mixed with solvent B. It is apparent that the solute cannot be recovered in highly pure form by a liquid-liquid extraction as may be possible in a distillation. Thus to recover the solute, the extract must be subjected to some additional purifying operation such as evaporation, distillation, crystallization, or adsorption.

EXTRACTOR OPERATION

Extraction often is carried out in a packed tower. The more dense phase is introduced into the top of the column and the less dense phase is introduced into the bottom. To achieve mass transfer of solute C between solvent A and immiscible solvent B, these solvents must be in intimate contact; thus one phase must be dispersed in the other phase. The dispersed phase travels through the continuous phase in the form of droplets. It follows that in order to obtain flow of the dispersed phase through the continuous phase, the two phases must be of different densities. Further, for continuous, countercurrent contacting, this density difference between phases must exist throughout the entire packed tower since the density of the phases may change significantly due to transfer of the solute.

DEPICTION OF LIQUID EXTRACTION

Since it is difficult to represent a system of three components on a rectangular diagram, a triangular diagram frequently is used. In Figure 11-1, A and B are the two solvents and C is the solute. A feature of the triangular diagram is that at any point the summation of the concentrations of components A, B, and C always is 100%.

A common characteristic of liquid extraction systems is that the mutual solubility of the solvents A and B increases with an increase in the concentration of solute C. This is illustrated in Figure 11-1, where, at a sufficiently high concentration of solute C, solvents A and B become completely miscible and a single-phase system results.

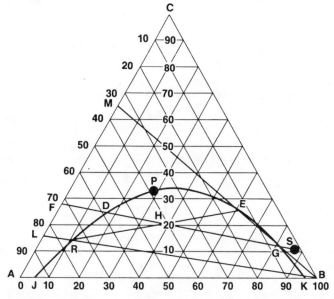

Figure 11-1. Equilibrium relation—triangular diagram.

MUTUAL SOLUBILITIES

Figure 11-1 is a triangular diagram representing a system in which water and benzene are the two solvents (A and B, respectively) and an organic acid is the solute C. Benzene is contacted with the aqueous feed solution to extract the organic acid. Point J represents the solubility of benzene in water and Point K represents the solubility of water in benzene. Curve JRPEK represents the equilibrium among these three components at a particular temperature. Any point under this curve represents a mixture which will separate into two liquid phases. A point outside the curve represents the composition of a single homogeneous phase.

There exists a definite concentration relationship between the two liquid phases at equilibrium. In Figure 11-1, the feed to the extractor is a solution of organic acid in water represented by Point F. The solvent to the extractor is partially stripped benzene of a composition represented by Point S. The feed and solvent form a mixture of the composition represented by Point H. If the extractor consists of one equilibrium stage, mixture H will separate into two phases so that the composition of the extract will be represented by Point E and the composition of the raffinate by Point R. The composition at Point E will be in equilibrium with the concentration at Point R.

The ratio of the concentration of solute in benzene to the concentration of solute in water is called the distribution coefficient for this temperature:

$$K_D = \frac{x_E}{x_R} \tag{11-1}$$

This distribution coefficient is similar to the Henry's Law constant in absorption operations. For a single solute which is only sparingly soluble in the two solvents, the distribution coefficient would be the ratio of the solubilities of the solute in each of the two liquid phases. For more soluble materials (higher solute concentrations), the distribution coefficient may be significantly different than the ratio of the solubilities in the two solvents.

In Figure 11-1, line ER connects the composition of an extract phase with the composition of a raffinate phase with which it is in equilibrium. Such lines are known as *tie lines*. These tie lines move vertically as the compositions of the two phases approach each other until only a single phase exists as shown in Figure 11-2. The point on curve JRPEK where a single liquid phase is formed is called the *plait point* (Point P). The interfacial tension approaches zero as the plait point is approached.

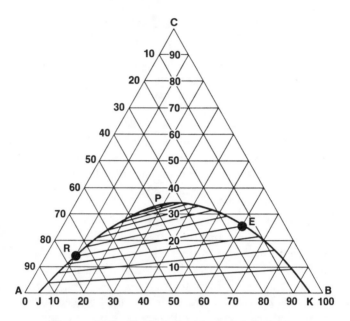

Figure 11-2. Tie lines on triangular diagram.

EFFECT OF TEMPERATURE AND PRESSURE

In most cases, solubility of the solute increases at higher temperatures; however, the change in solubility with temperature may not be the same in both solvents. Thus, the distribution coefficient for a solute between two solvents may increase or decrease as the temperature rises.

Since solubility usually increases at higher temperatures, above some temperature normally there will exist one homogeneous phase regardless of composition. This temperature is known as the *critical solution temperature*. At lower temperatures, both the composition of the mixture and the temperature will determine whether one or two liquid phases exist. However, the vapor pressure of the solvents also increases at higher temperatures. In some systems, vaporization of the liquid phase occurs before the critical solution temperature is reached.

Solubility of a solute is only slightly influenced by pressure. This effect can be predicted from the principle of LeChatelier. If the volume of the liquid phase increases with an increase in solute concentration, a higher pressure of operation will decrease solubility.

INTERFACIAL TENSION

There exists an interfacial tension between the two liquid phases. Quite often the interfacial tension between the two liquid solvents is altered markedly by the presence of the solute. While high values of interfacial tension tend to increase the difficulty of dispersing one phase in another, a large value of interfacial tension will promote coalescence of the dispersed phase droplets. On the other hand, low values of interfacial tension may produce an emulsion of the dispersed phase. The tiny droplets of such an emulsion do not separate easily from the continuous phase, which makes operation of the extractor very difficult.

The interfacial tension between the two phases cannot be calculated as the difference between the individual phase surface tensions measured against air. Generally interfacial tension is reduced by the presence of a dissolved solute. Donahue and Bartell empirically correlated interfacial tension and mutual solubilities of binary pairs of liquids in the absence of a solute [2]. Treybal reported that this correlation also predicted eight different ternary systems from available data [3]. His modified correlation is shown as Figure 11-3. In this figure x_{AB} is the mol fraction of

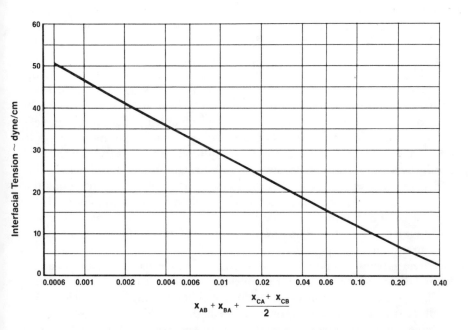

Figure 11-3. Treybal correlation for interfacial tension. (From Treybal [3]. Reprinted from *Liquid Extraction* by permission. Copyright © 1963, McGraw-Hill.)

solvent A dissolved in solvent B, x_{BA} is the mol fraction of solvent B dissolved in solvent A, x_{CA} is the mol fraction of solute C dissolved in solvent A, and x_{CB} is the mol fraction of solute C dissolved in solvent B. For binary liquid systems, Girifalco and Good showed that there is a relationship between interfacial tension and the hydrogen-bonding characteristics and molal volumes [4].

SOLVENT SELECTION

The two solvents for practical purposes should be immiscible; however, in most cases there is some mutual solubility of the solvents such as is indicated in Figure 11-1. The solvent selected should exhibit a high selectivity—it must dissolve the maximum amount of the solute and a minimum amount of the other solvent. The distribution coefficient should be large to reduce the number of theoretical stages required in the extractor. Since the solute C must be recovered from solvent B in the extract and any dissolved solvent B recovered from the raffinate, lines from Point B on Figure 11-1 can be extended through the extract and raffinate compositions to intersect line AC at Points M and L respectively. The farther the displacement of points M and L from the feed (Point F), the greater the selectivity of the solvent and the larger the amount of separation obtained per theoretical stage.

The capacity of the solvent for dissolving the solute must be large, otherwise the solvent circulation rate required may be uneconomical. Also, the solvent selected must be separated easily from the solute. The cost of separation and recovery of the solute and solvent significantly influences the economics of the entire liquid-liquid extraction operation.

The solvent must have a significant difference in density from the feed otherwise the hydraulic capacity of the extractor will be low. Further, this density difference still must exist after transfer of the solute. Thus the extract and raffinate phases across any tie line (as shown in Figure 11-2) must be of different densities if contacted in a continuous manner. Francis suggests that the formation of two phases of equal density can occur in many ternary systems [5,6].

The solvent should have a low viscosity, otherwise the column capacity will be reduced and the rate of settling of the dispersion will be slow. The solvent chosen must not produce such a low interfacial tension after solute transfer that an emulsion is formed. In addition, the solvent selected should be readily available and inexpensive. Many organic solvents pose special restrictions in their use due to flammability or high-vapor pressure. Also, the solvent selected should be nontoxic and

Table 11-2
Miscibility of Various Solvents

1. Water
2. Diethylene Glycol
3. Triethylene Glycol
4. Furfural
5. Diethyl Ether
6. Benzene
7. Cyclohexane
8. n-Heptane

Source: Oberg [1]. Reprinted by special permission from *Chemical Engineering*, Vol. 70, No. 15, 1963. Copyright © 1963, by McGraw-Hill, Inc., New York, N.Y. 10020.

noncarcinogenic and not corrode common materials of construction, so as to improve ease of handling and reduce capital cost of equipment.

Oberg and Jones present a simplified method for determining the miscibility of various solvents [1]. Typical solvents are listed in order in Table 11-2. Water at the top of this table is virtually immiscible with n-heptane at the bottom of the table. Each solvent is completely miscible with those located within two positions of it in the table. There is a relatively high miscibility with those located three away from it in the table. On the other hand, there is a relatively low miscibility with those located four away from it in the table. Any liquids located five or more positions away from each other in the table are practically immiscible.

ALTERNATE CALCULATION PROCEDURES

In distillation calculations, the system is depicted by rectangular coordinates that plot the concentration of light key in the vapor vs. the concentration of light key in the liquid. It is possible to depict a liquid-liquid extraction in a similar manner. As shown in Figure 11-4, the concentration of solute in the extract phase can be plotted against the concentration of solute in the raffinate phase. The slope of this equilibrium curve is represented by the distribution coefficient.

EQUILIBRIUM CONSIDERATIONS

The equilibrium between the extract and the raffinate is characterized by the same activity in both phases. In this case Equation 11-1 can be rewritten in terms of the activity coefficients:

$$K_D = \frac{\gamma_{CR}}{\gamma_{CE}}$$

(11-2)

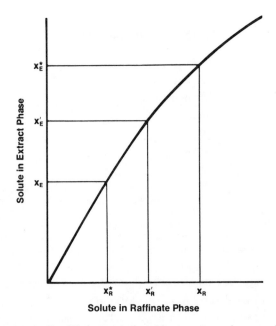

Figure 11-4. Equilibrium relationship—rectangular coordinates.

where γ_{CR} is the activity coefficient for solute C in the raffinate and γ_{CE} is the activity coefficient for solute C in the extract.

If the purpose of the extraction operation is the separation of two solutes (component C and component D) which are present in the feed mixture, the selectivity of the solvent B for each of the two solutes must be considered. The degree of separation of the two solutes is given by:

$$S_D = \frac{K_{DC}}{K_{DD}} \tag{11-3}$$

which is the ratio of the distribution coefficients for the two solutes. In such systems, activities can vary due to interactions between components. The degree of separation can vary substantially with concentration as the two solutes vie for the same limited amount of solvent.

RATES OF MASS TRANSFER

To produce mass transfer of solute between the two solvents a driving force is necessary. This driving force usually is expressed in terms of the concentrations of solute in the two phases and the departure from equilibrium values. The rate of mass transfer of solute C from the feed (solvent A) in the extract (solvent B) is:

$$N = K_E a A Z (x_E^* - x_E) \qquad (11\text{-}4)$$

Alternately, the rate of mass transfer of solute C for the raffinate phase is:

$$N = K_R a A Z (x_R - x_R^*) \qquad (11\text{-}5)$$

These relationships are illustrated diagramically in Figure 11-4.

If we consider the mass transfer from the two-film theory, the transfer through the extract liquid film from the interface is:

$$N = k_E a A Z (x_E' - x_E) \qquad (11\text{-}6)$$

Likewise, the transfer through the raffinate liquid film to the interface is:

$$N = k_R a A Z (x_R - x_R') \qquad (11\text{-}7)$$

The resistance to mass transfer through each film is the reciprocal of the film mass transfer coefficient. As is true in other forms of mass transfer, the resistances in the two films are additive. Thus we have the overall resistance in the extract phase:

$$\frac{1}{K_E} = \frac{1}{k_E} + \frac{m}{k_R} \qquad (11\text{-}8)$$

Similarly, in the raffinate phase:

$$\frac{1}{K_R} = \frac{1}{k_R} + \frac{1}{m k_E} \qquad (11\text{-}9)$$

In these equations m is the slope of the equilibrium curve as illustrated in Figure 11-4.

If the distribution coefficient representing the concentration of solute in the extract to the concentration of solute in the raffinate is large, m will have a value greater than unity and the main resistance to mass transfer will be in the raffinate phase. If the distribution coefficient is small, m will have a value less than unity and the main resistance to mass transfer will be in the extract phase.

REACTIVE SYSTEMS

If solvent B is a solution that contains a material that will react with solute C, the solubility in the extract phase will increase. If the reaction is rapid, the reactant in solvent B will diffuse toward the liquid film and react there with the solute C diffusing through the interface. In this case the diffusion of the reactant in solvent B may control the mass transfer rate. However, fast reactions in the extract phase usually exhibit the main resistance to mass transfer in the raffinate phase. If the reaction is slower, solute C will diffuse some distance into the main body of solvent B before the reaction is completed. In most cases, a chemical reaction in the extract phase increases the rate of mass transfer.

When the reaction between solvent B and solute C is irreversible, the value of x_E^* approaches zero. Such would be the case if H_2S were extracted from LPG using an aqueous solution of caustic soda as the solvent. However, if the chemical reaction is reversible so that the solute can be recovered, then x_E^* will have a low value that is dependent on the concentrations of the reactants and the temperature. Such a system might be the extraction of H_2S from LPG using an aqueous ethanol-amine solvent. The extract phase subsequently would be regenerated to permit reuse of the amine solvent.

DISPERSED PHASE

In designing an extractor, it is necessary to select which of the two solvent phases will be dispersed with the object of maximizing the rate of mass transfer. Some criteria for this selection are:

1. Maximize interfacial area.
2. Minimize liquid-film resistance.
3. Maximize column capacity.
4. Avoid coalescence within the packed bed.

A consideration in the rate of mass transfer is the interfacial area available. If the phase with the largest volumetric flow is dispersed, the surface area available for mass transfer from the droplets is maximized.

In most systems, dispersion of the organic phase into the aqueous phase results in the formation of stable, normal-shaped, dispersed phase droplets. However, Blanding and Elgin reported that in certain systems irregular-shaped, dispersed phase droplets were produced when the aqueous phase was dispersed into the organic phase [7]. They also reported that nonuniformity of the droplet shape affected the flooding rate.

If one of the liquid films offers the major resistance to mass transfer, that high-resistance phase should be dispersed to maximize mass transfer rates. This is done to reduce the required distance the solute must be diffused in the phase in which resistance is greatest.

If the higher viscosity solvent is the continuous phase, the dispersed phase droplet rate of rise will be reduced. This increases the contact time between phases and the total mass of solute transferred; however, a high viscosity continuous phase lowers the column capacity. If the higher viscosity solvent is the dispersed phase, the rate of diffusion of solute in the dispersed phase will be reduced. Breckenfeld and Wilke reported that dispersed phase viscosity had little effect on hydraulic capacity [8].

Ballard and Piret suggest operation with systems in which the continuous phase wets the tower packing [9]. Since the dispersed phase will not wet the packing, coalescence of the dispersed droplets by contact with the packing pieces is minimized. When the dispersed phase wetted the packing, these investigators found that it formed rivulets or flowed as a film over the surface of the packing. Ceramic packings are wetted preferentially by aqueous solvents, while plastic packings are wetted preferentially by organic solvents. Metal packings will wet by either an aqueous or an organic solvent depending on the initial exposure of the metal surface.

COLUMN CAPACITY

If the dispersed phase flow is increased gradually, drop frequency per unit of column volume becomes greater. Eventually the number of dispersed phase droplets becomes so great that this phase fills the interstitial voids in the packed bed so that coalescence and flooding occurs. If the continuous-phase flow is increased, eventually its velocity will become as large as the velocity of the dispersed phase. Since the dispersed phase no longer can flow in the opposite direction to the continuous phase, dispersed-phase holdup increases rapidly and flooding occurs.

Most investigations of the flooding rates in packed columns have been carried out using binary pairs of solvents without solute transfer. Thus, such correlations represent the maximum possible flow rates since solute transfer usually affects the properties of the two phases so as to reduce hydraulic capacity.

Crawford and Wilke determined the maximum hydraulic flows in a 12-in. diameter column packed with Raschig rings [10]. They reported the flooding velocities of each phase based on the column cross-sectional area. The capacity of the column decreased significantly as the packing size was reduced. The sum of the square roots of the continuous and dispersed phase velocities at flooding was found to be constant for a given packing and pair of liquids. The limiting velocity for each system therefore was taken to be the square of this sum. These limiting velocities were expressed as a Reynolds number and used as the ordinate of a flooding correlation. The characteristic packing diameter was expressed as the reciprocal of the packing surface area.

Crawford and Wilke found that the best empirical fit of their data was obtained when these Reynolds numbers were related to the expression:

$$\left[\frac{\mu_c}{\Delta\rho}\right]^{0.5}\left[\frac{\sigma_i}{\rho_c}\right]^{0.1}\left[\frac{a_p}{\epsilon}\right]^{0.75}$$

To expand the scale of their log-log plot, the square of this relationship was used as the abscissa.

In the development of a flooding correlation for gas-liquid contacting, originally the term a_p/ϵ^3 was used to characterize the size and shape of the tower packing (see Chapter 1). In less than ten years, the packing factor (F) had been adopted to describe the particular packing involved, since F could be determined experimentally. This correlation was modified by Nemunaitis, et al. by substituting $F\epsilon^3$ for a_p in the abscissa based on their subsequent work with ceramic Intalox® saddle, metal Pall ring, and ceramic Raschig ring packings [11]. This modification permitted use of the correlation with larger size and higher capacity packings for which the packing factor (F) had been determined previously.

Their modified flooding correlation for liquid-liquid contactors is shown as Figure 11-5. The values for surface area and $F\epsilon^2$ for commonly used packings are given in Tables 11-3, 11-4, and 11-5. The correlations to predict maximum capacity of liquid-liquid contactors do not provide the same degree of reliability as offered by correlations for gas-liquid columns.

The original Crawford and Wilke correlation was based on eight different binary liquid systems which are listed in Table 11-6. The void fractions for packings tested had a maximum value of 0.74. The liquid properties varied as follows:

liquid viscosity	0.58 to 7.8 cps
liquid density difference	9.4 to 37.2 lb/ft^3
interfacial tension	8.9 to 44.8 dyne/cm

The modified correlation was based on data from six different tower packings with ϵ having values up to 0.94. All of these flooding data were based purely on hydraulic flow data with no mass transfer of solute occurring. The extrapolation of Figure 11-5 or its use outside the range of applicable physical properties should be done with considerable caution.

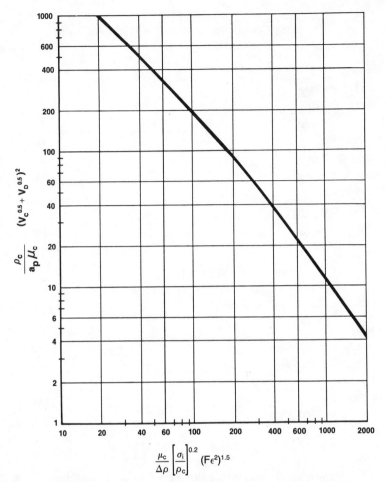

$$\frac{\mu_c}{\Delta\rho}\left[\frac{\sigma_i}{\rho_c}\right]^{0.2}(F\epsilon^2)^{1.5}$$

Figure 11-5. Modified Crawford-Wilke correlation for extractor flooding capacity. (From Crawford [10]. Reproduced by permission of the American Institute of Chemical Engineers.)

Also, the approach to flooding should be checked both at the bottom and at the top of the column.

Nemunaitis, et al., report that flooding in two commercial treaters removing mercaptans from gasoline using an aqueous caustic soda solution occurred at 20% of the values given by Figure 11-5. More recent commercial experience with treaters removing H_2S from LPG using an aqueous ethanolomine solution also showed flooding occurs at 20% of the values given in Figure 11-5. For these treaters, in which the hydrocarbon phase is dispersed and the aqueous continuous phase flow velocity (V_C), is only 5% to 10% of the dispersed phase flow rate (V_D), it is suggested that design flows not exceed 12% of the flooding velocity

Table 11-3
Flooding Correlation Values for Metal Packings

Packing	Surface Area ft^2/ft^3	Fε^2
#25 IMTP® Packing	62	37.9
#40 IMTP® Packing	46	22.6
#50 IMTP® Packing	30	17.2
#1 Hy-Pak® Packing	53	41.2
#1½ Hy-Pak® Packing	35	26.9
#2 Hy-Pak® Packing	26	24.5
1 in. Pall Rings	63	49.7
1½ in. Pall Rings	39	36.6
2 in. Pall Rings	31	25.1

Table 11-4
Flooding Correlation Values for Plastic Packings

Packing	Surface Area ft^2/ft^3	Fε^2
#1 Super Intalox® Saddles	63	32.3
#2 Super Intalox® Saddles	33	24.0
1 in. Pall Rings	63	44.9
1½ in. Pall Rings	39	33.6
2 in. Pall Rings	31	22.3

Table 11 - 5
Flooding Correlation Values for Ceramic Packings

Packing	Surface Area ft^2/ft^3	Fε^2
¾ in. Intalox® Saddles	102	73.9
1 in. Intalox® Saddles	78	47.8
1½ in. Intalox® Saddles	59	28.0
2 in. Intalox® Saddles	36	22.4
¾ in. Raschig Rings	74	125
1 in. Raschig Rings	58	89.5
1¼ in. Raschig Rings	45	63.7
1½ in. Raschig Rings	37	48.2
2 in. Raschig Rings	28	35.3

Table 11 - 6
Experimental Systems for Capacity Correlation

Continuous Phase	Dispersed Phase
Water	Gasoline
Glycerine	Gasoline
Carbon Tetrachloride	Water
Carbon Tetrachloride	Glycerine
Water	Methyl isobutyl ketone
Glycerine	Toluene
Naphtha	Water
Water	Naphtha

Source: Crawford [10]. Reproduced by permission of the American Institute of Chemical Engineers.

given by Figure 11-5. These practical observations indicate that additional work is needed to provide a more precise basis for design of such extractors.

PRESSURE DROP

In liquid-liquid systems, the pressure drop primarily is due to the hydrostatic head through which the phase must flow. The average fluid density is slightly different than that of the continuous phase due to the volume occupied by the dispersed phase holdup. Of course, there is a resistance to flow, however this frictional pressure drop normally is much less than the hydrostatic head. In extractors, the operating temperature should be maintained low enough or the operating pressure high enough to prevent any vaporization at the point of minimum column pressure.

PACKING SIZE

The use of Figure 11-5 is limited to extractors with packings selected to provide interstitial spaces that are larger than the dispersed phase droplet size. Gaylor and Pratt show that for each pair of liquids there is a critical packing size [12]. The dispersed phase droplet size is independent of flow rate so long as the packing is larger than this critical size. Liebson and Beckmann report that the critical packing size frequently is near $1/2$ in. [13]. Because of this effect, packing of $3/4$ in. or larger size ordinarily should be specified. To avoid channeling and reduced contacting efficiency at the column wall, packing size should not exceed $1/8$ the column diameter [1].

One of the primary functions of tower packing in extractors is to increase the flow path length for the dispersed phase. This increases the contact time between phases thus producing a greater amount of solute transfer. The tower packing also maintains a relatively uniform distribution of flow of both phases throughout the entire column cross section. Further, the packed bed distorts the dispersed phase droplets which results in fresh surfaces being made available that promote increased mass transfer. Another important function of the tower packing is to eliminate backmixing of the continuous phase which would result in a reduced mass transfer driving force. To accomplish these functions, the packed bed must not contain too large size interstitial voids or have too few pieces of packing per unit volume. For these reasons, the packing selected normally is no larger than 2-in. size, and many times $1\frac{1}{2}$-in.-size is the desired maximum.

DETERMINATION OF STAGES

Any design procedure requires a calculation of the number of mass transfer stages required, and then a determination of the packed depth required to achieve such a stage. The use of the equilibrium stage concept in liquid-liquid extraction is similar to its use in distillation operations. A theoretical stage of mass transfer is one from which the extract and the raffinate leave in equilibrium. Stated in a different manner, the ratio of the concentration of solute in the extract to the concentration of solute in the raffinate equals the distribution coefficient.

If the solvent A and the solvent B are immiscible or only slightly miscible, then their flows through the extractor essentially are constant. In this case, Figure 11-1 can be redrawn as illustrated by Figure 11-6. On the abscissa are values of mol fraction solute C in the solvent A on a solvent B free basis. These values represent raffinate compositions such as from J to P in Figure 11-1. On the ordinate are values of the mol fraction of solute C in solvent B on a solvent A free basis. These values represent extract compositions in equilibrium with the raffinate compositions which are connected by tie lines as illustrated on Figure 11-2. They are compositions such as from K to P on the curve JRPEK in Figure 11-1.

The number of theoretical stages required can be determined from Figure 11-6 by means of a stepwise procedure similar to the McCabe-Thiele method used in distillation calculations (see Chapter 6). An operating line QT first must be constructed below the equilibrium curve NO just developed from equilibrium data. Line QT can be drawn by material balance on the solute quantities in the feed and solvent since these

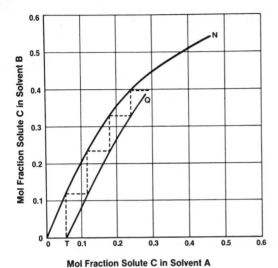

Figure 11-6. Determination of number of equilibrium stages.

rates and compositions are known. Point T represents the composition of solvent B entering the column and the composition of the raffinate leaving the column. Point Q represents the composition of the extract leaving the column and the composition of the feed in solvent A entering the extractor. The ratio of x_E to x_R on curve NO is the distribution coefficient. The value of x_R at point T usually is fixed by a specification for percentage recovery of the solute in the feed.

As an example, assume a feed containing 28 mol % solute C and 72 mol % solvent A enters the extractor at the top. The solvent is pure immiscible solvent B entering the bottom of the extractor at the rate of 375 mols solvent per 1,000 mols feed. It is desired to recover 85% of solute C in the feed as extract leaving the top of the column. By material balance on the streams leaving the extractor, the raffinate will contain 5.5 mol % solute and the extract will contain 38.8 mol % solute. In Figure 11-6, the top column conditions are represented by $x_R = 0.280$ and $x_E = 0.388$. The bottom column conditions are $x_R = 0.055$ and $x_E = 0$. The operating line is slightly curved since the flow of solvent A phase decreases from 1,000 mols to 762 mols while the flow of solvent B phase increases from 375 mols to 613 mols due to solute transfer. From a stepwise procedure, it is determined that this extraction requires 3.8 theoretical stages.

Where the transfer of solute is followed by a rapid, irreversible chemical reaction in the extract phase, the value of x_E^* approaches zero. The preponderant resistance to mass transfer will occur in the raffinate phase. In this case, the use of a transfer unit rather than a theoretical stage is more helpful for design purposes (see Chapter 3 and Chapter 4). The number of transfer units required may be calculated directly from the concentrations of solute in the feed and raffinate:

$$N_{OL} = \ln \left[\frac{x_F}{x_R} \right] \tag{11-10}$$

Thus, removal of 99.5% of the H_2S from a hydrocarbon liquid feed by contacting it with an aqueous alkaline solvent will require 5.3 transfer units.

CHOICE OF DEVICE

When only one theoretical stage is required, usually a liquid mixer followed by a settling tank is used. This probably was the earliest device used for liquid extraction; however, it requires a large inventory of solvents. Spray columns can be used where the density difference between phases is large. However, such towers become excessively tall if N_{OL} is three or greater because of the large values of H_{OL}. This low efficiency partially is due to axial mixing which shows an increasing effect as column diameter becomes larger.

Whenever two to seven theoretical stages are necessary, packed columns are the preferred devices. Sieve-plate columns also have been employed for these same applications. The perforations in the trays serve to produce the dispersion while the downcomers (or upcomers) conduct the continuous phase from tray to tray. Because packed and sieve-trayed columns impart only a minimum of energy to the system, they are preferred for low interfacial tension systems (< 12 dyne/cm) to avoid emulsification.

When ten or more theoretical stages are required, the packed depth needed may make the tower excessively tall: therefore, specifying a mechanical contactor may permit the use of a shorter column. These contactors use rotating disks or impellers to disperse one phase into the other. Another type of mechanical contactor uses centrifugal force to produce radial-flow mixing of the two phases. Such devices particularly are useful when the difference between the density of the light phase and the density of the heavy phase is 2% or lower.

STAGE EFFICIENCY

The problem of specifying the depth of packing in an extractor is not a straightforward determination. As discussed by Nemunaitis, et al., their tests produced a lower apparent H_{OL} value for beds of 1-in. size packings when 2-ft deep beds were used than when the bed depth was 5 ft [11]. This work showed that the efficiency is practically independent of velocity so long as the continuous phase velocity is at least 80 ft/h. At lower rates, backmixing of the continuous phase tended to reduce the efficiency. The dispersed-phase velocity produced only a very minor effect on efficiency. These data for three types of packing are shown in Table 11-7. Further, this work indicates that 1-in. metal Pall ring and 1-in. ceramic Intalox® saddle packings develop H_{OL} values which are only about 40% of the values for empty spray columns.

Table 11 - 7
Transfer Units Developed with 1 in. Packing
MEK-Kerosine-Water System

Packing	2 ft Bed Depth	5 ft Bed Depth
Metal Pall Rings	1.20	1.86
Ceramic Intalox® Saddles	1.11	1.86
Ceramic Raschig Rings		1.42

Source: Nemunaitis [11]. Reproduced by permission of the American Institute of Chemical Engineers.

Eckert indicated that the rate of mass transfer decreased rapidly as the residence time of the dispersed-phase droplets in the continuous phase increased [14]. Thus, the act of formation of the dispersed-phase droplets contributes significantly to the overall mass transfer. Therefore, the use of packed beds of 6 ft to 10 ft in depth followed by redispersion tends to minimize column height.

Eckert further showed that the packed depth necessary to achieve an equilibrium stage of mass transfer decreased only slightly with an increase in the continuous-phase velocity when this rate was greater than 80 ft/h. However, he found a small increase in the depth required to achieve an equilibrium stage with an increase in the dispersed phase velocity. Sherwood has postulated that at low rates the interfacial area increases with the dispersed phase flow rate; while at higher rates the interfacial area attains a nearly constant value [15].

Seibert et al., reported that the overall volumetric mass transfer coefficient varied directly with flow rates; however, it was much more affected by the dispersed phase rate compared to the continuous phase rate [16]. These investigators also observed that the overall mass transfer coefficient initially increased rapidly with an increase in continuous-phase velocity above zero; however, above a continuous-phase velocity of 40 ft/h, the mass transfer coefficient approached a fixed value. The overall mass transfer coefficient increased almost linearly with the dispersed-

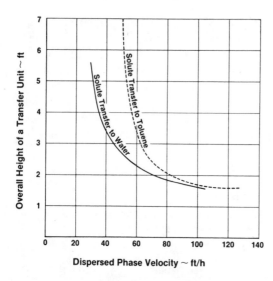

Figure 11-7. Efficiency of #15 IMTP® packing with acetone-toluene-water system and with the water phase continuous. (From Seibert [16].)

phase velocity. Their data for #15 IMTP® packing is shown in Figure 11-7 with the aqueous-phase continuous.

Sherwood stated that the rate of mass transfer may depend on whether the extract or raffinate is the dispersed phase for systems in which mass transfer occurs because of differences in solubility. Siebert et al., observed that the overall mass transfer coefficients were significantly greater for a system of low interfacial tension (butanol and water) than for a system of high interfacial tension (toluene and water). They also found a tendency for mass transfer efficiency to be dependent on the direction of solute transfer. Industrial experience indicates that the rate of mass transfer is independent of which phase is dispersed in systems in which the transferred solute subsequently is consumed by a chemical reaction.

⊚ Based on commercial experience, Table 11-8 has been prepared to show the packed depth required for various numbers of transfer units

Table 11 - 8
Packed Bed Depths Required
for Modern Packings

Transfer Units Per Bed	Packing Size		
	1 in.	1½ in.	2 in.
1.5	4.3 ft	5.2 ft	6.2 ft
2.0	7.1	8.5	10.1
2.5	9.8	11.8	14.0

per bed. This table is based on mobile organic/aqueous systems and the use of metal slotted-ring or ceramic saddle packings together with high-performance dispersion plates. Generally, a single packed bed is not deeper than 12 ft before another dispersion plate is installed. The use of deeper beds results in a relative loss of efficiency for each additional foot of packing.

EXTRACTOR INTERNALS

Because of the differences between gas-liquid contacting and liquid-liquid contacting, column internals of somewhat different design from those described in Chapter 9 are required. Of course, the light phase enters the bottom of the column and the heavy phase enters the top of the column. The most common manner of operating an extractor is with the light phase dispersed. Thus, the interface between phases will be located at the top of the column above the beds of packing.

At the bottom of the packed bed, it is necessary to form the light-phase dispersion. While this dispersion could be produced by one device and a separate packing support plate used to hold the packed bed, such an arrangement is not desirable since the packing support plate can affect adversely the light-phase dispersion rising through it. Therefore, the packing support plate and the light-phase dispersion plate can be combined as illustrated in Figure 11-8. By design, the light phase pools beneath this plate to a sufficient depth necessary to cause it to flow through the orifices in the plate due to the difference in densities between the two phases. These orifices set the light-phase dispersion into the packed bed that rests on the top surface of this plate. The continuous phase enters the downcomers above this plate at the bottom of the packed bed. The heavy phase is discharged from the downcomers below the pool of light-phase liquid under this plate.

The design of a disperser/support plate involves specifying the number, location, and size of the orifices which disperse the light phase. The velocity of the dispersed phase through these orifices usually is limited to not more than 70 ft/min to avoid possible formation of an emulsion. Such emulsions consist of very fine droplets which do not coalesce nearly as quickly as a conventional dispersion of larger-size drops. Orifice sizes of 0.19-in. to 0.25-in. diameter commonly are used, although sizes as small as 0.14-in. and as large as 0.31-in. diameter have been utilized. When the dispersed-phase superficial velocity (V_D) exceeds 130 ft/h, generally the number of orifices per ft^2 is increased rather than the orifice size being enlarged. If the continuous-phase superficial velocity (V_C) exceeds 60 ft/h, additional downcomers should be installed through

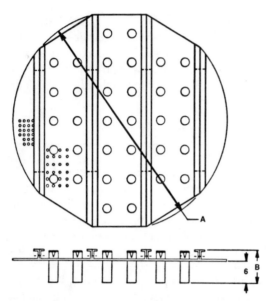

Figure 11-8. Disperser support plate. (Courtesy of Norton Company.)

the disperser plate. Obviously, these additional downcomers displace some number of the light-phase dispersion orifices so that the light-phase flow capacity is reduced.

Since disperser plates of the design shown in Figure 11-8 operate by difference of densities between the two phases, this same plate can be used for redispersion under each succeeding bed of packing through which the light-phase passes while traveling up the column. Obviously, these plates must be sealed to the supporting tower-ledge with a gasket to prevent leakage.

Each packed bed usually is equipped with a bed limiter at the top to prevent disturbance of the upper surface of the bed due to operational upsets. The heavy phase is introduced into the column through a distributor similar in appearance to that shown in Figure 9-11. However, the orifices in such a continuous phase distributor are sized to provide a low entrance velocity (not greater than 170 ft/min) so as to avoid disturbing the dispersed phase which is rising through it. A similar design of feed sparger is used in the inverted position to introduce the light phase below the bottom dispersion plate. Risers are added to this sparger so as to discharge the light-phase about 1 in. above the bottom of the continuous-phase downcomers. Again the entrance velocity is low to avoid creating turbulence on the lower surface of the light-phase pool below the disperser plate.

In those cases where the heavy phase is dispersed, a different arrangement of column internals is necessary. Now the interface between phases will be located at the bottom of the column below the beds of packing. In such cases, the packed beds are supported on conventional packing support plates as illustrated by Figure 9-2. Again a bed limiter may be installed on the top of each bed of packing.

The heavy-phase dispersion is formed at the top of the packed bed by use of a modified design of the dispersion plate shown in Figure 11-8. This plate is installed in an inverted position using a gasket on a ledge located 8 in. to 12 in. above the top of the packed bed. Similar plates are installed above each packed bed to reproduce the heavy-phase dispersion. The light-phase is introduced into the column through a distributor similar to Figure 9-11 that is installed in the inverted position below the bottom packing support plate. The heavy-phase is fed to the top disperser plate through a sparger of similar design to that previously described.

COALESCENCE OF DISPERSED PHASE

In general, the higher the interfacial tension the more rapidly coalescence will occur. The more viscous the continuous phase the slower will be the rate of coalescence of the dispersed phase. The coalescing zone of the column must be designed from settling principles. This may require enlarging the column diameter in order to reduce the velocities if the packed bed is operating at high flow rates.

The interface between phases should be kept several feet away from the column outlet to avoid entrainment of continous phase droplets in the coalesced dispersed phase. If coalescence is difficult to achieve, a small size packing or a mesh which is wetted perferentially by the dispersed phase may be employed to help coalesce the dispersed phase droplets.

The presence of trace impurities may have a pronounced effect on column operation. Many times such impurities collect at the interface between the two phases. Modification of the liquid properties at the mass transfer interface can affect both the capacity and efficiency of an extractor. It is common practice to provide a means of removing a small quantity of liquid from the interface periodically in order to purge impurities from the system.

INDUSTRIAL APPLICATIONS

Although liquid-liquid extraction usually is not the first choice of separating processes, it has been employed in the following commercial applications:

1. Removal of sulfur compounds from liquid hydrocarbons.
2. Recovery of aromatics from liquid hydrocarbons.

3. Removal of waxes and resins from lubricating oils.
4. Separation of butadiene from other C-4 hydrocarbons.
5. Separation of homogeneous aqueous azeotropes.
6. Separation of asphaltic compounds from oil.
7. Manufacture of hydrogen peroxide.
8. Removal of phenolic compounds from waste water.
9. Extraction of glycerides from vegetable oils.
10. Recovery of acetic acid from digesters and fermenters.
11. Refining of tall oil and methylated tall oil.
12. Recovery of rare earths in phosphor manufacture.
13. Extraction of tar acids from coal tar.
14. Recovery of hormones, vitamins, and antibiotics.
15. Purification of uranium, tantalum, and columbium.
16. Recovery of copper from leach liquor.

EXAMPLE PROBLEM

An aqueous process effluent contains 3.4 lb of a valuable organic compound per 1,000 lb of H_2O. Since the organic material has a somewhat higher boiling point than water, an extraction of this organic with a solvent appears to be the least expensive method for recovery of the solute. This organic solute is highly soluble in aromatic solvents that are almost immiscible in water. In order to enable recovery of the solute from the extract by means of a simple stripping operation, a high boiling aromatic liquid (p-diethyl benzene) will be used as the solvent.

Laboratory tests conducted at the effluent temperature of 80°F give the following distribution coefficients when the compositions of each phase are expressed in lb solute per 1,000 lb solvent.

Concentration in Water	Concentration in DEB	K_D'
2.1	21.1	10.05
1.7	14.2	8.35
1.2	8.7	7.25
0.7	4.3	6.14
0.2	1.2	6.00

What would be the column diameter and packed depth required to recover at least 95% of the solute present in 41,140 lb/h of aqueous effluent?

The data from the laboratory tests can be used to construct an equilibrium diagram on rectangular coordinates as in Figure 11-9. To recover

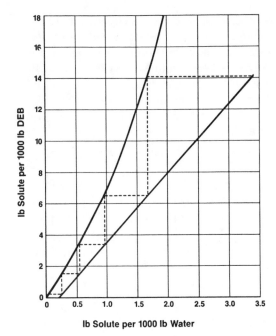

Figure 11-9. Equilibrium diagram for example problem.

95% of the solute would give a concentration of 0.17 lb solute per 1,000 lb H_2O in the raffinate. Assuming the DEB solvent is solute-free, we can establish the condition at the bottom of the extractor. This condition will lie on the X-axis of the equilibrium diagram.

Since DEB and H_2O are almost immiscible and the amount of solute transferred is small compared to the total mass-flow rates of the solvents, the operating line for this column will be essentially a straight line. Next, we will fix the slope of the operating line by choosing the DEB solvent flow rate so as to avoid a pinch against the equilibrium curve. Further, since we are using a packed column, we will attempt to specify a sufficient DEB flow rate so that no more than five theoretical stages of mass transfer are required. For this extraction, therefore, the DEB flow rate will be set at 9,400 lb/h.

By material balance, the concentration of solute in the extract will be 14.1 lb solute per 1,000 lb DEB. We now have established the condition at the top of the extractor that can be located on the equilibrium diagram. The operating line will join the compositions at the top of the tower with the compositions at the bottom of the tower on this diagram.

A McCabe-Thiele procedure is used to step off the equilibrium stages required as has been illustrated in Figure 11-6. For this extraction, 4.3 theoretical stages are necessary for 95% solute recovery.

Since the volume of aqueous feed solution is much greater than the volume of DEB solvent, the water-phase will be dispersed into the solvent-phase in order to generate the maximum interfacial area for mass transfer. The packing selected will be 1-in. stainless steel Pall rings which will be wetted initially with DEB solvent. From Table 11-3, this packing has a surface area of 63 ft^2/ft^3 and the value of Fϵ^2 is 49.7.

Now that all flow rates have been determined, the modified Crawford-Wilke Correlation (Figure 11-5) can be used to calculate the required column diameter. The following physical properties are needed:

Physical Property	Top of Column	Bottom of Column
Continuous phase density	53.17 lb/ft^3	53.06 lb/ft^3
Dispersed phase density	62.32 lb/ft^3	62.22 lb/ft^3
Continuous phase viscosity	0.82 cps	0.76 cps
Interfacial tension	32.0 dyne/cm	43.3 dyne/cm

The abscissa value for Figure 11-5 at the top of the column is:

$$X = \frac{0.82}{9.15} \left[\frac{32.0}{53.17} \right]^{0.2} (49.7)^{1.5} = 28.4$$

The ordinate value at flood from the correlation is 720, therefore:

$$\frac{53.17}{63(0.82)} [V_C^{0.5} + V_D^{0.5}]^2 = 720$$

Thus, $V_C^{0.5} + V_D^{0.5} = 26.45$

From the flow rates of feed and extract, the ratio of V_C to V_D is determined to be 0.272. Therefore at flood V_D is 302 ft/h and V_C is 82.1 ft/h.

If we select a 60-in. ID column, the dispersed phase rate will be 33.5 ft/h and the continuous phase rate 9.1 ft/h. At the top, this column will operate at 11.1% of flooding velocities.

The abscissa value for Figure 11-5 at the bottom of the column is:

$$X = \frac{0.76}{9.16} \left[\frac{43.3}{53.06} \right]^{0.2} (49.7)^{1.5} = 27.9$$

The ordinate value at flood from the correlation is 730, therefore:

$$\frac{53.06}{63(0.76)} [V_C^{0.5} + V_D^{0.5}]^2 = 730$$

Thus, $V_C^{0.5} + V_D^{0.5} = 25.67$

At flood, the dispersed phase velocity is 286 ft/h and the velocity of the continuous phase is 76.9 ft/h. For this 60-in. ID tower, the bottom will be operating at 11.7% of flooding rates.

From Table 11-8, the extractor will require two beds of packing each 7.9 ft deep to produce the 4.3 transfer units. Since λ is 1.62, HETP is less than H_{OL}; however the prudent designer probably would specify a 60-in. ID column with two beds of 1-in. Pall ring packing each 10 ft deep due both to the low superficial liquid velocities as well as to the high viscosity of the continuous phase increasing the resistance to mass transfer. Each packed bed would be equipped with a high-performance dispersion plate at the top, a bed limiter, and a conventional packing support plate.

NOTATION

A	Column cross-sectional area (ft^2)
a	Interfacial area (ft^2/ft^3)
a_p	Surface area of packing (ft^2/ft^3)
F	Packing factor
H_{OL}	Overall height of liquid transfer unit (ft)
k_E	Extract liquid-film mass transfer coefficient (lb mol/h $\cdot$ $ft^2 \cdot \Delta x$)
k_R	Raffinate liquid-film mass transfer coefficient (lb mol/h $\cdot$ $ft^2 \cdot \Delta x$)
K_D	Distribution coefficient
$K_E a$	Overall mass transfer coefficient for extract (lb mol/h $\cdot$ $ft^3 \cdot \Delta x$)
$K_R a$	Overall mass transfer coefficient for raffinate (lb mol/h $\cdot$ $ft^3 \cdot \Delta x$)
m	Slope of equilibrium curve
N	Solute transferred (lb mol/h)
N_{OL}	Number of overall liquid transfer units
S_D	Degree of separation
V_C	Continuous phase superficial velocity (ft/h)
V_D	Dispersed phase superficial velocity (ft/h)
x_E	Mol fraction solute in extract
x_E^*	Equilibrium mol fraction solute in extract
x_E'	Mol fraction solute in extract liquid film
x_F	Mol fraction solute in feed
x_R	Mol fraction solute in raffinate
x_R^*	Equilibrium mol fraction solute in raffinate
x_R'	Mol fraction solute in raffinate liquid film
Z	Packed depth (ft)

γ	Activity coefficient
ϵ	Void fraction of packing
μ_C	Continuous phase viscosity (cps)
ρ_C	Continuous phase density (lb/ft^3)
σ_i	Interfacial tension (dyne/cm)
$\Delta\rho$	Density difference (lb/ft^3)

REFERENCES

1. Oberg, A. G., and Jones, S. C., *Chemical Engineering*, Vol. 70, No. 15, 1963, p. 119.
2. Donahue, D. J., and Bartell, F. E., *Journal of Physical Chemistry*, Vol. 56, 1952, p. 480.
3. Treybal, R. E., *Liquid Extraction*, 2nd Ed., Chap. 4, McGraw-Hill, 1963, p. 132.
4. Girifalco, L. A., and Good, R. J., *Journal of Physical Chemistry*, Vol. 61, 1957, p. 904.
5. Francis, A. W., *Industrial and Engineering Chemistry*, Vol. 45, 1953, p. 2789.
6. Francis, A. W., *Industrial and Engineering Chemistry*, Vol. 46, 1954, p. 205.
7. Blanding, F. H., and Elgin, J. C., "Transcripts of American Institute of Chemical Engineers," Vol. 38, 1942, p. 305.
8. Breckenfeld, R. R., and Wilke, C. R., *Chemical Engineering Progress*, Vol. 66, 1942, p. 305.
9. Ballard, J. H., and Piret, E. L., *Industrial and Engineering Chemistry*, Vol. 42, 1950, p. 1088.
10. Crawford, J. W., and Wilke, C. R., *Chemical Engineering Progress*, Vol. 47, No. 8, 1951, p. 423.
11. Nemunaitis, R. R., et al., *Chemical Engineering Progress*, Vol. 67, No. 11, 1971, p. 60.
12. Gaylor, R. N., and Pratt, H. R. C., "Transactions of Institution of Chemical Engineers" (London), Vol. 35, 1957, p. 267.
13. Liebson, I., and Beckmann, R. B., *Chemical Engineering Progress*, Vol. 49, No. 8, 1951, p. 423.
14. Eckert, J. S., *Hydrocarbon Processing*, Vol. 55, No. 3, 1976, p. 117.
15. Sherwood, T. K., *Absorption and Extraction*, Chap. 8, McGraw-Hill, 1937, p. 256.
16. Seibert, A. F., Humphrey, J. L., and Fair, J. R., "Evaluation of Packings for Use in Liquid-Liquid Extraction Processes," University of Texas, 1985.

APPENDIX

Metric Conversion Table

Term	Convert From	Convert To	Multiply By
Absolute Temperature	°R	°K	0.5556
Area	ft²	m²	0.09290
Capacity Factor	fps	m/s	0.3048
Density	lb/ft³	kg/m³	16.02
Diameter	ft	mm	304.8
Diffusivity	ft²/h	cm²/s	0.2581
Enthalpy	Btu/lb	kcal/kg	0.5556
Gas-Film Mass Transfer Coefficient	lb-mol/ h•ft²•atm	kg-mol/ h•m²•atm	4.883
Gravitational Constant	ft/s²	m/s²	0.3048
Heat Capacity	Btu/ lb•°F	kcal/ kg•°C	1.000
Heat Flow	Btu/h	kcal/h	0.2520
Heat Transfer Coefficient	Btu/ h•ft³•°F	kcal/ h•m³•°C	16.02
Height Equivalent to a Theoretical Stage	ft	mm	304.8
Height of a Transfer Unit	ft	mm	304.8
Humidity	lb H₂O/ lb BDG	kg H₂O/ kg BDG	1.000
Interfacial Area	ft²/ft³	m²/m³	3.281
Kinematic Viscosity	ft²/h	cSt	25.81
Kinetic Energy	ft-lb	kg-m	0.1383
Liquid-Film Mass Transfer Coefficient	lb-mol/ h•ft²•mol/ mol	kg-mol/ h•m²•mol/ mol	4.883
Liquid Rate	gpm/ft²	m³/m²•h	2.445
Mass	lb	kg	0.4536
Mass Flow	lb/h	kg/h	0.4536
Mass Velocity	lb/ft²•h	kg/m²•h	4.883
Mass Velocity	lb/ft²•s	kg/m²•s	4.883
Molar Flow	lb-mol/h	kg-mol/h	0.4536

(Cont)

Metric Conversion Table (Continued)

Term	Convert From	Convert To	Multiply By
Overall Gas Mass Transfer Coefficient	lb-mol/ h•ft^3•atm	kg-mol/ h•m^3•atm	16.02
Overall Liquid Mass Transfer Coefficient	lb-mol/ h•ft^3•mol/ mol	kg-mol/ h•m^{3}mol/ mol	16.02
Packed Depth	ft	mm	304.8
Packing Diameter	in.	mm	25.40
Pressure	atm	kg/cm^2	1.033
Pressure	psi	kg/cm^2	0.07031
Pressure Drop	in. H$_2$O/ft	mm H$_2$O/m	83.33
Superficial Velocity	fps	m/s	0.3048
Surface Tension	lb/in.	dyne/cm	175,100
Temperature	°F	°C	0.5556 (°F-32)
Vapor Capacity Factor	lb$^{0.5}$/ ft$^{0.5}$•s	kg$^{0.5}$/ m$^{0.5}$•s	1.220
Viscosity	lb/ft•h	cps	0.4134

GLOSSARY

Absorption factor—Ratio of the slope of the operating line to slope of the equilibrium curve in absorption operations.

Absorption operation—Transfer of a solute from a gas phase to a liquid phase.

Azeotrope—Boiling liquid mixture which has the same vapor composition as the liquid composition.

Bed limiter—A column internal on top of a packed bed to prevent expansion of the bed.

Bottoms—The high boiling liquid product effluent from a distillation column.

Capacity factor—Superficial vapor velocity corrected for vapor and liquid densities.

Concurrent scrubber—Scrubber in which the gas and liquid flow in the same direction.

Countercurrent scrubber—Scrubber in which the gas and liquid flow in opposite directions.

Critical pressure—Pressure required to liquify a gas at its critical temperature.

Critical solution temperature—Temperature above which two liquids are completely miscible.

Critical temperature—The temperature above which a liquid phase will not exist regardless of pressure.

Cross-flow scrubber—Scrubber in which the gas and liquid flow in perpendicular directions.

Debutanizer—Column that removes C-4 hydrocarbons from the feed.

Demethanizer—Column that removes methane from the feed.

Depropanizer—Column that removes C-3 hydrocarbons from the feed.

Diatomic gas—Gas whose molecules consist of two atoms.

Disperser plate—Tower internal that produces dispersed drops of one liquid phase in the other liquid phase.

Distillate—That portion of the condensed overhead vapor from a distillation column that is withdrawn as product.

Distribution coefficient—Ratio of solute concentration in extract phase to solute concentration in raffinate phase.

Drag coefficient—Measure of a force exerted on a body in the direction of fluid flow.

Driving force—Force responsible for producing a change.

Dry line—Line on a plot that represents a property of a packed bed with gas flow only.

Dumped packing—Bed of individual packing elements that are randomly oriented.

Entrained liquid—Liquid droplets transported in a flowing gas.

Equilibrium curve—Line on a plot that represents the compositions of two phases that are in equilibrium.

Equilibrium ratio—Ratio of the composition of one phase to another phase with which it is in equilibrium.

Extract—The effluent of an extractor that has been enriched in dissolved solute.

Extractive distillation—Distillation in which a high boiling solvent is added to alter the relative volatility of components in the feed.

Extractor—Device for transferring a solute between two immiscible liquid phases.

Feed point—Location in a column at which the feed is introduced.

Flash zone—Portion of a column in which a liquid is partially vaporized.

Flooding—A liquid holdup sufficient to invert phases within the interstices of a packed bed.

Flow parameter—Square root of the ratio of liquid kinetic energy to gas kinetic energy.

Fluidized bed—Bed in which the solid elements are suspended in a rapidly moving gas phase.

Foam—Low density frothy mass formed on the surface of a liquid.

Form drag—Force exerted on a body by parallel flowing fluid due to the shape of the body.

Fractionator—Device that physically separates a mixture of components in the feed, usually by distillation.

Fume scrubber—Device used to remove an offensive substance from a gas stream.

Gas-film controlled—Mass transfer operation in which the principal resistance is in the gas film.

Gas quench tower—See *Quench tower.*

Gas scrubber—See *Fume scrubber.*

Heavy key—Principal high boiling component of a feed mixture.

HETP value—Mass transfer height that provides one theoretical stage of separation.

Hold-down plate—A heavy tower internal used to prevent fluidization of the top surface of a packed bed.

Hydraulic loading—Degree of maximum fluid handling capacity of the device.

Hyperbolic tower—A column whose shell takes the shape of a hyperbola in a longitudinal section.

Interfacial area—Area of contact between two different phases.

Interfacial tension—Resultant of cohesive forces acting at the interface between two immiscible liquids.

Irrigation points—Openings from which discrete streams of liquid flow.

Irrigation rate—Volumetric liquid flow per unit of column cross-sectional area.

Lambda factor—Ratio of slope of equilibrium curve to slope of operating line.

Lean solution—Solvent that contains a small quantity of solute.

Light key—Principal low boiling component of a feed mixture.

Liquid distributor—Tower internal that provides uniform liquid flow onto a packed bed.

Liquid-film controlled—Mass transfer operation in which the principal resistance is in the liquid film.

Liquid holdup—Quantity of liquid present in a packed bed.

Liquid retention—Quantity of liquid remaining in a packed bed after discontinuance of feeds.

Loading point—Flow rates at which the vapor phase begins to interact with the liquid phase to increase interfacial area in a packed bed.

Logarithmic average—Mathematical average based on a logarithmic function.

Lower loading point—Maximum flow rates at which the pressure drop is proportional to the square of the gas rate for a packed bed.

Mass velocity—Mass flow rate based on column cross-sectional area.

Maximum operational capacity—Maximum vapor rate that provides normal efficiency of a packing.

Overhead—Low boiling vapor product from a distillation column.

Packed bed—Confined volume of elements designed to improve contacting between two phases.

Packed depth—The vertical height of a packed bed.

Packing factor—Number relating the pressure drop to flow rates through a particular tower packing.

Pasteurization—Removal of small quantities of low-boiling components at the top of a distillation column.

Pressure distillation—Distillation at pressures greater than 5.5 atmospheres.

Pressure drop—Reduction in pressure due to resistance to flow through a device.

Pumparound—Section of a column over which the liquid is recirculated.

Quench tower—Column that rapidly cools a hot gas stream.

Raffinate—The effluent of an extractor from which dissolved solute has been removed.

Reboiler—Heat exchanger that vaporizes a liquid to provide energy to a distillation operation.

Rectifying section—Section of a column that condenses high-boiling components in the vapor.

Reflux—Condensed liquid returned to a distillation column to rectify the rising vapor.

Reflux ratio—Ratio of reflux flow to distillate product flow.

Regeneration—Removal of solute from a rich solution to permit reuse of the solvent.

Relative volatility—Ratio of the equilibrium ratio of one component to that of another component.

Removal efficiency—Degree of elimination of a substance.

Rich solution—Solvent that contains a large quantity of solute.

Sensible heat load—Difference in heat content due to temperature change with no change of phase.

Single-component vapor—Vapor phase that contains but one chemical substance.

Solvent—A liquid that is capable of dissolving a solute.

Splash deck—Row of separated horizontal slats onto which liquid rains.

Split stream—Operation in which a fluid stream is divided into two or more streams.

Stripping factor—Ratio of the slope of the equilibrium curve to the slope of the operating line in stripping operations.

Stripping operation—Transfer of solute from a liquid phase to a gas phase.

Stripping section—Section of a column that vaporizes low-boiling components in the liquid.

Superficial velocity—Rate of flow based on the column cross-sectional area.

Support plate—Tower internal that is located at the bottom of a packed bed to support the weight of the packing.

Theoretical stage—A mass transfer stage from which the two phases leave in equilibrium.

Tower internals—Devices used to facilitate performance of tower packings.

Tower packing—Elements designed to promote contact between two phases.

Trayed columns—Towers containing a series of horizontal plates for contacting two phases.

Trays, angle—Trays consisting of a series of separated horizontal angle irons.

Trays, baffle—Trays consisting of a series of staggered horizontal baffles that are vertically offset.

Trays, counterflow—Trays on which the vapor and liquid flow countercurrently either through the same or separate openings.

Trays, sieve—Trays that are perforated to allow vapor flow upward through liquid flowing horizontally from the inlet to the outlet downcomer.

Trays, valve—Trays in which the perforations have caps that deflect the upwardly flowing vapor that passes through liquid flowing horizontally from the inlet to the outlet downcomer.

Turndown ratio—Ratio of maximum hydraulic flow to minimum flow at constant efficiency.

Vacuum crude still—A vacuum tower that processes the bottoms from an atmospheric pressure distillation of crude oil.

Vacuum deaeration—Removal of dissolved air from a liquid at pressures less than atmospheric.

Vacuum distillation—Distillation at pressures less than 0.4 atmospheres.

Vacuum still—A distillation column operating at a pressure less than 0.4 atmospheres.

Vapor capacity factor—Superfacial vapor velocity corrected for vapor density.

Vapor distributor—Tower internal that produces uniform vapor flow into a packed bed.

Vapor/liquid equilibrum—Relationship of vapor composition to the liquid composition with which it is in equilibrium.

Void fraction—Proportion of unoccupied space in a bed of tower packing.

Wall flow—Quantity of liquid that flows down the wall of a column.

Wall wiper—Tower internal designed to intercept liquid flowing down the column wall.

Wash bed—Packed bed used to remove minor contaminants from a gas stream by scrubbing with a liquid.

Water cooling—Reducing water temperature by partial evaporation into an air stream.

INDEX